# Teleconferencing:
# Maximizing Human Potential

Robert A. Cowan

**Reston Publishing Co.,Inc.**
*A Prentice-Hall Company*
**Reston, Virginia**

**Library of Congress Cataloging in Publication Data**

Cowan, Robert A.
    Teleconferencing.

    Includes bibliographical references and index.
    1. Teleconferencing.  I. Title.
HF5718.C69  1984        384        83-21236
ISBN  0-8359-7549-5

Printed in the United States of America

## *Dedication*

To Joan M. Cowan and William Meardon, Sr.

# Table of Contents

# *Acknowledgements*

Teleconferencing is an extension of human communication and interaction. There are many people who have contributed to the field and helped me refine my approach to the field. First, James Gardiner and his patience in working with me over the years was invaluable in shaping my ideas about telecommunications. Much of the description included in this book of personality characteristics which constitute effective telecommunicators is based on Jim's research in interpersonal communication.

The progressive thinkers at the Highlander Center in New Market, Tennesee led me to understand our natural interest in information that is relevant to our lives and helped me to put video production in its proper perspective. Others who have helped me over the years include: Shelia Herriott Hood who had faith in my skills and helped to start my work in two-way video teleconferencing in Alaska; Chief Peter John of Minto, Alaska, who helped me learn how to listen to others; Nancy Holmes, who guided much of my thinking and encouraged me to seek out real people and value their contributions.

Jenny Fouts Cowan believed in me, made the writing of this book much easier and contributed many helpful editorial comments. Glenn Southworth, President of Colorado Video, changed my thinking about the role of full motion teleconferencing. Ben Park recognized my teleconferencing projects as innovative and Martin Elton promoted in the uniqueness of my work. Arthur C. Clarke's writing and wisdom taught me more about integrated communication systems than anyone.

Finally, Robert W. Cowan who became one of my best researchers, and taught me that you do not have to be a runner to win a race.

# *Preface*

It seems that the topic of "teleconferencing" is everywhere. Articles in the airplane magazines, trade journals, and television programs extoll the virtues of electronic meetings of one type or another. Major firms are holding satellite video conferences and satellite earth stations are beginning to pop up as flowers in the spring. Terms like "transponder," "uplinks," "audio conferencing," "electronic mail," "store and forward," and countless others are being casually thrown around at conferences and possibly by the people in your organization.

In the midst of this confusion, there is a growing explosion in the teleconferencing area as more and more companies, both large and small, are turning to one or more of the current teleconferencing technologies in an attempt to make their organizations more effective.

There is nothing magical about teleconferencing. It is the result of the simple recognition of a need, a basic understanding of the uniqueness of the medium and sufficient attention to the technical and people-oriented details involved. Teleconferencing is not something to try just to "keep up with the Jones'," it is an integral part of the strategic planning process that will effect the way you and your company does business.

The success stories have been impressive. Some firms have been able to save millions of dollars by completing jobs ahead of schedule. Some have been able to reach thousands of customers and clients with their sales messages instead of hundreds. Educators have delivered needed education across the country instead of to small groups. The list goes on. . .

Teleconferencing, and the technologies that support it, are still maturing. There is much we do not know about human interaction via electronic networks, but a few guidelines are emerging. As imprecise as they are, they may be the building blocks for the future. The object of this book is to give you some of those guidelines that have emerged from thousands of hours of teleconferencing, observation, and introspection on the nature of electronically augmented human communication—there is no reason for new users of teleconferencing systems to re-invent the wheel. Once you initiate your own teleconferencing efforts you will find that your unique situation will call for variations to the concepts mentioned in this book, much as a public speaker varies his approach depending on the character of the audience he or she faces.

This book is mainly intended for those who want to increase their understanding about this new technology that may rival the introduction of the computer in its effect on organizations. This book will give you an idea about how such technologies may benefit you and your organization, and how your organization will be affected. This book will also provide a number of references to teleconferencing activities on the part of many firms and educational institutions, as well as *ad hoc* teleconferences used for marketing purposes. The key ingredient has been sufficient planning and the development of a well defined purpose and specific outcomes to be achieved. For those in an educational environment, parts of the book will suggest some techniques that will help you become more effective. There are countless examples of corporations, businesses and educational institutions using teleconferencing with exceptional results. You can review the material and determine yourself whether some of these approaches make sense for your business or organization.

To understand some of the media's strengths and weaknesses, a portion of the book will discuss the technologies of the industry. The information presented is not designed to make you a technician, nor will it give you the level of technical understanding to implement a complex satellite communications network—there are enough firms that specialize in the technical details. What this book will stress are the human factors and how they relate to technical design.

If, after reading the description of the technologies available, you wish to pursue the development of some teleconferencing capabilities the book will give you guidelines for developing budgets, determining savings, and assessing benefits. You will be able to gather the information you will need to sell your idea to management or, if you are a manager, the information you will want someone to prepare for you. The book will help you focus on the details and specific objectives that are critical in the successful implementation and operation of any teleconferencing effort—whether it be a one-time satellite demonstration of a new product or a full-blown teleconferencing network linking geographically separated offices.

Perhaps it may be of importance for me to discuss some of my philosophy as to why I think teleconferencing is worth the time and effort necessary to produce this book. First, there is a tremendous human resource in this country which is underutilized simply because there has not been an easy way to tap this potential. Teleconferencing provides a mechanism for maximizing much of that resource by making it possible to easily link (network) people by providing the ''human connection.'' Second, the more the users understand about the media through which they are communicating, the more effective their personal communications. The goal is the effective communication of human information (thoughts, knowledge, creativity). Third, with their ability to network people with similar interests in search of common goals, the systems hold great promise to enrich our lives. The combination of "High Tech—High Touch" is precisely the reason why these teleconferencing systems hold such appeal. *For the first time, the electronic technologies are providing us with the mechanisms to reach out and communicate where there was little or no communication before.*

There are many vendors providing teleconferencing equipment. Rather than attempt an exhaustive discussion of each of the vendors, I will concentrate on a major vendor or teleconferencing service provider in each technology group and describe specific offerings in detail. I believe many introductory books that attempt to review all the available products fall short of the mark for a variety of reasons: unintentional reporting bias and insufficient knowledge about each of the products covered. I will avoid the problem by limiting the discussion to only a few of the products that I feel have a solid record of reliability. I will mention, however, the various other manufacturers for your future use in acquiring additional information. After reading the book, you will have sufficient knowledge to evaluate the offerings of other vendors *in light of your own special needs.*

Teleconferencing is one of the most exciting developments in human communications. The shape of the horizon before us will be formed by people like yourself: people who have needs to communicate with others in a more effective manner; people who believe that success follows an understanding of the basic principles; people who creatively apply these principles to their own unique environments.

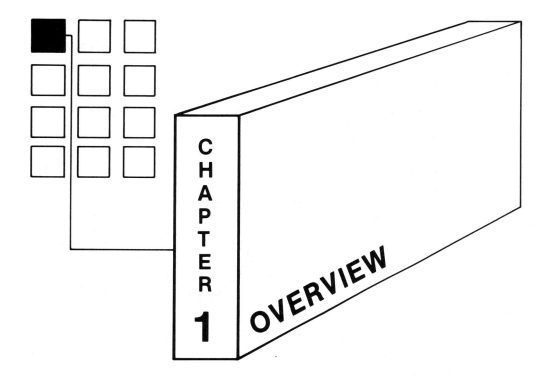

## CHAPTER 1 OVERVIEW

**P**robably the first question that needs to be addressed is "What is teleconferencing?" This question was easier to answer five or ten years ago than it is today, and it will be easier to answer today than five to ten years in the future. Basically, *teleconferencing is a term that is applied to an electronic gathering of three or more individuals at two or more locations.* Along with this concept go all the technologies supporting that type of communication. Today, those technologies include a whole host of devices.

The technologies fall into two basic groups: visible and invisible systems. The devices in the conference rooms that are seen and used by the participants are called visible systems; the devices (transmission systems) that link the conference rooms or locations together are called invisible systems. As we describe the various systems in this book, you will begin to appreciate the interrelatedness of the user, the user devices, and the transmission systems.

The most widely publicized form of teleconference is the satellite video teleconference. It tends to be a large, one-time conference that sends visual images to many locations around the globe. However, there are a host of other types of teleconferencing systems, including audio-only, audio with the capability of sending graphic images (audiographic), computer-based systems, and several other forms of visual communication. There is considerable activity taking place in each technology as businesses, governments, health care providers, educators, and others begin to explore how teleconferencing can link people.

The growth in the teleconferencing industry by business, education, and government has been significant over the past several years. Current investments in teleconferencing (e.g., installations and communication charges) are running at about $2 million per month.[1] The investment rate in 1982 increased 1,000 percent over the same period in 1981. The number of business meetings held via teleconferencing is expected to increase from 89,400 in 1981 to 1.8 million in 1986.[2] Projections indicate that in 1986 $124 million will be spent on teleconferencing rooms alone! The use of teleconferencing for occasional meetings (the *ad hoc* teleconferences) are increasing at the rate of about 30 percent per quarter.[3]

Our pure need to exchange information of all types is growing as well. In 1982, over 4 million electronic messages were sent from the 1 million communication terminals in the United States.[4] By 1992, the number of messages is expected to climb to over 21 billion! In a survey sponsored by the International Information/Word Processing Association in 1982, the 2,000 respondents indicated that electronic mail is the most anticipated application to be added to word processing systems.[5] The survey also indicated that 27 percent of the corporations have plans to implement electronic mail in 1982, and 35 percent have long-range plans to do so.

At the start of 1982, there were over 60 private companies that owned satellite communication networks, about half of them manufacturing firms.[6] Xerox, in its study of communication trends, decided that by 1990 teleconferencing will account for roughly 20 percent of all data communications traffic.[7] The market for satellite services was $146 million in 1981, will rise to $1.2 billion in 1985, and will rise to $2.9 billion by 1991. Table 1-1 puts these forecasts in perspective.

AT&T predicts that teleconferencing can replace 16 percent of all international trips (Figure 1-2).[8] Of that 16 percent, 6 percent can be replaced by audio, 52 percent by audiographic, and 42 percent by full-motion video systems (Figure 1-3). AT&T also found that while international travel has been increasing at a compound rate of 5 percent per year, international telephone calls have been increasing at 30 percent per year, indicating a growth in communication patterns.

The next logical question is "What are these businesses and associations doing with their teleconferencing?" The following examples illustrate the range of applications which have been in place for several years. In the visual area, one company (TeleConcepts) is now offering a satellite video press conference service for corporations; for a fixed sum, a company can reach ten major cities with one-way television and provide the press with the opportunity to ask questions via telephone lines.[9] Allied Van Lines reached 1,300 people with one program at a cost of less than $85 per person, while past meetings were attended by 660 people at a cost of $266 per person. Instead of the traditional nine regional product announcement meetings over a three-week period, Ford used satellite teleconferencing to introduce the EXP sports car to 20,000 sales staff and dealers in one day. The Catholic Telecommunications Network started operation in mid-1982 and will be used for radio and television programming for the general public, along

## TABLE 1-1
### Teleconferencing Trends and Projections

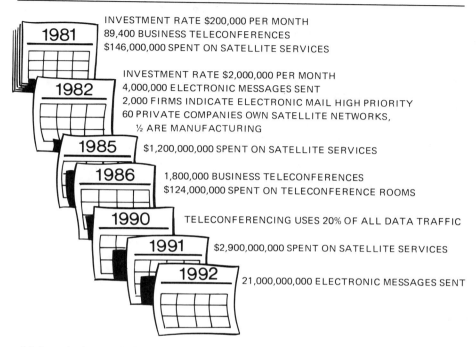

**1981**
INVESTMENT RATE $200,000 PER MONTH
89,400 BUSINESS TELECONFERENCES
$146,000,000 SPENT ON SATELLITE SERVICES

**1982**
INVESTMENT RATE $2,000,000 PER MONTH
4,000,000 ELECTRONIC MESSAGES SENT
2,000 FIRMS INDICATE ELECTRONIC MAIL HIGH PRIORITY
60 PRIVATE COMPANIES OWN SATELLITE NETWORKS,
½ ARE MANUFACTURING

**1985**  $1,200,000,000 SPENT ON SATELLITE SERVICES

**1986**  1,800,000 BUSINESS TELECONFERENCES
$124,000,000 SPENT ON TELECONFERENCE ROOMS

**1990**  TELECONFERENCING USES 20% OF ALL DATA TRAFFIC

**1991**  $2,900,000,000 SPENT ON SATELLITE SERVICES

**1992**  21,000,000,000 ELECTRONIC MESSAGES SENT

with instruction and teleconferencing.[10] Aetna Life and Casualty's teleconferencing facility, which just extends eight miles, was used for 1,700 meetings in six months by 11,300 users! Who said useful teleconferencing had to mean signals bouncing across vast numbers of miles?[11]

The hotel industry has been involved in the teleconferencing business. By establishing their own network arrangements, the hotel chains believe that they can draw large groups to teleconferencing-equipped hotels. Holiday Inn started its broadcasts in June 1980 with a program for TRW Corporation and subsequently established its own formal teleconferencing network called "HI-Net."[12] One of the newer networks announced is operated by the Marriott hotel chain, which made its debut in mid-1982 with a major program featuring television journalist Howard K. Smith.

Other success stories are these: the American Library Association presented key sessions in 62 cities; Hewlett Packard reached 35 cities with its three-hour program to announce new products; Johnson & Johnson networked 35 cities to reach 2,000 physicians with a program on hip replacements; United Technologies used a two-hour live satellite broadcast to introduce a new corporate division to 12 other company locations; the battery division of Gould used satellite broadcasting to announce one of their new products to the world; and Bache Halsey Stuart Shields, Inc., introduced a new financial service to 13 other locations around the country.[13]

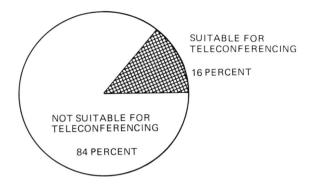

**FIGURE 1-2**
Potential Teleconferencing Displacement of International Travel
*Source: AT&T.*

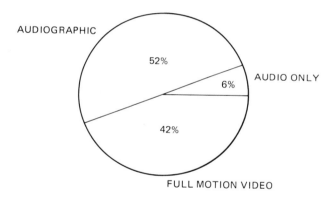

**FIGURE 1-3**
International Teleconferencing Modalities
*Source: AT&T.*

The use of two-way cable television systems is expanding—even into the home itself—but in a different way than you might expect. In Higashi Ikoma, Japan, town residents can demonstrate cooking right from their own kitchens to others throughout the city and receive call-in questions about the food preparation.[14] Research indicates that since the system was first installed in 1978, about 50 percent of the people who have the cable system have actually produced their own programs. United Press International's *Newstime* uses low-cost slow-scan television technology to distribute general news and news programs for women to over 950,000 homes via cable television systems.[15]

Alaska has been using audio teleconferencing for legislative purposes since 1978, when the Legislative Telecommunications Network was established.[16] The network is used by citizens and legislators alike to exchange information concerning legislation. Research Health Services, a health care corporation in Kansas City, uses audio conferencing for regular management meetings and the delivery of educational materials to its managed hospitals and nursing homes in a four-state area.

The use of text communication systems for both messages and conferences has been on a rapid rise. Deluxe interactive communication terminals are being placed in hotel rooms in Colorado so that guests will have access to a variety of electronic message services.[17] Coca-Cola has exchanged its telephone messages for computer messages to achieve a reduction in mistakes and delivery delays, and more sharing of general information via its computerized bulletin board system. American Building Products was able to save thousands of dollars on a plant move by equipping both movers and contractors with communicating terminals to quickly handle the hundreds of daily questions concerning the complex project.[18] A large tennis racket manufacturer is equipping all of its sales force with communications terminals so that they will have access to the company computers from the client's store for orders, delivery dates, order status, and inventory questions.[19] Travelhost has recently ordered 500,000 terminals to place in hotel rooms so that guests will be able to access a comprehensive electronic mail system, as well as airline schedules, stock market quotations, and restaurant guides.[20] A number of major hotel chains, like Holiday Inn and Marriott, have initiated their own satellite networks to increase the utilization of existing conference facilities.

Association members scattered across the United States regularly share personal strategies on fundraising and public relations via computer conferencing.[21] A group of independent consultants across the United States cooperatively work on studies and prepare final reports on a New Jersey computer conferencing system without having to meet face-to-face. The use of electronic mail and conferencing systems has grown to such an extent that Airfone intends to expand its aircraft-to-ground communications systems to link passengers' carry-terminals with their computer systems back at the office.[22]

There are as many variations in the application of teleconferencing as there are users. However, some basic statements can be made as to the areas in which teleconferencing can have some impact:

1. Introduction of new policies which impact corporate operations.
2. Motivational programs to improve productivity.
3. Conferences and support services for field personnel.
4. Educational programs for specific audiences.
5. New product announcements to press, field personnel, dealers, distributors, users, and clients.
6. Introduction of new marketing and advertising programs.

7. Presentations to shareholders at annual meetings to expand their sense of participation.

These categories can be compressed even further into the areas of management communication, education, and marketing. Examples of management communication would include engineering and production staff located miles apart discussing the manufacture of a new product, ensuring that the product will arrive in the market place in the shortest possible time with the fewest possible production problems. The marketing department could announce a new product to field sales people so that everyone gets the same information, with subsequent meetings to discuss product acceptance and new sales strategies.

Teleconferencing can be used to reach many with education where it was previously either too costly or literally impossible to reach all those that needed the education. The range of potential educational applications can be as varied as the organizations themselves. Programs that lead to advanced degrees and supervisory training to improve a company's bottom line are common. Education can be divided into two major categories: (a) education that improves productivity, in which the outcome of the educational event leads to the implementation of actions that result in a direct increase in sales or production output or that result in reduced expenses for the delivery or manufacture of a product or service, and (b) education as a marketing tool. The content of these programs can vary from preventive maintenance for machine operators to motivational training to education on the application of Theory Z in American industry. Many also look at education as a form of marketing; through the educational process, sales and revenue are generated.

Although some would consider marketing as a form of management communication, I will make a distinction between the two based on the audience and purpose. Management communication focuses on staff and tactical communication, whereas marketing's market is external and in some manner is designed to impact revenues. Although many corporations are engaged in marketing efforts that are directed internally (promoting *esprit de corps*), these efforts are more motivational in their nature. Included in the marketing approach would be programs for sales agents not directly employed by the business, in other words, those individual businessmen that sell your product—the sales force's "extended family."

Obviously, one of the next questions is "Why teleconferencing?" Some of the benefits of teleconferencing are:

1. Reduced travel time and distance.
2. Presentations are given once, with everyone hearing the same information.
3. Better use of staff and executive time.
4. Audience access to broader resources.
5. Information disseminated quickly and allowance for clarification at time of delivery.

6. Increased communication frequency.
7. Increased communication with field staff when other media are not viable alternatives.
8. Reduced lead time to implement new projects.
9. Feedback.
10. Ability to reach many people at the same time with a single message.
11. The "event" can have more impact than a more traditional meeting.

Many consider teleconferencing to be a travel substitute. The popular opinion is that teleconferencing will be an acceptable sutstitute to displace the costs of travel, but that may not be the only reason. According to some:

> Economic facts of life have also spurred the growth of this new business . . . Costs of travel and accommodations have risen at a rate some estimate to be as high as 45% annually and growing complaints from executives about lost time and discomfort endured during travel have played a significant role, as well.[23]

When finding time for video and audio teleconferencing is a problem, the use of computer conferencing or electronic mail may be indicated. In a recent article on electronic mail, it was noted that "In international business in particular, phoning can be very expensive. You have both the cost for the phone usage itself and the cost of the executive time wasted in telephone tag."[24]

It may be necessary for economic reasons to focus on travel cost displacement issues, but cost should not be the primary criterion by which the decision is made. Teleconferencing is simply not the same as being there. There is no question in the minds of teleconferencing experts that teleconferencing does a poor job of replacing the social interactions that take place in a person-to-person meeting. A letter is not the same as a chat with someone over a glass of wine. An "I love you" over the telephone is not the same as the words uttered face-to-face. Watching a movie on television is not the same as seeing it in a theatre with several hundred others. A record is not the same as attending a concert. Each setting brings with it unique dynamics which add or distract from the communications process. How else but through text can one take several days to compose thoughts which emerge as one or two cogent paragraphs that have maximum meaning and impact. With electronic media, however, there is an immediacy that cannot be captured in any other way—a remote participation in which a portion of our senses are moved to environments far away. These electronic media may not be the same as being there, but they provide us with access to events that were previously impossible to attend. This is one reason that the term "value-added" is often used in conjunction with teleconferencing. It means that in addition to simple travel cost displacement, new communications options and benefits are possible.

The belief that teleconferencing should be analyzed in light of value-added benefits is becoming more widespread. According to Joanne Milberger of the International Association of Business Communicators, "Teleconferences do not appear to be replacing meetings, but rather to be providing an avenue for new and additional ones. They are simply a new way of conducting business."[25] It is interesting to note that the advantage of the Alaska audio conferencing system has not been travel cost reductions:

> No good case was found for travel avoidance, since only 11.5% indicated they would have traveled to testify with LTN. However, the unquantifiable benefit of information gained applies—82.8% would not have traveled to the State Capitol and their testimony would have been lost.[26]

There is conflicting data on the extent to which teleconferencing actually reduces travel costs. In fact, some companies see an overall increase in travel and communication costs, but they also see increased revenue. However, once teleconferencing is in place for a period of time, there will be greater and more effective use of the teleconferencing systems and less travel. Since communication costs are usage sensitive, they will rise as the new technologies are used more, but the gain is increased productivity with reduced travel time and the benefits that come from increased communication.

Productivity is another issue that has been raised when the topic of teleconferencing is mentioned. White- and blue-collar productivity (or the lack thereof) has been discussed in the professional journals for the past several years. In the 1970s, office productivity increased roughly 4 percent, while factory productivity increased 85 percent. Many feel that one of the reasons for the significant difference in productivity gains is the level of investment in capital equipment in each area. For example, the 1970s investment in each office worker was roughly $10, while the investment in each factory worker was $100.[27] More recent research by Ruprecht & Wagoner supports the hypothesis that office automation systems do increase productivity. Based on studies of automated and nonautomated environments, managerial productivity in automated offices will be increasing from 3 to 28 percent, while clerical productivity will rise from 18 to 24 percent.[28] Since teleconferencing is considered by many of the experts in office automation as part of the "office of the future" concept aimed at improving productivity, one might expect teleconferencing to enhance productivity as much or more as other office automation devices.

Since one of teleconferencing's strongest applications is in education, it is interesting to look at some national business statistics in that area. In a recent survey of over a thousand organizations, the results indicated that over 70 percent of U.S. organizations are offering programs in supervisory skills and orientation.[29] Management skill development, communication skills training, technical updating, time management, and safety training are all offered by over

50 percent of the firms surveyed. And the demand for productivity-related education will increase.

The need for education increases the more a worker is involved in the manipulation of information, and our society is certainly moving toward an information society. Only 13 percent of our work force is involved in manufacturing today, and currently 60 percent of our work force is involved in the production or processing of information.[30]

There appear to be other problems facing business as well. Many of these problems seem to be communication-based. For example, in a recent study by the Rockefeller Institute on the reasons why a customer stops buying, it was found that almost 70 percent of the customers changed their buying habits because they felt an attitude of indifference was shown by the company.[31] Only 14 percent changed because they were dissatisfied with the product! The perception of ''indifference'' can be related to (a) insufficient time to make the necessary contact, (b) lack of technology to reach the customer base, or (c) an organizational attitude which does not encourage customer contact. For some, teleconferencing can provide a mechanism to reach large numbers of customers more efficiently, as well as permitting greater customer input as to satisfaction with the product. In this way, teleconferencing becomes part of a broader telemarketing strategy.

So there appear to be many reasons for considering teleconferencing as another communications option. What have other companies experienced as they developed teleconferencing capabilities? According to Booze-Allen, in a study of teleconferencing users who use teleconferencing at least twenty hours a month, found that:[32]

1. Ninety percent were very satisfied with their teleconferencing use.
2. Three-fourths perceived an increase in personal productivity.
3. Three-fourths experienced a decrease in travel expense.
4. Three-fourths experienced less time away from their home offices.
5. One-half reported increasing meeting efficiency.
6. One-half perceived a decrease in the time needed to reach decisions.
7. One-half noted increased amounts of communication among the various parts of the organization.
8. One-third reported an improvement in decision quality.

Yet all is not rosy in the field of teleconferencing. There are many who do not feel that teleconferencing justifies the expense involved. A large part of the problem is educational: there is insufficient knowledge about the scope of teleconferencing and its applications. In his article in *Fortune,* J. Cooney said that one satellite company's offerings

. . . included one of the odder new ideas, videoconferencing, which is based on the premise that you can't really know what's on the boss's mind unless he appears on a screen at your home office, where you can watch for facial twitches, see whether he needs a haircut, or if the boss is female makes raucous sexist jokes.[33]

John Naisbitt, in *Megatrends,* also believes that teleconferencing has a limited future:

Teleconferencing. That is another trend that will not happen. Talking with people via television cannot begin to substitute for the high touch of a meeting, no matter how rational it is in saving fuel and overhead. If it is of little importance, use teleconference. Be appropriate. But we have to face it: there is no end to meetings. Teleconferencing is so rational, it will never succeed.[34]

There are many regular teleconferencing users that would simply disagree with those statements. In fact, the total number of teleconferences in 1982-83 is estimated to be 2.5 million.[35] In addition, there are a number of executives that have a ''gut level'' feeling that improving communication improves the competitive advantage of the company. Executives are beginning to feel that they *have* to get ''up to speed'' in some of these newer technologies just to keep ahead of their staff members. Lincoln National Life Insurance Company's planning vice president, Richard Kischuck, finds that ''You begin to feel that you're missing out on very important information if you're not plugged in.''[36] But plugged into what? Teleconferencing is only a *conduit* for information, not an end in itself. In a business environment, teleconferencing is the express lane for human communication, but it is important to consider the organizational issues, the value of information, and the new demands for participatory management.

## Chapter 1 Notes

1. W. Thomas and C. Thomas. "Investment trends in teleconferencing." *Educational and Industrial Television*, August 1982, 34–35.

2. "Growth in teleconferencing." *Words*, February–March 1983, 12.

3. "*Ad Hoc* teleconferencing trends." *TeleSpan Newsletter*, September 15, 1982, 11.

4. J. Seaman. "Electronic mail: Coming at you." *Computer Decisions*, October 1982, 128–160.

5. "A summary of the AOC 1982 survey of word processing users." *International Information/Word Processing Association*, November 1982.

6. "Study predicts private satellite networks will be up fifteenfold by 1991." *Industrial and Educational Television*, November 1982, 11.

7. W. Sonneville, "Digital electronic message service: To form a more perfect union." *Business Communications Review*, January–February 1982, 9-16.

8. "AT&T discusses survey of international teleconferencing needs." *TeleSpan Newsletter*, October 15, 1982, 3.

9. "Satellite press conference launched." *TeleSpan Newsletter*, August 15, 1983, 12.

10. "Summaries." *TeleSpan Newsletter*, October 15, 1982, 9.

11. "The facility at Aetna Life." *Educational and Industrial Television*, February 1983, 18, 20-21.

12. K. Hunter, "A cautious welcome for hotel conferencing." *Video Systems*, April 1982, 29-33.

13. "Conference by satellite—a selection of case studies." *Educational and Industrial Television*, August 1982, 36-39.

14. J. Hecht, "Fiberopolis." *Omni*, December 1982, 120-122, 124, 126, 128.

15. G. Southworth, "Using narrow band video." *Video Systems*, April 1982, 11-13.

16. "Case study of Alaskan legislative network available." *TeleSpan Newsletter*, September 15, 1982, 21.

17. "An entrepreneur who sees the boom in two-way television." *Data Communications*, May 1982, 79-80.

18. H. R. Northhaft, "Making a case for using electronic mail." *Data Communications*, May 1982, 85-93.

19. "Newsfronts." *Data Communications*, October 1982, 46.

20. "Tall order in Texas." *Computer Decisions*, December 1982, 66.

21. H. R. Northhaft, "Making a case for using electronic mail." *Data Communications*, May 1982, 85-93.

22. H. Brody, "Telephones fly high." *High Technology*, September–October 1982, 26, 29.

23. "Videoconferencing: New option for marketing communication." *Telemarketing*, September–October 1982, 33.

24. J. Seaman, "Electronic mail: Coming at you." *Computer Decisions*, October 1982, 142.

25. "News." *Video Systems*, October 1982, 8.

26. "Case study of Alaskan legislative network available." *TeleSpan Newsletter*, September 15, 1982, 21.

27. M. Cornbluh, "The electronic office: How it will change the way you work." *The Futurist,* June 1982, 37-42.

28. J. B. Dykeman, "Editorial: Ring around the collar?" *Modern Office Procedures,* November 1982, 10.

29. "HRD facts & figures: What kinds of training do U.S. organizations do?" *Training/HRD,* November 1982, 86.

30. T. Richman, "Peering into tomorrow." *INC.,* October 1982, 45-48.

31. L.A. Arredondo, *Telecommunications: Management for Business and Government.* New York: Telecom Library, Inc., 1980.

32. C. Ungaro, "Teleconferencing focuses on a new era." *Data Communications,* September 1982, 85-97.

33. J. Cooney, "Lowering skies for the satellite business." *Fortune,* December 13, 1982, 161.

34. J. Naisbitt, *Megatrends: Ten New Directions Transforming Our Lives.* New York: Warner Books, 1982, 46.

35. "Survey for public television station predicts growth in teleconferencing." *TeleSpan Newsletter,* June 15, 1983, 3.

36. M. Lasden, "Make room for executive workstations." *Computer Decisions,* December 1982, 120.

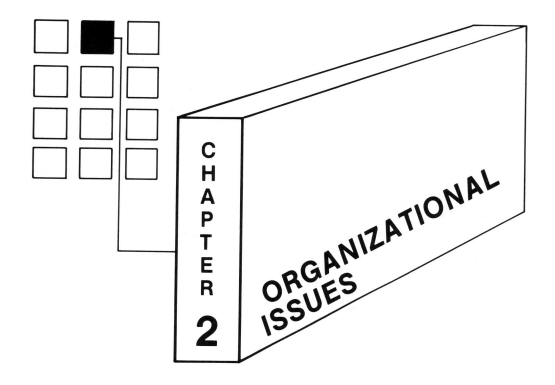

CHAPTER 2

ORGANIZATIONAL ISSUES

Teleconferencing is still a fairly new medium, and there are some technical issues that are being addressed every day by users and equipment manufacturers alike. *However*, the number-one problem in the implementation of teleconferencing is organizational, not technical! Putting aside some of the human-factor aspects (how teleconferencing users interface with the hardware), *the very nature of the organizational environment in which the teleconferencing system is placed will have significant impact upon the degree of success achieved.* As John Naisbitt pointed out in his book *Megatrends*, the "information age" is not just around the corner—it is with us now. Unfortunately, few realize exactly what that means either on a personal level or on a more abstract corporate level.

It would seem that we all have this mental picture of the Information Age that begins circa 2001—a Buck Rogers setting where the glow of amber phosphor screens reflects off the white lab coats of the executives gathered in the corporate electronic "war room" as they review the results of the latest computer simulations associated with the introduction of a potential new product. In fact, the advertising that appears in the current flood of publications appeals to that image, but some businesses are not waiting until 2001 (See Figure 2-1). More and more we are seeing military terms being used in the business setting. The latest catch phrase is "C³I"—Command, Control, Communication, and Intelligence. Competitive monitoring, planning, and ACTION are the key words. A recent ad in *Defense Electronics* by HRB-Singer has appeal beyond the military audience

**FIGURE 2-1**
Recent Military Teleconference

*Credit: Courtesy of the Public Service Satellite Consortium, Washington, D.C.*

for which the ad was intended. I would not be surprised to see a similar advertisement in a major business publication.

---

### INTELLIGENCE IS THE BEST DEFENSE

Today's electronic battlefield demands command decisions that are fast and well informed. $C^3I$ systems from HRB-Singer give you the Intelligence to see the total picture for quick assessment and the $C^3$ to take effective action.

Our $C^3I$ capabilities cover all phases of the threat . . . In strategic applications, information collection, processing and correlation keep you abreast of the changing threat situation to aid in your defensive planning. Our early warning systems enable you to monitor enemy strength on a day-to-day basis, and determine their intentions . . . In the tactical mode, our $C^3I$ systems give you the information you need to make quick, effective decisions.

If you're a decision-maker, looking for a system that can give you the total picture, contact . . .[1]

---

There are many corporations around the country that are looking for just such a system to help manage the complex information world they face. *The critical issue, however, is the quality of the human component at each end of the information pipeline—the technology is only the conduit.* All of these technologies are interrelated, and we need to keep that in mind. As we expand our communication options and begin to communicate in entirely new ways, it will change how we conduct business, how we organize ourselves, and even how we think.

It is not enough that we try to predict what technologies will emerge during the next few years; we must try to understand the human impact of the technology. As Isaac Asimov noted: "The important thing to predict is not the automobile, but the parking problem; not the television, but the soap opera; not income tax, but the expense account; not the bomb, but the arms race."[2]

As Weinberg noted in his book on General Systems Theory, a system is a collection of parts, no *one* of which can be changed without affecting the entire system.[3] Providing increased communication capability to all or portions of an organizational system will change the entire system, and today's systems are not simple.

## The Management Environment

One of the major trends in business today is participative management. The reasons are many, but the complexity of the business environment is one of the factors. The current rate of change, which seems to be for the most part technologically based, makes it difficult to look to the past for historical trends to guide us into the future. This lack of "guideposts," and a growing understanding of the interrelatedness of almost everything, increases the frustration as we try to make the "correct" decision. The sheer amount of information that we receive is increasing at geometric rates, making it difficult to decide when enough information has been gathered to make a sound decision. We are consumed by the fear that just as soon as we make a decision, we will receive that *one* critical piece of information which changes the entire picture. All this boils down to is the simple fact that there is too much information for a single manager to handle. Decisions require more participation and more collective thought. This means a change for the manager, who must share in the decision process yet retain the responsibility for the outcome—by no means an easy task.

Another factor which increases the complexity of our business environment is the continuing concentration of economic power in our county. Mergers are in the news more often than the start-up of a new firm. The 500 largest firms in the United States produce as much as the remaining 400,000 companies.[4] The independent worker constitutes only 10 percent of the labor force, while one-third of the labor force work for the top 500. There is much that indicates a continuing move in our country toward centralization, and with centralization comes a greater amount of interaction and a multiplicity of effects. On the other hand, there are some that believe that we are moving toward decentralization: toward an "electronic cottage industry." In actuality, we are probably moving toward centralized economic power and a decentralized work force. Regardless of the direction, teleconferencing can play a vital role in networking key human resources.

As the organizations become larger, the performance level drops, due in large part to the increasing length of the communications/decision path. The checks and balances become more rigid, and the organization has difficulty in reacting swiftly. This built-in resistance to sudden change can have a beneficial damping effect which keeps the organization from making irrational moves, but it also serves to keep the organization from making swift rational moves as well. Herein lies one of the key weaknesses of a large corporation—DECISION TIME. This is the time it takes for information to reach the correct people, the time to react to the information, the time to bring the necessary people into the decision process, and the time to move from decision to implementation.

An organization, however large, may find that TIME is key to its growth potential. With the current trend for shorter decision turnaround times (the time from initiation to action), more are turning to the use of communication systems, such as teleconferencing, to keep the turnaround time within competitive limits and provide the necessary input to maintain high decision quality. Cleveland, in his excellent article entitled "Information as a Resource," notes:

> The ultimate "limits to growth" of knowledge and wisdom are TIME (time available to human minds for reflecting, analyzing, and integrating the information that will be "brought to life" by being used) and the CAPACITY of people—to analyze and think integratively.[5]

Our current view of an organization in holistic terms comes from the Land of the Rising Sun and Theory Z's focus on increased organizational communication, especially from the bottom up, instead of the more traditional top down approach we learned from Theory X. There is little doubt that increased attention to interpersonal relationships, increased communication, and increased use of consensus decision making are the current evolutionary directions.

With the development of greater interpersonal interaction, there is a reduction in the number of layers between worker and manager. In fact, the new term "working manager" is a result of the increasing push toward greater production-management communication. Even within a business framework, our traditional responsibility-oriented organizational chart is changing as we recognize that overlapping responsibilities are more characteristic of the nature of things. Unfortunately, this shift to a combination of horizontal, vertical, and even diagonal structures creates new management control challenges associated with the advancing web of accelerated communication.

Without a doubt, teleconferencing can be an excellent information-sharing tool for problem solving, but it is also an effective means to identity and formulate problems as well. Our computers can provide analysis in seconds, communication satellites can transmit the information around the world at the speed of light, BUT HAVE WE ASKED THE RIGHT QUESTION? As the organization and competitive environment increase in complexity, so does the difficulty of recognizing, formulating, solving, and implementing the "correct" solution to the "right" problem. The organizational failure to find and solve problems correctly is becoming so common that researchers now call it Error of the Third Kind.[6] Basically, it is the "probability of solving the 'wrong' problem when one should have solved the 'right' problem."

The difficulty arises when we fail to see the division between *operational* problem solving and *strategic-planning* problem solving. In the first case, the concern is with the solution phase; in the second case, the focus is on finding the most organizationally relevant problem to solve. Mitroff notes that individuals have different capacities for operating in each mode (finding versus solving) and suggests that by identifying the strengths of individuals and increasing communication, an organization can increase its probability of correctly solving the right problem:

> Instead of asking the question WHO should choose, the question HOW the choice should be made may actually be more important. If anything, our preliminary work suggests that the choice of a problem, its formulation, its solution, and its final implementation ought to be made by decision makers who are appreciative of all four perspectives. This does not require that a problem solver give up his or her preferred style . . . What it does require is that they be prepared to broaden their perspectives so that they can compensate for their weaknesses—in effect, their blind spots.[7]

In this context, teleconferencing can be an effective vehicle in implementing such an approach; it can "network" the most appropriate individuals, whatever their geographic location, so that the issues can be addressed in an integrated fashion.

The manager is now faced with changing organizational dynamics, and the term "managerial competence" takes on new meaning and importance. In order to maintain the necessary command and control functions, the information feedback loop response time must be fast, and the information in the loop must be accurate. When that is combined with the need for increased interpersonal communication skills, the need for a new breed of manager emerges. Harris feels that the

> . . . tough minded bosses will give way to executive types who are concerned about the seven "S's": structure, strategy, system, superordinate goals, skills, style and staff. They envision subordinates as colleagues from whom they seek cooperation and consensus.[8]

Pascale and Althos, in their book *The Art of Japanese Management: Applications for American Executives*, defined the Seven S's as:

☐ Strategy: The plan of action.

☐ Structure: The way a firm is organized.

☐ System: How information moves in the organization.

☐ Staff: Human demographic characteristics.

☐ Style: Behavior of management and executives.

☐ Skills: Organizational and people strengths.

☐ Superordinate goals: The purpose to which the organization is dedicated.[9]

Teleconferencing, in its many forms, can impact the structure, system, and style by maximizing staff and skills.

## Changing People Factors

In the past, individualism has not been one of the more desired employee qualities. Taylor's early Theory X work certainly reflected a view of the work environment that is different than that desired by today's new worker.[10] The types of reinforcements that were the foundation of Taylor's observations are no longer as effective in our day and age. The new "perks" are participation in management decisions and the opportunity to see a job through to the end. Thomas Sheppart, associate professor of management and international business at the University of Texas, says:

> Younger employees are indifferent to the traditional penalties for noncompliance; they have a strong desire to be heard and a driving need for recognition as individuals . . . They see job satisfaction rather than pure income level as a sign of success. Not that they wouldn't want the material things too, because they do; it's just that they are conditioned to want more out of life and see these things, not as rewards for hard work, but as the rights of Americans of their generation.[11]

Sheppart is not alone in his assessment of the situation. Bailyn, in an insightful article entitled "Resolving Contradictions in Technical Careers or What If I Like Being An Engineer?", wrote:

> My research suggests that the right to report directly to a higher level of management than previously would be an important part of a career reward. Such an arrangement brings the employee closer to a level in the organization where overall goals are formulated, and thus eases his or her search for organizationally relevant problems to work on.[12]

Through this access to the organization's policy formulation stage, many feel that they can make a more substantial impact on the nature of the firm.

We are also seeing the emergence of new life style values. Wellness, creative use of leisure time, greater focus on family, and quality personal interactions are heading the success criteria list. One traveling educator I met said that her idea of Life was not night after night in an each-room-looks-the-same motel, nor was it ten hours out of every week driving from place to place. "I got a degree for this?" was her plea. A complainer? No, just someone who wants to spend a few evenings with her children. Someone who wants more from life than plastic dinners and an ulcer. She was alone. She was away from the professional stimulation of the others in her firm. By being on the road so much of the time, she felt like she was outside the company, unable, by her absence, to help shape the policies that would affect her. The rise in single parent families, as well as the growing importance of family relationships, is increasing the resistance to travel.

Reductions in scheduled air flights by our nation's air carriers is requiring an increase in layovers in airports and is increasing the level of travel fatigue for all those that must be mobile, especially executives who are becoming less tolerant of the wasted time at airports. The result is that meetings either are held less frequently or are delayed until problems escalate to the point where action is mandatory.

Many people who spend a great deal of time traveling actually like their jobs—in principle. When they do have client contact, the job may be very rewarding. But it is the time between positive encounters that is not enjoyable. These satisfaction variables have a very significant financial impact. For example:

1. What does it cost an organization if a critical person quits?
2. How long would it take to find a replacement? What would happen to sales during that time?
3. What impact does the temporary reduction in service have on the client's view of the organization?
4. Once hired, how long will the new employee be ineffective because he or she does not "know the ropes?"
5. Finally, how can you be sure that the replacement is going to like the job any better than the old employee?

Sensitivity to these issues can result in unexpected financial gain, or at least loss avoidance.

Actually, the directions of management and individuals are complementary. Today's manager needs greater participation to make a decision and today's worker wants to participate. Both are looking for quality: quality in the products they sell and quality in their lifestyles. Both are seeking greater interpersonal communication. Unfortunately, one of the problems is that the organizational communication structures which will permit this covergence to occur are developing at a much slower rate than the competitive environment demands. In the right situation, teleconferencing can create a more timely communications structure.

## Changing Value of Information

One of the approaches being used as an organizational coping mechanism for the current flood of information is to move the decision-making responsibility to the lowest possible level. A typical problem with this approach has been that the information necessary to effectively make the decisions has not flowed downward with the responsibility. Naturally, this results in frustration for both upper- and middle-level management. On one hand, upper-level management is bothered by the low decision quality on the part of middle management, and, on the other hand, middle-level management feels that upper-level management does not keep them informed and fails to provide access to the information necessary for them to do the job. The critical question is "How much information is enough to get the job done?"

As Peter Drucker noted, information and knowledge are the "central capital, the cost center, and the crucial resource of the economy."[13] We must treat information and all those involved in the information process seriously. Information is unlike any other commodity. It has some rather unusual characteristics, and it is useful to look at the subject from a fresh perspective. The more we understand about the nature of information, the better we will be able to manage it and maximize its utility. Since information is necessary for an organization and since there is an organizational cost in its collection, analysis, and dissemination, it may be useful to think of information's contribution margin.

Before we approach information as a substance, let's look at how information is malleable, how it changes through the human communication process. Information is shared in two ways: in parallel and serial fashions. In parallel communication, a number of people hear information from a single source at one time. In serial communication, information is passed from one person to another. Serial communication is significantly more prone to the introduction of error than parallel communication, which is one of the reasons why teleconferencing is preferred by some users who need to get the same important message to a number of other individuals.

Information error has three different characteristics: addition, deletion, and modification. First of all, information is *added* to the original message each time it is repeated. Statements are expanded upon to "make more sense." Often the person repeating the message will add other related pieces of information in order to maximize the communications event. Second, information is *deleted* from the original message. Information is retained by the listener that (a) the listener wanted to hear, (b) seemed important at the time, (c) made sense, and (d) seemed unusual or had special significance. The other information is lost. Third, information is *changed* in the repeating. By and large, any qualified statements in the message will become definite statements. Obviously, the more you can reduce the number of steps a message takes (the repetitions) to reach the end user, the higher the probability that the information will be received as intended. However, information itself has some rather unusual characteristics that need discussion.

Information breeds. The more information there is, the more it seems to grow and expand. New information leads to more information. Our entire news, publication, and book industries derive their profits from keeping us current with new information.

Information can be compressed. Much like a numerical average reduces individual numbers, information can be reduced as well. *Reader's Digest*, along with a host of other similar publications in the sciences and business, distill information to its "critical" components. However, any time information is compressed it loses something, either incidental or critical.

The value of information is always relative. Remember that the assignment of significance to a piece of information is performed by the individual doing the reporting. Reporting bias, the time of day the information is heard, and the mood of the reporter all impact the communication process. For example, make two copies of a relevant article from a magazine, underline the important statements on only one copy, put both copies in your desk, and leave them for a year. Then remove the article with no markings and underline the important statements. Compare the two. You will immediately see how your perspective has changed over time.

Information is never 100 percent accurate. As the general semanics people say, "The word is not the thing. Words only represent something else." A map does not accurately reflect the territory it represents. Granted, you can come close—but only for one precise moment in time. Each time you copy the information (share or transmit it) something will always change, much as an enlargement of a 35-mm slide is never as good as the slide itself.

Information can only be shared. Information cannot be exchanged or given in the traditional sense. Unlike something material that I give you, such as money, if I give you information, we both will have the knowledge. This is one of the most unique aspects of information—I can give information to as many people as I want and I will still have it!

Information's value changes with time. First, information has little value in the initial stages. See Figure 2-2. Just as a line cannot be drawn on a piece of paper when only one dot is present, we need a certain amount of information before we can determine a direction. Second, there is a peak value to the information when sufficient data has been amassed to make a decision with a high probability of quality. Normally, this is after the passage of some time. Third, beyond that point, the flood of information makes the decision process more difficult and the utility declines. Fourth, information develops a negative value with the passage of additional time. Decisions that are based on information that is outdated may be costly to the organization. Fifth, the value of information rises as it is recognized as historical data. When used as a guidepost or as a point in a trend analysis, information can once again significantly increase in value.

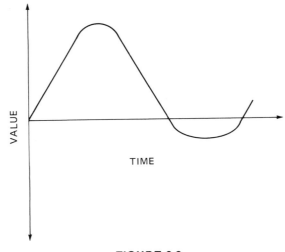

**FIGURE 2-2**
Information's Value Over Time

The cost of acquiring information is variable. See Figure 2-3. There is a relatively high initial cost associated with the design and implementation of an information capture system. The costs decline as the process is streamlined, only to increase due to storage and manipulation costs associated with growing volumes of information.

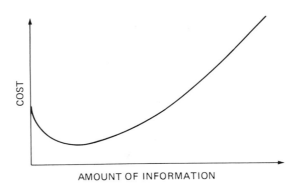

**FIGURE 2-3**
Information Acquisition Costs

The usefulness of information to an organization varies with its dissemination. The sharing process increases the baseline of common information upon which decisions are made. When few individuals have access to relevant information, the utility is low. However, as the sharing process continues, the value increases. But, again, there is a point where distribution can lead to a decline in utility. Unfortunately, too many believe that information hoarding is what gives them organizational security, and they manipulate the distribution of information in their own best interests. *Without a doubt, this counter-productive behavior is one of the most serious problems facing companies that need COMPLETE information NOW.* The new information technologies will only be successful if the organizational environment supports participative sharing of information. As Cleveland noted:

> Participatory decision-making implies a need for much feedback information, widely available and seriously attended. That means more openness and less secrecy—not as an ideological preference, but as a technological imperative.[14]

## Productivity Factors

I spoke not too long ago with a manager about the implementation of a word processing system in his organization. When the topic of increased productivity arose, he commented that the free time generated would just be used by the clerical staff to drink more coffee or talk on the telephone. This view is not all that uncommon and points up the problem that American industry has in looking at productivity issues as we move away from the pure production industry into an information-oriented environment.

While the goal of teleconferencing and other office automation systems is increased productivity, it is unfortunate that we do not have effective ways to measure office productivity. The most commonly used methods for the justification of a teleconferencing system are: cost displacement, value-added (sometimes called cost-benefit), and technological imperative. The cost displacement model is probably the most commonly used method of determining the benefits of a teleconferencing system. Commonly, these dollars are referred to as "hard dollars." They are identifiable, and the savings are considered real and tangible. In teleconferencing there is a significant problem with cost displacement models: the accuracy of the forecast is directly dependent on the validity of the assumptions concerning the extent to which travel is reduced. While current industry figures indicate that a 10 to 20 percent reduction in travel can be achieved, there is significant variation between companies.

The value-added model is where teleconferencing begins to provide some benefits. However, value-added benefits tend to be "softer" and more difficult to quantify. Some organizations may see the benefit immediately; others may feel that value-added benefits are simply a smoke screen. Let me give you some examples of value-added benefits that are difficult to quantify:

1. Sales people spend less time on the road. To what extent will more revenue be generated, or will the time saved be wasted?

2. Now ten people can participate in an educational program instead

of the one individual that traditionally traveled to an educational program. Does the one individual do a good job of teaching the others after the seminar? What value is there in having ten well-trained individuals instead of one?

3. A number of individuals can receive the same information at the same time. What is the cost of poorly received messages and other informational errors?

4. It is now possible for distant supervisors to meet with management once a week instead of once a month in person. What are the revenue ramifications of such meetings? Are problems identified earlier and corrected, thereby saving dollars?

5. Information can reach individuals in a matter of minutes instead of days. What is the competitive advantage in this rapid information dissemination?

These questions do not have easy answers. However, it will become increasingly important to develop guidelines that assist managers through these uncharted waters.

Technological imperative simply means that if you don't do *something*, you will go out of business. The health care field is filled with technological imperative purchases—one hospital buys a piece of equipment and the others follow suit. If a major competitor buys a device that may capture a new market, you may have no choice but to purchase the equipment to "keep up." In some ways, teleconferencing has become a subject of the technological imperative. There are a number of firms jumping on the satellite teleconferencing bandwagon simply because others are doing it.

Teleconferencing, as well as other systems, should support managers and professionals. Research indicates that managers and professionals account for upward of 75 percent of all office costs.[15] As a result, even small increases in productivity can have considerable financial impact on an organization. Even the typing of a memo has become increasingly expensive. The cost of supplies, equipment, and personnel time now comes to $7.54 per message, and if the memo is revised in any way before it is sent out, the cost increases to $12.90.[16] These clerical costs have been encouraging more direct communication between the sender and receiver to bypass clerical costs, with efforts to reduce the "paper trail" as much as possible.

While there is little doubt that teleconferencing can save time, I have a concern that organizations will not agressively seek to convert free time to productive time. If no managerial action is taken, there may well be longer coffee breaks taking place. It is critical that management-employee responsibilities be cooperatively reassessed in light of the time savings. For example, the introduction of a technology which produces a 20 percent increase in available time should be matched with a modification in the employee's yearly goals.

We have certain stereotypes of what can be done in a given period of time using traditional means. We base our staffing on what we feel is a reasonable personnel load to accomplish certain tasks, based on our past experience. A sales manager who spent many years on the road will define territory based on past experience of what is possible in a given amount of time. As soon as technology is added, the rules of the game change. Unfortunately, few managers make a concerted effort to understand the ways in which these devices create surplus time, so the basic expectations and assignments do not change significantly once the new technologies are in place. Naturally, a gradual increase in expectations will result until a more natural level is reached, but the rate of increase needs to be managed. In a technologically enhanced environment, the user's responsibilities should be increased.

What are some of the statistics concerning time savings with the use of teleconferencing systems? A review of the literature shows that, on the average, an increase in productivity from 10 to 20 percent can be expected, and hard dollar expenses for travel will be reduced by 10 percent. It is estimated that these figures will increase as workers develop greater understanding of the technologies and begin to apply the concepts to a broader cross-section of tasks.

## Summary

Because we understand so little about the contribution margin of information, we are poor managers of information technologies. Our computer systems are probably the best managed of the lot, but only from an operational viewpoint. There are few businesses and educational institutions that have started to use the power of the computer as a device to assist in our management of information beyond financial statistics. Even fewer organizations have sought to consolidate information technologies under a single management structure. Only in this way can organizations take advantage of the dynamic interrelatedness or cross-elastic nature of information systems. As long as the management of information devices is disconnected, the effectiveness of information transfer will be less than optimal. All too many look at communications costs in the same fashion as energy costs: target areas for cost reduction. Effective management is the key focal point. The past methods of containing costs, such as fewer calls and memos, do not link well with increased profits.

As we look at the various teleconferencing technologies, keep in mind ORGANIZATIONAL FIT. The most attractive video teleconferencing system may be the worst possible selection, given the organizational needs. The technological mix should support the company's mission statement and objectives and not modify those directions; the communications systems should fit the company, not the company fit the communications system.

As with any new technology, we tend to view a new system in light of our past experiences with what we perceive as related systems. Caution is advised because teleconferencing contains a complimentary, yet unique set of technologies. They are as different as the letter and television, the telephone and radio, the in-person lecture and the video tape. While communications is a common factor, each technology emphasizes different aspects of the communications process.

## Chapter 2 Notes

1. HRB-Singer, Inc. "Intelligence is the best defense." *Defense Electronics*, 14(2), December 1982, 8–9.

2. H. T. Smith, and W. H. Baker, "Reckoning with the future." *Words*, February–March 1983, 30–31.

3. G. M. Weinberg, *An Introduction to General Systems Thinking*. New York: John Wiley & Sons, 1975.

4. R. Williams, "Reindustrialization past and present." *Technology Review*, November–December 1982, 49–57.

5. H. Cleveland, "Information as a resource." *The Futurist*, December 1982, 36.

6. I. I. Mitroff, "On the error of the third kind: Toward a generalized methodology for future studies." In H. A. Linstone & W. H. Clive Simmonds (eds.), *Futures Research: New Directions*. Reading, MA: Addison-Wesley, 1977.

7. Ibid., 51.

8. P. R. Harris, "New office technologies force redefined roles." *Information System News*, December 13, 1982, 44.

9. R. T. Pascale, and A. G. Althos, *The Art of Japanese Management: Applications for American Executives*. New York: Warner Books, 1981.

10. F. W. Taylor, *The Principles of Scientific Management*. New York: Harper & Brothers, 1911.

11. "Training today: How this decade's "generation gap" affects productivity." *Training/HRD*, November 1982, 87.

12. L. Bailyn, "Resolving contradictions in technical careers or What if I like being an engineer?" *Technology Review*, November–December 1982, 46.

13. H. Cleveland, "Information as a resource." *The Futurist*, December 1982, 35.

14. Ibid., 39.

15. J. J. Connell, "Managing human factors in the automated office." *Modern Office Procedures*, March 1982, 51–64.

16. H. R. Northhaft, "Making a case for using electronic mail." *Data Communications*, May 1982, 85–93.

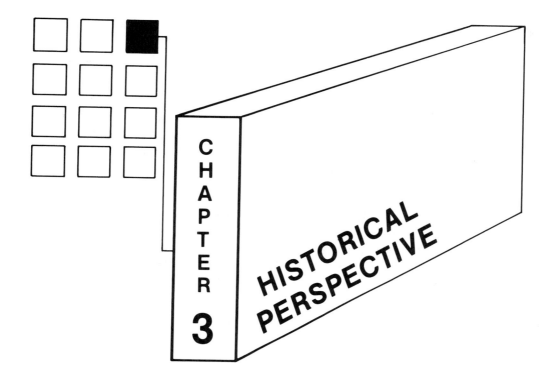

C
H
A
P
T
E
R
3

HISTORICAL
PERSPECTIVE

**L**ike much of the electronic technology that we see all around us today, teleconferencing systems are still in their relative infancy—most being less than two generations old for all practical purposes. Before talking about teleconferencing in depth, it may be useful to take a quick glance backward at some of the developments in the communications field for a perspective as we prepare to look at current issues and future trends. What is interesting to observe, as we rewind our history tapes, is how the use of these technologies changed with maturity. *It is fairly easy for today's technologically sophisticated reader to laugh at some of the earlier efforts in the field of communications, but we need to focus on the maturation process—the changing nature of the applications.* We will be looking backward with almost 100 years of perspective. As we review past efforts to apply new, now commonplace technologies, keep in mind that teleconferencing is also a rather new application. One can only wonder what individuals 100 years hence will think of today's teleconferencing efforts.

The drum dialog between distant African villages and rising clouds of smoke from several hills in the remote American west both represent some of the earliest forms of nonelectronic teleconferencing. Although primitive by some standards, the development of these communication modalities was extremely innovative—few other cultures developed similar capabilities. Although the common factor is the need for communication and interaction, the methods and applications are different. The drum's communication range was somewhat limited, but it certainly was not limited by tropical rain. Smoke signals had a much greater communication range, and there was little noise to alert enemies. If these two systems had co-existed in the same culture, the users could have selected the best communications system for the environmental conditions.

As the need for communication speed increased beyond the capabilities of the messengers on foot and horseback, new methods were explored. In 1790, Claude Chappe built a fairly large network of semaphore stations on hill tops in France.[1] From a high vantage point and with a colored flag in each hand, the semaphore operators would change the position of each flag to pass messages to several receivers many miles away. In 1815, the Rothschilds used carrier pigeons to track the progress of the battle of Waterloo.[2] When Napolean was defeated by Wellington and Blücher, the timely news brought by this information system enabled the Rothschilds to make significant shifts in their investments that netted them a fortune. The value of information was beginning to be realized on a large scale. Throughout the world many were seeking to devise methods of communicating more quickly. The pony express, that great American tradition which lasted less than two years before being replaced by other methods, was indicative of the lengths we would go to in order to move information in the fastest possible manner.

## Telegraph

Samuel F. B. Morse ushered in the electronic era with the telegraph in 1844. Morse was a man of the arts, the first liberal arts professor in the United States, and the man who started Vasser college. Morse's first telegraph message between Washington and Baltimore was ''What hath God wrought!'' and may have been more prophetic than was realized at that time. This phrase was repeated 118 years later in 1962 by John F. Kennedy when he spoke to Lagos, Nigeria, on the first transatlantic telephone call via satellite.[3]

## Telephone

The telephone was a watershed device that significantly altered the character of our society and of the world. In 1876, the significance of ''Mr. Watson, come here. I need you!'' was simply that Mr. Watson came! No prepared prose was used to introduce the technology. Unlike an astronaut uttering ''One small step for a man . . .'', the beauty of Bell's statement is that it resulted in immediate action. The value of the device was immediately realized, BUT NOT BY EVERYONE.

In 1877, running short of funds, Bell tried to sell his telephone patents to Western Union for $100,000. Western Union considered the notion of the telephone ''fantastic'' and rejected Bell's proposal. Here is an exerpt from Western Union's minutes of the historic meeting:

The telephone is so named by its inventor, A. G. Bell. He believes that one day they will be installed in every residence and place of business . . . Bell's profession is that of a voice teacher. Yet he claims to have discovered an instrument of great practical value in communications which has been overlooked by thousands of workers who have spent years in the field . . . Bell's proposal to place his instrument in almost every home and business place . . . is fantastic . . . In conclusion the committee feels that it must advise against any investments in Bell's scheme. We do not doubt that it will find users in special circumstances, but any development of the kind and scale which Bell so fondly imagines is utterly out of the question.[4]

Several months following the writing of this report, Western Union discovered its mistake and attempted to enter the telephone business. In 1879, Western Union gave up the fight and resigned from the telephone business.

It has often been said that we proceed into the future looking behind us, and so it is with new communications systems. There were many who had no idea how to handle the new communications modalities that were emerging around the turn of the century. Perhaps no other device received as much skepticism as the telephone. Bell was not quick to realize the importance of telephone communication for business, although the first public telephone call in 1877 was a news story relayed to the *Boston Globe*. In fact, many of Bell's early demonstrations of the telephone were more like radio broadcasts than anything else. Perhaps because of his background as an educator, rather than a businessman, Bell felt that his device could be used to extend the lectures of great thinkers into the homes of the public. Bell saw the telephone as a tremendous educational tool and was quick to point out the possibilities to anyone who wanted to listen. In 1877, a cartoon in the New York *Daily Graphic* showed a man talking to groups connected by telephone. The concept of teleconferencing by telephone was born![5]

Around 1890, Bell arranged several demonstrations of the telephone in what could be called a mass distribution mode. Nearly 2,000 people in Providence, Rhode Island, heard the "Star Spangled Banner" played in Boston.[6] A concert played in Madison Square Garden was heard by 800 people in Saratoga and by guests in a telephone executive's home, where they danced to the music. Unfortunately, all these demonstrations were considered a "side show" by the public, and little value was seen in the device. It is interesting to note that only now are we returning to some of the earlier thoughts Bell had about the application of his device.

Radio had a similarly mixed beginning. When Guglielmo Marconi demonstrated the wireless in 1895 in Bologna, Italy, he felt that radio had tremendous applications for the military. It was only after the Italian government dismissed the concept that Marconi went to England to introduce his technology. In addition to the military demonstrations, Marconi used the wireless to transmit minute-by-minute reports on the internationally famous Kingstown Regatta boat race to the Dublin *Daily Express*—an effort that gained Marconi worldwide attention. Coverage of the America's Cup and subsequent development of transatlantic communication increased the public's awareness of radio's great speed. These applications were the most representative of what we now call "competitive advantage."

Oddly enough, one of the biggest users of this new form of communications was a fruit shipping firm called United Fruit. United Fruit was surprisingly advanced in its thinking. As one of the largest shippers of bananas in the world, United Fruit found that the wireless enabled it to change the routes of its banana boats so that they could arrive at the ports that offered the highest prices. Since many of the boats could hear one another, a great deal of information was shared between the captains concerning weather and other topics of interest—a crude form of wireless teleconferencing, but effective. By recognizing the application for telecommunications (communications over distances), United Fruit became the one of the world's largest shipping firms.

The advent of wireless voice communication came without the fanfare of Bell or Marconi's inventions. Reginald Fressenden introduced voice communication to the world on Christmas eve, 1906, when he picked up his violin, played a few bars of "O, Holy Night," sang a few verses, read from the book of Luke, and played a phonograph record of a woman singing from Handel's "Largo."[7] United Fruit ships as far away as the West Indies heard the broadcast, then placed orders for the equipment, which would enable employees not familiar with Morse code to understand radio messages.

Still, there was little widespread excitement about radio. Much like the telephone, it seemed a "frill," and many of the early demonstrations seemed to be without significance at the time. For example, an early pioneer in radio, Dr. Lee DeForest, staged musical broadcasts from the Eiffel Tower and broadcast Enrico Caruso live.

Although marine communication was expanding, there was little being done with radio until the newspapers started to develop their own stations. Interestingly enough, the newspapers saw their ownership of a radio station as a way to increase newspaper sales. In the beginning it was a technique that worked quite well. The concept was simple enough: between musical selections, read just enough of the news story over the air to prompt listeners to buy a copy of the paper. In the early 1920s, William Scripps' *Detroit News* was one of the first newspapers to start its own radio station. Westinghouse, on the other hand, entered the radio station business primarily to produce programs that would entice people to buy its radios.

The revolution in radio came in 1922 when the first commercial was aired. Until that time there were no commercials on radio, but one station, WEAF, owned by American Telephone and Telegraph, broke tradition. AT&T rationalized that it, and it alone, had the authority to air messages for money. AT&T stated that what it was promoting was a new form of coin telephone booth in which anyone could pay his money and address the world, instead of only one other person. Now there was a financial incentive for owning a radio station. It was no longer a toy or simple promotional activity. Radio had come of age.

In retrospect, the early uses of radio were somewhat amusing. Commercials were lengthy and written in a rather academic style with compound, complex sentences that were difficult to understand when heard. When the first plays were broadcast, the actors could not get used to reading their lines in front of a microphone. So early radio plays were delivered from studios which were set up just like a stage, with the microphones hidden in the lamps so as to not distract the actors and actresses. It took years before actors in radio productions could develop the necessary oral skills to compensate for the lack of visual contact with the audience. It was soon discovered that it was possible to use words to appeal to the audience's imagination—the "mind's eye." Writers found that they could create mental images that would have been impossible to create on the stage. Orson Welle's Halloween surprise broadcast, *The War of the Worlds*, is a perfect example of how actors and scriptwriters were able to maximize the medium and build images of an invasion from Mars by space creatures that were real enough to shake an entire nation.

In the mid-1920s another major change in the new medium occurred when Dr. John Brinkley started a small radio station in Milford, Kansas, which he used as a forum from which to sell his patent medicines. Although his technique of prescribing drugs to people who wrote in describing their problems was the focus of efforts by the American Medical Association to revoke his broadcast license, Brinkley is credited with initiating the concept of public service broadcasting. In cooperation with the Kansas State College in Manhattan, Brinkley launched the "College Of The Air." People who could not attend formal classes could now work toward their degrees via radio without leaving their homes. Within two years, over 150 colleges and universities built their own educational radio stations. Although the vast majority of these educational stations were forced off the air due to pressure from commercial enterprises, the notion of educational broadcasting was born, and a portion of Bell's dream had been realized.

Before leaving the subject of radio, it should be mentioned that the single most agressive group in the development of teleconferencing has been the radio amateurs. Since the turn of the century, radio amateurs have conducted multiparticipant discussions on every possible topic. Their radio "round tables" continue to exist today as interested parties meet weekly to discuss alternative lifestyle activities, technical issues, civil defense, and many other topics. These individuals have audio teleconferencing protocols down to a fine art and have provided those in the teleconferencing field with invaluable advice on how to conduct large group audio discussions.

## Television

Although television has been around about as long as radio, it took even longer to gain a foothold. It is difficult to believe that although the first television images were produced as early as 1884, it was not until 1939 that the first public showing of television took place. Our American television standards were not in effect until 1941, and national standards for color were adopted as late as 1953. Television has come a long way since the early days when performers had to compensate for the poor-quality cameras by wearing green makeup and purple lipstick in order to look natural. But the biggest breakthrough in the video field came in the early 1970s with the introduction of portable video equipment.

Previously, television meant large studios, technicians, and other professionals. The new portable units permitted ordinary people to capture events on video tape with new freedom from the confines of the studio. The new "volksvideo" proved that everyday individuals could operate their own equipment and produce their own programs. While these efforts lacked the polish of professional productions, they added a new dimension of honesty and truth. It was from these early pioneers in the hills of Appalachia that I learned that as production quality increased, the more people distrusted the honesty of the message being conveyed. The more tightly a program is edited, the more people believe that the content is being manipulated. I learned that when there is viewer interest in the subject matter, the quality of the production has little impact; when interest is low, the production value needs to be great to compensate.

## Satellites

In 1945 an article appeared in the special interest publication, *Wireless World*, that was overlooked by a war-weary nation, but which caught the attention of the military.[8] In that landmark article, Arthur C. Clarke described the technical details involved in establishing communication satellites that would orbit the earth. Clarke specified the exact position and distance from the earth at which an orbiting satellite would appear stationary to ground observers. It was not until the mid-1960s that Clarke, author of *2001: Space Odyssey* and renowned futurist, saw his prediction come true as the first geostationary satellites were placed in orbit. In the mid-1970s another major development introduced video teleconferencing to an entire nation. In 1974, the National Aeronautics and Space Administration launched its sixth Applications Technology Satellite (ATS-6). ATS-6 was unique for several reasons. First, it was the first satellite that was specially designed for two-way television, so that people in two different locations could see and hear one another. Second, ATS-6 had a much larger antenna, which could concentrate its energy in small geographic sections so that smaller, low-cost receiving stations could be placed in rural areas. Hanging in space 22,300 miles above the equator, ATS-6 regularly linked users in Appalachia, the Rocky Mountain states, and Alaska. In Alaska, people who had no regular television service and had poor telephone communication were suddenly able to participate in discussions with others as far away as 1,000 miles.

Initially, ATS-6 was used to transmit prerecorded programs to various locations, with token question-and-answer periods at the end of the transmissions. Eventually, however, the users discovered that the real benefit of the satellite was that users could interact, enter into a dialog with others. New electronic friends were made, and relationships were established. A few years after the NASA demonstration ended, I was in Washington and saw a woman who looked very familiar. I introduced myself and discovered that she was a physician I talked to every week via ATS-6. Dr. Wilson, a marvelous person, said, "Bob! I didn't recognize you without the television set frame around your face!" Although she died a few years later of cancer, our electronic friendship was just as rewarding as any face-to-face friendship.

## Summary

With the advent of each medium there have been tendencies to project into it the characteristics of similar existing modalities. Newspaper writing styles were used when radio first appeared. Traditional stage movements were used when television was first developed. Traditional stage movements were even used when radio first appeared. Many felt that the telephone would never be accepted as a daily communications medium because it was impossible to see the person at the other end. There were a number who felt that telephones would never replace the letter as a preferred method of interpersonal communication because the telephone was too interactive. The letter, on the other hand, permitted the author to completely develop a thought without interruption.

Today, we recognize that each medium is, in fact, unique. When we select a medium, we select it on the basis of the message we wish to communicate. Most understand that there are times when a letter is a much better method for communicating some types of information than a telephone call. Books have not been replaced by audio recordings of the author reading the information.

As the various methods of communicating with groups electronically are discussed in the following chapters, it is important for you to keep in mind that: (a) these modes are different from some of the existing technologies with which we are familiar and (b) if you have had some negative experiences with teleconferencing, it is important that judgment not be rendered too quickly due to the newness of the medium. *In all probability, poor experiences with teleconferencing are a result of misapplication of the technology and a lack of attention to the new human factors—the mistaken belief that teleconferencing is "just like" something else with which we are familiar.*

## Chapter 3 Notes

1. H. Busignies, Communication channels. *Scientific American*, September 1972, 99–113.

2. J. Naisbitt, *Megatrends: Ten New Directions Transforming Our Lives*. New York: Warner Books, 1982.

3. S. W. Head, *Broadcasting in America: A Survey of Television and Radio*. Boston: Houghton Mifflin, 1972.

4. G. L. Archer, *History of Radio to 1926*. New York: The American Historical Company, 1938.

5. E. Barnouw, *A Tower in Babel: A History of Broadcasting in the United States to 1933*. New York: Oxford University Press, 1966.

6. Ibid.

7. Ibid.

8. A. C. Clarke ''Extra-terrestrial relays: Can rocket stations give world-wide radio coverage.'' *Wireless World*, October 1945, 305–308.

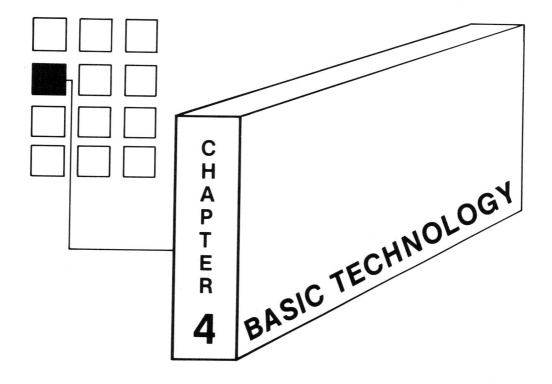

**CHAPTER 4**

**BASIC TECHNOLOGY**

It is difficult to discuss teleconferencing without some introduction to the basic technological aspects. This is necessary for several reasons. First, the level of teleconferencing sophistication (read: cost) is described in technical terms that an effective consumer needs to understand. Second, should you decide to put together your own system, you need to know how it all functions so you can design a system that will work. Third, if you hire a consultant to do the work for you, it is extremely helpful to know a little about what the consultant will be talking about. If you know absolutely nothing, the consultant will spend time educating you—and that is not service that the consultant provides free of charge. In this chapter, I will introduce some of the physics of communication, the various transmission systems that move the signals from "here to there," and give a brief introduction to the individual teleconferencing systems.

## Basic Physics

The first area to cover is some of the very basic physics involved in telecommunications. There are a number of technology-based terms that are frequently mentioned when discussing teleconferencing equipment, and a description of the fundamental physics will make it easier to understand statements made in this book and by others in the field.

## Frequency

You may be familiar with the term "frequency," but you may not know what it really means. Look at Figure 4-1 for a moment.

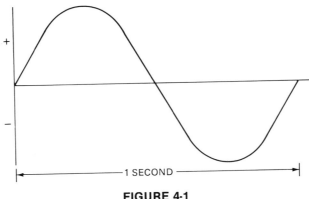

**FIGURE 4-1**
One Cycle Per Second

As you can see in the figure, the line first goes up, goes back through the center, goes down, and then goes back to the center once again. The complete movement (zero, positive, zero, negative, zero) is called a "cycle." If the cycle in Figure 4-1 took one second of time to complete, it would have a frequency of one cycle per second. Figure 4-2 shows another wave-like line, but this time you can see two complete cycles in the one-second time period, or a frequency of two cycles per second.

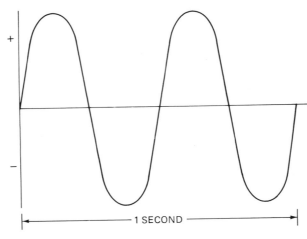

**FIGURE 4-2**
Two Cycles Per Second

When radio communication was in its developmental stages, engineers often shortened "cycles per second" to just "cycles." It got to the point that others listening to conversations or reading technical papers could not figure out if "cycles" was referring to cycles per second, cycles per minute, or cycles per year. In order to end the confusion, the engineering community agreed to name cycles per second after an early pioneer in the field of radio communication, Heinrich Hertz. Now, one cycle per second is called a "Hertz" and is abbreviated "Hz" (e.g., 2 Hz would be two cycles per second).

To avoid writing all the zeros associated with frequencies of thousands and millions of cycles per second or more, the following terms are used:

$$1,000 \text{ Hertz} = 1 \text{ KiloHertz (1 KHz)}$$
$$1,000,000 \text{ Hertz} = 1 \text{ MegaHertz (1 MHz)}$$
$$1,000,000,000 \text{ Hertz} = 1 \text{ GigaHertz (1 GHz)}$$

To convert the concept of frequency into more understandable terms, imagine a large bass drum. Hitting the surface of the drum with a drum stick, as seen on slow-motion equipment, shows us that the drum stick pushes the drum material away from its normal resting position. As the drum's skin moves outward, the air molecules are packed more closely together, and the air pressure increases and moves toward the listener. Since the surface of the drum is elastic, it wants to return to its normal position after it has been struck. However, since it is elastic, when it gets back to its normal position it does not immediately stop. Instead, it moves through the at-rest position (zero) and extends beyond the normal position. How fast the drum skin moves back and forth determines the frequency of the sound generated. Now it is creating a very small vacuum (negative air pressure). The surface of the drum will continue to move back and forth until it finally comes to rest in its normal position. All this happens very quickly, and we cannot normally see it move, but we may be able to feel the vibrations with our fingers. The range of our hearing is from 20 to 20,000 Hz. Quite a range, but our ears are substantially less sensitive to the very low and very high frequencies.

**Bandwidth**

Three factors affect communication costs: the distance involved, the duration of the communication, and the bandwidth required. Early in the development of the telephone, communication engineers found that it was going to be very expensive to develop a system that was capable of reproducing the complete human hearing range (20 to 20,000 Hz). So they decided that since the human voice used a range of frequencies between 100 and 5,000 Hz, their telephone system did not have to reproduce frequencies higher than what the human voice generated. They experimented further and found that the voice could be reasonably well understood if the frequency response of the telephone was limited to between 200 and 3,400 Hz. Using the electronic equivalent of an axe, the engineers literally cut off all the higher and lower frequencies. In order to communicate among themselves more precisely, the engineers said that the difference between the highest frequency and the lowest frequency would be called "bandwidth," or the width of the band of frequencies to be transmitted. In the case of the telephone, the bandwidth is roughly 3,200 Hz (3,400 Hz minus 200 Hz) for the voice and 800 Hz for special control signals, for a total bandwidth of 4,000 Hz (4 KHz).

The engineers also found that the telephone wire had a bandwidth considerably greater than the 4 KHz required for adequate voice communication and discovered a way to put several different voice communications on a single wire without the parties hearing one another. This was a major breakthrough for all the communication companies, for up until then each voice communication required its own individual wires, and installation was expensive. Now there was an economic incentive to pack as many voice communications as possible onto a single piece of wire and a reason to keep the bandwidth of a voice communication channel limited to 4 KHz.

If an FM radio station needed the ability to link its studio downtown with a transmitter on a distant hill, it would use telephone wires to connect the two locations. Since FM radio stations need to transmit frequencies from 50 to 15,000 Hz to handle the higher frequencies from the violins and flutes, they need the telephone company to provide them with a line that would have a bandwidth of at least 14,950 Hz. The telephone company will provide the service, but at a higher cost because (a) it would be losing the revenue from the two or three additional telephone conversations that would be displaced and (b) it would have to put in special equipment since its equipment was designed to handle just voice communication.

Television, like FM radio, needs more bandwidth than voice communication. If you look closely at your television screen, you will see that the picture is made up of a series of horizontal lines. The average television picture has 300 horizontal lines of information and approximately 430 individual points of light on each line, for a total of 140,000 discrete points of light, called "picture elements," on the television screen. In order for us to have a sense of motion, our television system sends 30 still images (frames) per second for a total of 4,200,000 picture elements per second, which equates to a bandwidth of roughly 4,500,000 Hz (4.5 MHz). The telephone company can pack over 1,000 telephone conversations into a 4.5 MHz bandwidth! As you can well imagine, anyone who wishes to use the telephone network for television pays a premium price for all that bandwidth.

In teleconferencing, as well as in other areas of telecommunications, the cost of communication increases with the bandwidth requirements. The further you deviate from the telephone company's standard equipment and offerings, the more costly communication becomes. For rough comparison purposes, an hour of audio bandwidth communication is $20, as opposed to $1,000 to $2,000 for television. Additionally, since special equipment is required to establish a television transmission link, it is a far more complex and costly process than simply picking up the telephone and dialing a number.

## Analog and Digital Communication

So far, we have discussed wave-type, or "analog," communications. Computers communicate using digital communication. Since computers are nothing more than very fast switching systems, computers and computer-like devices talk in on/off symbols called "bits" of information. Very much like analog systems, the bandwidth requirements for digital information are referred to in "bits per second" or "bps."

It is very difficult to equate analog and digital bandwidth requirements due to the unique nature of each transmission system. However, for illustration purposes, if a 4 KHz analog voice communication was converted to digital information, the digital system would need to operate at 64,000 bps (64 Kbps) in order to provide similar clarity. Similarly, a regular 4.5 MHz television signal would require a digital transmission system capable of handling 90 million bps (90 Mbps). The problem is that it takes about 10 bits of information to describe one analog wave, so more bandwidth is necessary for a digital system to transmit the same information as its analog counterpart. So what is the advantage of digital information? Frankly, in a number of situations digital information is a distinct disadvantage, but digital information is (a) less susceptible to interference and noise, (b) can be stored and manipulated by a computer far more easily than analog information, and (c) communication costs may be lower if special computer-oriented long-distance networks are used.

Realistically, current digital equipment can push only about 4.8 Kbps through a standard voice telephone line over long distances. Faster digital speeds are possible over shorter distances (less than five miles), but most teleconferencing is long distance and the faster speeds would not be applicable. However, there have been a number of fairly recent developments that may significantly increase the digital transmission speeds over regular telephone lines.

## Basic Transmission Systems

The problem of how you get from "here to there" exists no matter what type of teleconferencing system is used. In this section we will cover some of the more common transmission systems that are used in teleconferencing.

### Public Switched Network

A fancy name for the communications network we access through our telephones: more commonly called the "dial up" network. The United States has the most comprehensive telephone network in the world, and there are few places in our country where there are no telephones. For that reason, the public switched network (PSN) is ideal for teleconferencing purposes because it is possible to reach just about any location. It requires no special engineering to connect users; one simply dials a telephone and the connection is automatic. This capability is especially important to users who deal with many locations on an infrequent basis, as opposed to users who communicate with a few locations on a regular basis. Since the PSN has sufficient bandwidth for voice communication, the term ''voice grade'' is used to describe its capabilities.

## Long-Distance Alternatives

One method of reducing long-distance telephone charges is through the use of WATS (Wide Area Telephone Service) lines. Less expensive than direct-dial long distance, several varieties of WATS lines are available, ranging from service limited to adjacent states to national coverage. WATS lines are also available for intrastate use, but in some cases intrastate WATS calls may be more expensive than direct-dial calls. During the past several years a number of communication firms have offered alternatives to the traditional ''1-PLUS'' direct-dial long-distance service offered by the telephone companies. These firms use a combination of communication channels to offer long-distance service for less than direct dial rates. Companies like MCI, Western Union's Metro Service, Allnet, and others offer interesting options to the direct-dial network. Two words of caution for teleconferencing users evaluating long-distance alternatives. First, if you are using the service for an hour or more, make sure it is still less expensive than direct-dial rates or WATS service. Second, check out the quality of the service before a critical program. It has been my experience that some of the services have more noise in their communication lines, which may make it difficult to hear others when you are teleconferencing with several locations.

## Dedicated Lines

It is possible to obtain from the telephone company special lines that have been adjusted, or ''equalized,'' to provide sufficient bandwidth to carry much higher frequencies. Because these lines need to be adjusted to provide the increased service, they are not accessed through the telephone company's central switching system. Instead the telephone company will provide you with a pair of wires that, for all practical purposes, run directly from your location to the destination and are available for use 24 hours a day—you pay a fixed amount each month for unlimited use. Dedicated lines are also available for voice-grade service as well. If your public switched network long-distance audio teleconferencing costs are anticipated to be high, an option would be to install dedicated voice-grade lines between your locations. Again, the lines are available 24 hours a day and are much less expensive than the higher quality, equalized lines. It is possible to connect all facilities to one master dedicated line which links all of the locations.

## ''900'' Service

American Telephone and Telegraph (AT&T) originally started this service so that callers around the country could dial one number and listen to the latest sports scores or a host of other brief, prerecorded messages. Recently, AT&T has expanded the service so that callers can listen to a live or prerecorded lecture of any length. To use the "900" system, an originating firm connects a telephone line to its public address system and feeds the information to AT&T. To "eavesdrop" on the presentation, a caller simply dials the "900" number, listens, and then hangs up when the program is over. While the "900" service does not permit callers to ask questions, it does provide a way for up to 8,000 people who could not attend a presentation to listen as it is taking place. What some companies have done is to offer the program live and then play back a recording of the presentation for the next 24 hours so that callers can listen to the presentation at their convenience.

### T1 Carrier Systems

AT&T offers a special digital communication service which can support high rates of digital information up to 1.5 million bps (1.5 Mbps). The significance of the T1 carrier is that it is significantly less costly than AT&T's rate to carry a television signal. The reason the T1 is less expensive is simply that a T1 system uses just a pair of wires to handle the high-speed transmissions, while full television transmission would require an expensive microwave link (see explanation below). A number of manufacturers have been working on electronic systems that compress a regular television signal so that it can be transmitted through a T1 carrier system. A full discussion of compression techniques will follow.

### Cable Systems

Coaxial cable is a special wire which has the capacity to carry many communication signals. Although most commonly used to carry television signals, cable can be used to carry a large number of voice-grade communications as well, or a mix of television, voice, and digital communications. Because of installation costs, cable is normally useful when connecting locations are less than 15 miles apart.

### Microwave Systems

When longer distances are involved, or when the cost of cable is prohibitive, microwave transmissions are a viable alternative. Microwave transmitters can usually handle only one television signal and have a range limited to about 20 miles. The range is limited because the microwave transmitters operate at extremely high frequencies (12,000 MHz and above), which behave more like light than the more familiar AM, FM, or CB radio signals. Microwave signals have difficulty penetrating heavy rains, trees, and buildings, and they cannot reach over the horizon—they are limited to line-of-sight. To reach locations beyond 20 miles, a "repeater" is used which receives the originating microwave signal and then retransmits it to the next repeater or the final location. To obtain maximum power, microwave transmitters use parabolic, or "dish," antennas which focus the radio energy in specific direction. Microwave systems are used between high-communication-density locations due to the high cost. For example, a repeater location can cost as much as $50,000 when equipment, antenna tower, land purchase, access road, and establishment of electrical service are taken into account.

## Satellite Systems

Although Arthur C. Clarke developed the theoretical design in 1945, communication via satellite is a fairly recent development. Positioned 22,300 miles above the earth, communication satellites orbit the earth every 24 hours. When stationed over the equator, the satellites appear stationary to observers on the earth. A communication satellite is nothing more than a microwave repeater, but from its lofty vantage point the satellite can "see" transmitters and receivers over a wide geographical area. Internally, a satellite is composed of 24 receiver-transmitter pairs, with each pair called a "transponder." Each transponder is capable of repeating one television signal. The cost of an "earth station" to receive signals *from* a satellite has steadily declined from $20,000 to a current level of less than $7,000. The cost of equipment to transmit television signals *to* the satellite (called an "up-link") has not declined significantly and remain around $100,000. At the present time, there are thousands of earth stations owned by private individuals that are used to receive the many premium movie networks designed to feed America's cable television systems (as evidenced by the number of backyard 10-foot dish antennas pointed skyward). These home installations can just as easily receive satellite teleconferences, and the lack of confidentiality should be taken into account by potential users. One firm reported that immediately following a satellite teleconference, in which they announced a new product and toll-free numbers potential customers could use to obtain further information, their switchboards lit up with calls from private individuals who had watched the teleconference on their home earth stations. There are devices on the market which are intended to scramble television signals so that only locations with an unscrambler can view the television picture. There are two problems with scramblers, however. First, they tend to reduce the overall quality of the television image. Second, it is fairly easy for someone with average electronic skills to build an unscrambler.

There is one unusual characteristic about satellite communication that sets it apart from microwave communication—communication time delays. At the speed of light it would take your message about one-quarter of a second to travel the 44,600 miles from the transmitting station to the satellite and back to the receiving station. If the person on the receiving end responds, the message would take another quarter-second to reach you. The net effect is that you are seeing reactions to statements that you made a half-second earlier. While this may not seem like much of a problem, work at Bell Telephone Labs has shown that the time delay is sufficient to disorient those involved in highly interactive satellite teleconference discussions. This is one of the reasons why AT&Ts new video teleconferencing service, the Picturephone® * Meeting Service, does not use satellites to link its facilities.

---

*Picturephone® is a Registered Trademark of American Telephone and Telegraph.

## Laser Systems

A LASER (Light Amplification by Stimulated Emission of Radiation) is a device that creates a special beam of light that has tremendous capacity for carrying information. It has been estimated that a single laser beam could transmit all the telephone calls of the world simultaneously![1] Unfortunately, since a laser is basically a beam of light, fog, rain, and snow severly limit its range. As a result, the range of a laser is limited to less than a quarter-mile if reliable communications is desired. Even with this limitation, a laser is an excellent transmission device between buildings in major metropolitan cities where it is either impossible or too costly to install coaxial cable or microwave systems.

## Fiber Optics

Fiber optics are specially designed glass-like fibers that are used to carry laser beams considerably further than the quarter-mile range possible in the open air. Composed of extremely pure materials, fiber optics can carry laser signals many miles. A fiber optic system is still more expensive than a comparable microwave system, but it is being used in geographic areas where there are no more microwave channels available. In addition, fiber optic systems are not affected by weather and are immune to reception by unauthorized individuals.

## Packet Switched Networks

Packet networks are specially designed communication networks that are used exclusively to carry digital, computer-like information. Electronic mail and computer conferencing systems use packet networks because they are one-third as expensive as dial-up telephone lines and because the digital communication reliability is better than the public switched network. Currently, the largest providers of packet network services are Telenet, Tymenet, and Uninet. It is expected that Bell Telephone will be introducing its own digital communication network (Net 1000) in the near future.

## Compression Systems

Since communication costs increase with the bandwidth required, a new breed of "electronic funnels," called "compressors," are coming on the market. For example, television signals consume tremendous amounts of bandwidth (4.5 MHz) to move all the picture information. A number of years ago, screen watchers began to see that much of what was displayed on the television screen did not change from image to image. "What," they asked themselves, "would happen if you transmitted only the picture information that changed?" If you take a look at any of the news interview programs on television, you can begin to see why these engineers were so interested in the process. In most meetings, when the cameras are focused on the participants, the images change relatively little. When you look at an image of a financial sheet that is being discussed for two or three minutes, significant reductions in bandwidth could be realized. Although voice and computer signals are being compressed, most of the research effort is focused on television since its bandwidth requirements are so great (and expensive).

There are a number of ways that companies are approaching the problem. The basic categories of compression techniques are: *intra*-frame, *inter*-frame, and predictive. *Intra*-frame compression looks at each television frame, which is transmitted every 1/30 of a second, for similarities. For example, a large area of color (a blackboard) is described by the transmitting computer in one or two instructions instead of thousands to the receiving device which, in turn, recreates the color as described. *Inter*-frame compression compares a new television frame with the last frame sent and transmits the changed information. Predictive compression is a totally different approach to the compression problem. Much like inter-frame compression, the predictive technique is based on change, but where it differs is what it does with the *rate* of change. A predictive system might look at a person walking in front of the camera and say to the receiving unit: ''We both know what I just sent you. Here are some of the changes, but based on the rate of change I think that the next image will change like this.''

The manner in which these techniques are implemented varies from manufacturer to manufacturer. They use complex mathematical formulas (called ''algorithms'') as the basis of their compression techniques. Some algorithms work better in some situations than others, and each has its own particular list of advantages and disadvantages. The hardware is currently complex and expensive, but for the heavy teleconferencing user the reduced communication costs might more than justify the initial expense. Compressors perform truly amazing work. Converting a regular television image to digital information would require a transmission medium capable of handling 72 million bits of information per second. Compressors, on the other hand, pack essentially the same information into only 1.5 million bits per second (1.5 Mbps)! The 1.5-Mbps figure is a magic number because the telephone company's high-speed service, called a ''T1 carrier,'' is rated to handle 1.5 Mbps information. (See ''T1 carrier systems,'' above). There has been some exciting work done on compressing television images even further. It is now possible to transmit motion using only 56 Kpbs.[2] While the images do not move smoothly, there are some significant potential applications in cases where the primary use of a television system is graphic, with some motion available for meetings.

## Teleconferencing Systems

Each teleconferencing system has its own advantages, disadvantages, and costs. While you may be initially interested in only one form of teleconferencing, the following section will give you a brief introduction to each one of the current offerings before jumping into the detailed descriptions in the following chapters.

### Audio Conferencing

Audio conferencing is the most common form of teleconferencing and one of the least expensive. Reports from users indicate that audio conferencing can replace up to 40 to 50 percent of existing face-to-face meetings. With the addition of a visual component, the replacement percentage increases by only 10 to 20 percent. While it may be difficult to convince some executives that the visual component adds so little, the findings of current users must be acknowledged and should give us pause as we look at the costs and benefits associated with each of the technologies. In the audio conference the participants' telephones or speaker telephones are electronically linked so that all the participants can hear one another. The device that is used to combine all of these lines is called a "bridge." There have been many new advances in the field of audio conferencing technology, and the sound quality of the conference is significantly better than was previously possible. New speaker telephones have reduced the "hollow barrel" sound, and new bridge devices provide exceptional quality and flexibility.

## Audiographic Systems

When some form of written communication is necessary and there is insufficient time to mail the information ahead of time or when there is a need to respond on an *ad hoc* basis to questions or topics, then an audiographic system is an alternative. Facsimile, or "fax," has been around for years and does give the user the ability to transmit just about anything that is written on a piece of paper: financial charts, anatomical drawings, and certain types of photographs. One of the advantages of facsimile is that its product is a piece of paper. A simpler form of audiographics is the remote control of slide projectors. With this approach, a brief tone is transmitted over the telephone lines, much like the "beep" that you hear on film strip programs, and the projectors at each location advance one slide. One of the more exciting devices is the AT&T Gemini® * electronic blackboard. With this device, when someone writes on a special blackboard, the writing appears on television-like sets at the remote locations. The Gemini® has been very useful for corporations that tend to communicate in a "chalk talk" style.

## Slow Scan or Captured-Frame Television

Slow scan television (SSTV) or captured-frame television is a fairly old medium that has been gaining momentum. If you want the ability to transmit images from a television camera over the telephone lines, slow scan television may be an option. The only problem is that SSTV images do not move—they are a series of still images. A major advantage is that materials do not have to be sent out in advance, and if there is a need to discuss an image in more detail, the user simply points the camera at the object for inspection and sends another image. SSTV can transmit pictures of people, pages in books, three-dimensional objects that one simply could not get into a facsimile machine, X-rays, etc. However, the bandwidth is insufficient for full motion.

Television needs a bandwidth of 4.5 MHz to transmit moving images, but a telephone's bandwidth is only 4 KHz. If each picture was 4.5 million gallons of

---

*Gemini® is a Registered Trademark of American Telephone and Telegraph.

water, the full-motion television pipeline required to handle such a flow each second would have to be large. Telephone lines, by the water analogy, have been designed to handle a much smaller flow—approximately 4,000 gallons per second. It is literally impossible for a 4,000 gallon pipe to carry 4.5 million gallons per second. If we had a 4.5 million gallon tank (the TV screen), the regular television pipeline would fill that tank in one second. The smaller pipeline would fill the tank as well, but it would take much longer. This is the basis of slow scan television. While each regular television image, called a "frame," takes 1/30th of a second to transmit, the same frame transmitted via slow scan television takes 72 seconds.

An increasing number of companies are using either their own dedicated lines or satellite systems with greater bandwidth, so the time it takes to transmit an SSTV image is reduced—in a number of cases, the transmission time is less than eight seconds. At those speeds slow scan television is not all that slow. Since a majority of the uses for SSTV are graphic (overheads, material on paper, photographs, people) a transmission time of less than eight seconds is not objectionable.

## Videographic Systems

Regular users of SSTV will tell you that some of the reasons why they use SSTV are that they simply do not have the time to mail visual information to all the locations in their conferences ahead of time, that there are images that do not lend themselves well to other modes of transmission (such as facsimile), or that they cannot afford the cost associated with regular full-motion television. However, they will note that once they have a budget sheet or an engineering diagram on the screen, trying to describe the area they are talking about can be time consuming. It is fairly easy to mark an area that will be under discussion prior to the transmission or to use a small pointer indicating the region to be discussed, but it is sometimes difficult to think that far ahead—especially in an *ad hoc* discussion.

Videographic systems combine the advantages of SSTV with the advantages of audiographic systems. A user is able to transmit the desired picture and then pick up an electronic writing instrument to make notes that appear on all the viewing television sets. These real-time notes appear to make the image *seem* like full-motion television. Some of the more advanced systems enable all the participating locations to make their own notations, with each location's lines appearing in a different color for instant identification of the originator.

The true advantage of the videographic system is the ability to make notes over the image that has been transmitted. A complex financial sheet, medical illustration, or just about any other image where a presenter would have difficulty describing the location to be discussed lends itself to this form of system. Probably the closest analogies would be (a) a light pointer that people use when pointing out areas of interest on a projected slide and (b) the ability to make notes in a margin like one does with a transparency.

## Full-Motion Television

This is the type of teleconferencing most widely perceived as "teleconferencing." In this system, regular television cameras and television sets are used to provide a television image which approximates what we see on our home television sets. Actions made by participants are immediately seen by others. Full-motion television can be transmitted to other locations using the same high-bandwidth transmission systems used by the commercial television networks, or the television signals can be compressed—as long as the *illusion* of motion remains. Three types of configurations are common: one-to-many, one-on-one, and multiple site. The one-to-many situation normally uses a satellite to distribute the originating location's image to many receiving sites. If two-way communication is desired, individuals at the receiving locations call the originating studio by telephone. One-on-one occurs when two locations are equipped with transmission and reception equipment so that the participants can see and hear one another. AT&T's Picture-phone® Meeting Service links two similar teleconferencing rooms to provide one-on-one service. Multiple-site configurations permit three or more similarly equipped teleconferencing locations to interact. A multiple-site conference is technically complicated due to the problems of distributing the images of the participants at each location to all other locations.

### Store and Forward Systems

Store and forward systems are really composed of two technologies: electronic mail and computer conferencing. These systems enable various participants who cannot meet at the same time to exchange information. They store a participant's contributions and forward them to others when their schedules permit them to receive the information. These technologies were originally developed to meet a very specific need. In a number of situations, beginning with international communications, it was very difficult to have a number of individuals meet at the same time, even electronically. Differences in time zones and other factors became more complex as distance increased. To address those problems, technicians were able to program computers to simulate discussions on specific topics even though the participants were not able to meet at the same time. Recently, that technology has expanded to include audio and visual communications in addition to text. When participants are able to meet at the same time, it is called "synchronous communication"; when the participants exchange information at a time that is convenient for them, i.e., not at the same time, it is called "asynchronous communication."

*Electronic mail.* Actually, the need for this form of communication stems from an early need for written communication, called "record communication." Communication across time zones and the need for messages that were error free started the record communication process. Electronic mail is very similar to the early telegram, with several exceptions. With electronic mail it is possible to type in one message but a number of addresses. The central storage and switching system then sends the same message to all the addressees indicated. In actual use, someone wishing to send an electronic message connects to a central computer, enters the addresses and the message, and then terminates the connection with the computer. The central computer serves as an intermediate "storage" system and then "forwards" the messages. The forwarding process can be either automatic or manual. In the automatic mode, the central computer, after receiving the message, dials the computer terminal associated with each addressee and delivers the message. Generally, this delivery process takes anywhere from several seconds to several minutes following the completion of the original message. With the manual system, the central computer puts all the messages to an addressee into the electronic equivalent of a mail box associated with the individual. When an individual calls into the central computer, all the messages in the mail box are then delivered.

*Computer conferencing systems.* In a computer conference system, all the features discussed so far would be present, but with several important additions. Within the central computer's storage is an electronic version of topic-related file folders in which all the electronic mail pertaining to a specific topic is stored. In addition, options like voting, personal notebooks, and other features add to a computer conference system's flexibility. Using our marketing department as an example, one computer conference (file folder) might be dedicated to a product's problems. Another might be dedicated to reports on the competition. Another could be used to develop an annual sales report in which regional managers can add information and edit the document. The possibilities are endless—cooperative development of national personnel policies, research and development reports, ideas for new products, etc. Computer conferences can be very helpful as organizational tools and for the exchange of information prior to another form of teleconferencing. Meeting agendas can be developed by the group ahead of time, and items for review can be shared so that participants do not have to waste valuable time reviewing information during the synchronous conference—all the participants are "up to speed" prior to the real-time meeting. It is even possible to have the various participants in a real-time teleconference connected to the computer conference at the same time to discuss the various text items that were entered just moments before the meeting (such as the latest financial reports).

## Summary

In this section we have covered considerable territory. While teleconferencing can be as easy as setting up a conference call with the operator, more complex arrangements call for increased knowledge. You now have a brief overview of some of the technical basics, of how signals are moved between locations, and an introduction to the different teleconferencing options that exist. Many do not realize that there are so many ways to teleconference and fail to select the method, or methods, that would fit best with their business.

So far, we have focused on the technical factors, but the human factors are more important. Frankly, we are at a state of development in our technologies where they can do just about anything that we ask them to do. Unfortunately, we do not have a good idea about what we want them to do. With that fact in mind, let's shift our sights from the "High Tech" aspect of teleconferencing to the "High Touch," or human factors consideration.

## Chapter 4 Notes

1. International Telecommunications Union. *From Semaphore to Satellite*. Geneva: 1965.

2. Widergren Communications, Inc., (Widcom) of San Jose, California, recently demonstrated a 56-Kbps code which showed remarkable quality, given the very narrow bandwidth.

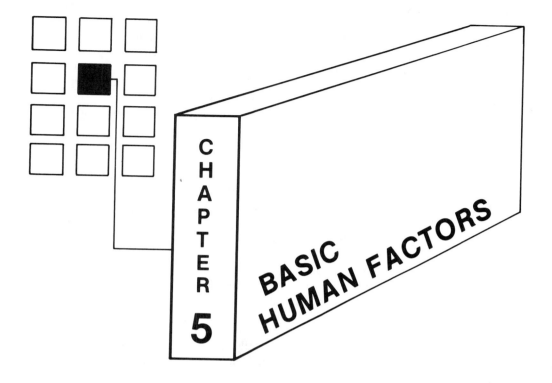

# CHAPTER 5
# BASIC HUMAN FACTORS

**N**ow that we have addressed some of the technical basics so that you can hold your own with consultants and others at conferences, we need to look at the human factors that are common to all of the teleconferencing systems. In this chapter we will look at a variety of factors: organization, individuals, attitudes prior to an event, the event itself, follow-up, educational factors, meetings, and *ad hoc* events. Rather than repeat certain aspects in each system's chapter, I want to cover the more general aspects at one time. I should note, however, that while some of these factors apply to text communication, there are some differences which will be covered in the chapter on electronic mail and computer conferencing.

## Organizational Factors

How an organization responds to teleconferencing will affect the outcome. There are a variety of relevant issues within the organizational frame work: commitment, placement, the innovator, objectives, expectations, applications within the mission statement, and communication needs.

### Organizational Commitment

An organization's commitment to teleconferencing has much to do with its eventual success. There continues to be disagreement about whether the approach should be "top down" or "bottom up," but in either case clear management support is necessary. By and large, upper-level management knows little about the way that its employees communicate, and a design originated by management may miss the mark. Those with a need to communicate should be the ones who become involved in the development of the project, with initial support from management and a clearly defined reporting channel back to management on the efforts.

### Organizational Placement

Who is in charge of teleconferencing in the organization? Often organizational placement is given little consideration. Placement is an important element when one realizes that an understanding of teleconferencing, associated training, scheduling, and other issues depends upon those that have the responsibility for the area. Teleconferencing has succeeded when there has been one or more very interested parties involved.

Let's take an example. You are considering an *ad hoc* teleconference for marketing purposes. Who should be responsible for the effort? Logically, the area that is developing the marketing program would be a prime contender. If marketing were to be the only user of teleconferencing, that would be an appropriate choice. But, like computer and telephone systems, teleconferencing is a corporate resource, and placement should reflect that viewpoint. Will marketing be eager to promote the use of teleconferencing to engineering, production, or personnel? Probably not. Marketing has too much to worry about. However, marketing may be the appropriate department for the pilot project. After the evaluation takes place, it may be worthwhile to look at developing a teleconferencing support function in the organization. Getting the right people trained and involving them with other groups where they can assist with communication efforts is key. If marketing were a heavy user, it might develop its own "expert" familiar with special teleconferencing applications in the marketing area who could work with the teleconferencing staff to handle the necessary logistics.

There is a growing awareness of the value of information as an organizational resource. Some firms are moving responsibility for their computer operations and telephone systems under an information resource position which operates at a vice-presidential level. Teleconferencing may belong there. In other organizations, human resource development (personnel and training) may assume responsibility for teleconferencing, since a significant portion of teleconferencing tends to be educational during the early stages. Perhaps the department that has responsibility for media (slide programs, video tapes, etc.) should have the responsibility, since the media group may have the technical expertise to operate some of the equipment, repair the systems, or install equipment.

One of the critical placement questions should be "If an initial pilot project is successful, who will make sure that the whole organization benefits from teleconferencing? Who will diffuse the innovation in the organization?" It is with those people that teleconferencing has the best chance of succeeding.

The organizational design of the system should reflect the nature of the media used and potential growth. Be careful that the decision to make the corporate communication center the ''technological showcase'' does not create psychological problems for day-to-day users. A showcase studio may provide some initial public relations benefits, but the long-term evaluation of the teleconferencing system will be based on use and benefits; those are the correct focus areas, not how fancy it looks. In one situation, it was determined that the corporate headquarters would be the main full-motion teleconferencing center, and the remote locations would be equipped with receive-only equipment and a basic telephone link for questions and answers. When the system began to develop a major role in education, it was discovered that considerable sums of money were being spent in flying the corporation's experts from their respective plants into the corporate office to make presentations. Providing transmission capability at each of the locations would have had a fairly fast payback period if the implementer had understood that a corporation's intelligence does not necessarily reside at the corporate headquarters.

There is one interesting factor that seems to be a common thread in teleconferencing systems: there needs to be a ''believer'' in the organization that works at the implementation of teleconferencing. There are no unusual characteristics that earmark this person as the logical choice, but there does need to be a basic belief in the concept. Probably the worst possible conditions would be to have teleconferencing assigned to someone that does not care about the medium. It may well be in the firm's best interests, during the formative initial stages, to place teleconferencing with the division that shows the greatest interest. In addition, it is critical to develop depth in the division or department. There have been a number of cases over the past years where the teleconferencing effort has significantly diminished when the innovator left the organization. When there are few trained to understand the dynamics of teleconferencing and its creative applications, the teleconferencing effort dwindles. If, based on a company's research, teleconferencing is an important part of the business, then developing wide-spread understanding and depth is important to protect the investment.

## Need for Clear Objectives

One of the reasons why teleconferencing fails is a lack of well-thought-out objectives as to what the teleconferencing system is to accomplish. As the popularity of teleconferencing increases, there may be a tendency for some firms to initiate teleconferencing without sufficient thought as to the expected outcome. The more detailed the objectives, the higher the probability of success. Those who become responsible for teleconferencing should be held accountable for the results of the system. Unless there is agreement on the part of those responsible for the teleconferencing initiative and management, considerable potential exists for an ineffective system.

One of the best ways to set initial objectives is to review the organization's mission statement and objectives. Through this process, it becomes easier to identify the firm's line of business and to structure the teleconferencing to support those objectives. Optimally, a teleconferencing enterprise should develop its own business plan, complete with mission statement, objectives, a plan of action, listings of the assumptions, and resources required to make the project a success. While this may seem to be quite a bit of work in the beginning, like most strategic planning, it provides the groundwork for future development and evaluation. In addition, when the teleconferencing concept is presented from this perspective it enables management to "buy off" on the approach. With written information that has received their approval, it is difficult for management to say that they did not understand the potential costs and problems that were involved.

Even if you are considering the installation of just a more sophisticated speaker telephone, it is worth giving some thought to the entire organization. What other segments of the firm could benefit from teleconferencing? Will placement of the equipment limit access by others? Are several speaker telephones units necessary? What are appropriate uses? Should there be several pilot projects scheduled so that an increasing number of individuals in the organization can learn about teleconferencing and test the potential in their areas? Should a conference room be equipped with a more sophisticated speaker telephone—the establishment of an "electronic meeting room?"

### Setting Realistic Expectations

There is a tendency for those involved in teleconferencing to promote it too heavily. Overzealous supporters may tell management that teleconferencing will make significant reductions in travel costs or total costs in general. Do not set unrealistic expectations! Communications costs will increase. People who did not travel will begin using the teleconferencing system. The net effect will be an increase in some cost centers, and teleconferencing may prove to be more expensive than the travel costs saved. For that reason, do not lean too heavily on travel cost reduction as the primary rationale for teleconferencing. In addition, teleconferencing may not work as well as expected. Remember: it is the *users* who make teleconferencing a success or failure. Personalities may get in the way, some people might refuse to stop their travel, and, for a host of other reasons, the program may not be as spectacular as planned. It is important to keep all those possibilities in mind when promises are being made to management. There are too many lessons in history for us to ignore how resistant some organizations can be to change. Those in charge of the teleconferencing effort may be the wrong individuals, they may have insufficient training or poor interpersonal communication skills, or there may be insufficient financial and management support for the effort. A whole host of reasons may exist. The fact may be that teleconferencing simply does not have a place in your organization. I personally find it hard to believe, but the possibility does exist. If a particular teleconferencing approach fails in an organization, it is not that teleconferencing *per se* failed, but that the timing was not right or the available human resources did not support it sufficiently.

## Need to Communicate

There should be a real need for the users of a system to communicate. While this may seem obvious, there have been many systems installed simply because it seemed like a good idea. Surveys of potential users have their drawbacks, partly because those surveyed do not really understand teleconferencing and what it can do for them, nor do they really understand the extent of their communication needs.

One of the best ways to begin is to look at long-distance calls and existing travel statistics. Trends, once you have all the data, are pretty easy to spot. It may be difficult, however, to get all the information. It is common for the raw data to be scattered throughout the company, and many computer systems used to monitor financial activity do not have the flexibility to audit past activity in the detail that you need. Next, consider the trends in the organization. In other words, once you have an idea of what activity has taken place, you need to get a handle on where the organization is going. New branch offices, new market territories, and new competitive pressures may mean an increased need for communication beyond existing levels. All of this data will guide the organizational placement of teleconferencing, how the system will support the mission statement, and how it addresses current tactical needs and strategic implications.

## Individual Factors

The individual is the key element in the development of teleconferencing. There are biases and personal desires that will impact even the willingness to consider teleconferencing as an option. Let's look at some of those factors.

## Resistance to Travel Substitution

One of the lessons learned very early in the teleconferencing industry is that many people *like* to travel. They see travel as one of the benefits of the organization and as a way to get out of the office. In addition, they may feel that good communication takes place only face-to-face. It would be very difficult to disagree with that statement, but financial reality must enter the picture at some point in time.

Although management may have reached a decision that the cost of face-to-face meetings is too high, management cannot easily dictate that those affected will cooperate with a teleconferencing effort to the fullest possible extent. You will find, however, some who are willing to accept teleconferencing with open arms. Who are they? The ones that enjoyed travel at first, but are now sick of spending half their lives in a hotel or motel in a strange town. They have families that are growing up and need more attention. They are some of the younger employees who are looking for a quality of lifestyle that is not company centered. They are also the people who seem to spend a considerable amount of time traveling in poor weather—the kind of weather that takes something out of you physically and mentally after fighting the road for two or three hours. They are the people who are sick of spending time in an airport terminal waiting for a connecting flight, those who have a sick feeling in their stomachs when their flight is late taking off and they have only fifteen minutes to make a connection, or the executive who wants to travel but simply cannot leave the office.

Those are the people to seek out. They have a need to communicate and have placed an internal value on their time. They know their personal time is too valuable to spend it traveling. So, from an operational standpoint, it is important to identify those people who sincerely desire to travel less. Avoid spending time trying to make converts of those who have a personal need for additional travel.

**Resistance To New Innovation**

There will always be some reluctance to participate in something new. This fact of life has been with us since the beginning of time, and there is no reason to expect it to change. Resistance can be divided into several categories:

1. "Somehow the new innovation will take away from me certain things that I enjoy." Travel displacement when travel is enjoyed is a good example.

2. "I don't understand what this is all about." Here it may well be that the potential users really do not understand what is being proposed. Audiographic and visual communications systems are difficult to explain to some. The use of a videotape to show people how it operates might be helpful. Actual exposure is best.

3. "I understand it, but I don't see what it has to do with me." Here is the classic "what do I get out of it" area. People need to understand the technology in terms of how it can (a) make their lives easier, which is a quality-of-life issue; (b) increase their status in the organization; and (c) increase their potential for income by allowing them to reach more clients, close deals faster, etc.

4. "It sure seems like a waste of money to me." This is a tough area to address. First, the individual needs to have an appreciation for the growing value of time. While teleconferencing does not result directly in an increase in the number of widgets produced per hour (the "here and now"), it does have the potential to increase productivity of existing staff and puts off into the future the current need to hire additional personnel (the abstract). There are a number of times when the individual making the comment has not been given the "big picture," in which aggregate savings make the difference. How hard you try to reach this person with further arguments depends on the degree to which the person can impact the success of the entire project. If it is the chief operating office making the comment, then the road ahead will be extremely difficult until you can be successful in your persuasive effort.

5. "I don't think that I can operate all this equipment." Don't be too quick to say "Sure you can. It's easy!" You may find that the individual in fact has a reverse Midas touch and will never get the hang of it. Be realistic in indicating that education and direct supervision will be a part of the program. Be thankful that the response was not one of the previous four; at least he or she is past that point and is willing to give it a chance.

## The "Pheromone Factor"

Many times you will hear about the "sex appeal" of a technology. Some prefer to refer to new innovations in more basic terms that reflect a nonintellectual attraction or interest in a new product or offering. Rather than call this irrational response "sex appeal," the new term is "pheromone factor"—pheromones are the scents that are given off that attract members of the opposite sex. A bright red convertible would have a high pheromone factor to someone interested more in the impression created than in basic transportation. Someone who buys a particular toothpaste based on advertising which indicates that brushing with the product will not only keep the teeth clean but will make the user more attractive is responding to the pheromone factor. To those new to teleconferencing, full-motion video has the highest pheromone factor. The cameras, the color, and the special equipment all combine to create an appeal that is more emotional than rational. There are some that spend considerable amounts of money for video teleconferencing because of its impressive nature, believing that clients may find it impressive and credit the company with being advanced and "on the leading edge."

Audio teleconferencing systems are the most common form of teleconferencing in use today. In terms of price and performance, audio conferencing is hard to beat. Audio conferencing can involve literally any telephone anywhere in the world. It is easy to use, since most everyone is familiar with a telephone. Because the telephone is so common, audio teleconferencing seems to be viewed as less innovative when compared with some of the other visual systems.

Probably the greatest negative factor against audio conferencing is past experience with a conference call. Because many conference telephone calls are less than successful, I would venture to say that they have created more negative public relations for audio conferencing than any other single factor. What separates audio teleconferencing from the simple use of the telephone is *how it is used!* It is the attention to the human issues that turns a "conference call" into an "audio teleconference."

I do not know how many times I have talked about audio conferencing to prospective users who scoffed at the concept because the technology did not seem "different enough" to be special. It is not so much the technology that separates the good teleconferences from the bad; it is the application of the technology. I have seen millions of dollars worth of equipment wasted on a poorly conceived, poorly thought-out video teleconference that failed to recognize the human issues and use the medium to its fullest.

There is a prevalent misconception that the bigger and more sophisticated a system, the better it is. This simply is not true. Just as a small crystal radio set composed of only a handful of parts is nothing without programming from a distant radio station, teleconferencing is nothing without planning. For those who are interested in reliability, there are few things better than a telephone with a speaker connected to it. With increased complexity goes an equal increase in the potential for problems. This is one reason why seasoned satellite teleconference users insist on teleconferencing insurance for the programs. The more complex the equipment, the greater the probability for either human or electronic failure.

So beware of the pheromone factor. There is absolutely nothing wrong with entering into the high-technology end of teleconferencing for its marketing appeal, provided the company recognizes that fact upfront. The difficulty comes when the rationale is productivity, but attractiveness clouds the selection process.

## Pre-Encounter Factors

Now that you have an idea of some of the individual perceptions about teleconferencing, let's move to the more pragmatic problem of preparing individuals to become potential users of a system. In this section we will take a look at the following: identifying users, demonstrations, objectives, setting expectations, training, attention to details, equipment checkouts, and the concept of "user friendliness."

### Identification of Users

The question that you have to ask yourself as you attempt to implement a successful teleconferencing system is: "Which kinds of users can I get to use the system that will (a) require the least amount of preparation and (b) will use the system frequently enough to show others the value of the telecommunications system." To paraphrase a Management-By-Objectives rule: It may take 80 percent of your time to stimulate only 20 percent of the potential users to become involved in teleconferencing. Put your time where the probabilities are in your favor. If you have never implemented a teleconferencing effort before, be assured that you will have a learning process to go through as well, so why not experiment with the most friendly group of users you can find. After you get a few teleconferences under your belt, then begin to go after the hard-core, face-to-face people.

Several characteristics come to mind that you should look for in potential users of a teleconferencing system: (a) they have a great need to communicate; (b) they tend to be involved in new, innovative projects; and (c) they are "failure tolerant." The latter category is perhaps the most important. During the initial stages of any teleconferencing effort, there will be a few problems. The telephone company may have difficulty installing the lines, the equipment may have a few problems, you may be just getting your feet wet with teleconferencing and are not able to be as helpful as you would like to be in preparing people for some of the interaction problems that they will experience—all of these conditions add up to the possibility that the meeting or program may not go quite as planned. Failure-tolerant people seem to understand the risks that go along with new ventures and take problems in stride. It is with this group that you want to experiment and determine the limits of your teleconferencing system. There are others that will dismiss teleconferencing if they experience even the smallest problem, and they will be some of the most vocal in your organization as they describe their disappointment. The result, naturally, is that you end up spending a considerable amount of time in trying to undo the political ramifications of their less-than-satisfactory exposure when you could be learning more about how to make teleconferencing work more effectively in your organizational setting. Life is just too short to set yourself up for this kind of problem. So work with your failure-tolerant group until you have the "bugs" worked out of the system and then seek to expose others to it in a very orderly and planned fashion. Now after saying what you should do, I will add that it is all easier said than done. There may be no avoiding interaction with potential critics, but try to minimize your exposure to this group in the early stages.

**The "Demonstration"**

When you get your teleconferencing equipment installed, try to avoid the urge to set up a series of "dog and pony" shows in which you turn on all the equipment and demonstrate the various bells and whistles. You will get a number of comments like "That's nice," "Interesting," and "What do you plan to do with it?" There is little that is meaningful in showing people technology. There is little value in showing someone a large computer, with all of its spinning disk drives and blinking lights, and expecting him to immediately see the personal applications. So why not demonstrate teleconferencing in a meaningful way? Involve the individuals in an actual teleconference.

Ideally, teleconferencing should be relatively "transparent" to the user. That is, it should permit the user to focus on communicating the message rather than calling attention to itself. An initial introduction to teleconferencing should attempt to concentrate on the exchange of information. The best introduction is when two individuals who need to communicate meet via an electronic system. The ability to exchange information and the potential advantages are seen almost immediately. Because of the system's newness, it is not advisable to bring together potential users who have complex or extremely important items of information to discuss. Rather, seek to limit the demonstration to the exchange of a few typical working items. This will serve to reduce some of the pressure on you. Such an operational demonstration will enable the users to see the application of the technology in dealing with routine communications needs, rather than creating the perception that the system should be reserved just for important items. In addition, if there are any hardware problems, there is a reduced exposure level for the implementer of the teleconferencing system.

## Initial Objectives

Prior to the teleconference, it is important to determine the communication objectives of the participants. An implementer should be aware that there are voiced and nonvoiced objectives that are brought into an event. When you initially ask someone what he or she expects to accomplish, you will probably receive a general outline of the direction that the participants wish to take. But keep in mind that few are able to tell you precisely what they expect to accomplish in a communication. When we walk into a meeting, we bring with us a mental picture of the communication event and a fairly good idea about the desired outcome. How we expect to achieve that outcome is relatively unknown. For example, some will assume that the presentation of graphic material will be possible and fail to mention it in the initial developmental discussions. The result may surprise you and the user.

## Setting Realistic Expectations

NEVER promise that teleconferencing will be able to do anything for a potential user! That may sound like a strange statement, but there is no way that you can really know the actual needs of the various users. Educators in a business setting face this problem all the time. There is always a difference between "perceived" need and "actual" need. If individuals have little or no experience with teleconferencing and they have little understanding of their own communication practices, you cannot trust the accuracy of their statements which relate to desired system characteristics. You must watch and listen to how people use teleconferencing to see if teleconferencing is really applicable for them. In a number of cases I have seen those responsible for teleconferencing assure potential users that the system will be able to perform as desired, only to discover that there was a difference in definition between the implementer and user. The best way to approach the issue is to LISTEN and not automatically assume that you know precisely what the user wants to do. Suggest that there be an initial "experimental trial" of the system to see if there is any potential application. In few cases have I found that a group ends up using teleconferencing in the way that *I* initially anticipated they would use it. The problem was that I had a stereotype of how I thought they exchanged information without teleconferencing. They had their own thoughts concerning what teleconferencing was all about. Both they and I were wrong. As soon as the first session was over and the debriefing was initiated, I began to notice the light bulbs going off in their heads as the users began to develop their own applications. It is a wonderful process to watch.

In a pre-use discussion with potential users, I listen to their statements about the nature of their communication problems. I then review for them some of my experiences with what I believe to be similar groups. I make absolutely sure to tell them that teleconferencing may not be for them. I had one student approach me after the initial encounter session and ask me why it seemed I was trying to talk the potential users out of using teleconferencing. "You should have been more positive. You know it'll work for them!" was his plea.

A number of years ago I read a communications study in which a speech for tougher punishment for criminals was presented to two different audiences by the same person. The only difference was that in one speech the speaker was introduced as a district attorney and in the other speech he was introduced as a criminal. A survey of the audience members showed that the ''criminal'' had a significantly greater impact on the audience. Why? People perceived the criminal was acting ''against his own best interests,'' and the audience attributed greater credibility to his statements. One would have expected a speech calling for tougher laws from a district attorney, but not from a criminal. Likewise, potential teleconferencing users expect the implementer to ''hype'' or promote teleconferencing. If, however, you indicate that teleconferencing may not be for them, you are really making an honest, straightforward assessment—it may not be the best communication vehicle for them—and you are enhancing your credibility with the group as someone who is more interested in their success than the success of the system. There is certainly nothing wrong with this approach, because a true implementer of a teleconferencing system realizes that what is good for the users is what is good for the system—a system is an extension of its users.

## Training

Initially, those interested in using teleconferencing are not interested in esoteric discussions about the value of teleconferencing in the abstract; they need ''survival skills''! They know that they are about ready to jump into this new technology and are not ready to assimilate the scope of information that you may have—at least not initially. It is a good idea to let them focus on some of the more basic communication skills and leave some of the technological manipulation until later. They need immediate success and reinforcement. There are only three things that you should try to work with in the first pass: developing specific objectives, preparing their visual elements, and planning how they can get interaction started. That may not seem like much, but those three elements are the building blocks for electronic communication. Actually, they are simply extensions of what the potential users may currently do, but the basic elements become more critical in an electronic environment. In training first-time users, try to keep the introduction to less than 10 to 20 minutes. Discuss some of what happens during a teleconference, but keep the emphasis on setting objectives. Give them an audio tape with the sound tracks of several conferences in which users are doing things right—interacting, setting objectives, reviewing major points, using the names of the participants, sounding relaxed—and a one-page summary of major points to remember. Then hold a second meeting just to review the objectives and discuss the material heard on the audio tape. The business meeting is a little different and requires more attention to making sure that task responsibilities have been communicated and understood. Finally, reinforce some of the major points in the tape and reassure the user that he or she will do a fine job in the teleconference. The same kinds of anxieties that confront a public speaker face the teleconferencing user.

In all, try to keep the initial training sessions informal, relaxed, positive, supportive, and SIMPLE. One friend said that first-time teleconferencing users have the attention span of a ten-year-old and I would agree. The simple fact that there are so many other anxiety and personality variables running through their heads tends to create a short attention span. In the second session, the nervousness is significantly reduced, and by the day of the program it has diminished to a fairly normal level. On the day of the teleconference, get together for coffee and review the information that will be presented. During that time outline again what will happen and some of the problems that can be expected, e.g., lack of response to questions. Then go through a few simulated questions to see how they handle the process of interaction. Normally, one or two questions will get the user to focus on the critical issues.

## Support Materials

A good teleconference needs as much attention to detail as if the conference were held face-to-face. There is a tendency to forget this simple fact because teleconferencing can be so easy to establish. A thoughtful agenda should include the objectives of the meeting, the desired outcomes, and the decisions that need to be made. Who is to be present? Have they been involved in a teleconference before? What training is necessary before the meeting? Are there written materials that need to be reviewed prior to the teleconference? How long will it take the materials to reach the participants?

There is a greater need for planning when there is an increase in audience size or technological sophistication. There is nothing more disconcerting than to find out that one or more of the participants have not received critical written materials which will be referred to in the teleconference. It is also extremely unnerving to find that a typographical error has been made in the telephone numbers given to the conference call operator or that the incorrect teleconferencing bridge number has been given to the participants—with insufficient time to mail out a correction.

It is wise to develop a series of checklists to keep track of the many details involved in the development of a teleconference. Educational programs tend to require more preparation than meetings, and if the schedule calls for a number of programs to be in-process at the same time, then a checklist is the only way to ensure that all the details have been addressed. As an example, Figure 5-1 shows a typical checklist for an educational teleconference. Every attempt should be made to list as many details as possible, but unique situations and demands will always emerge. Your teleconference requirements may be quite different than someone else's. By keeping both a notebook and time line diagram, you make a road map available for others should the person responsible for the effort become ill or otherwise not be available.

## Equipment Checkout

While in Alaska, I spent some time with the crews that were manning a major National Aeronautics and Space Administration satellite-tracking station

SAMPLE TELECONFERENCING SCHEDULE

WEEKS

| TASK | -5 | -4 | -3 | -2 | -1 | 0 | +1 | +2 | +3 |
|---|---|---|---|---|---|---|---|---|---|
| IDENTIFY NEED | X | | | | | | | | |
| IDENTIFY RESOURCE | X | | | | | | | | |
| MEET WITH RESOURCE | X | | | | | | | | |
| SET TENTATIVE TIME | X | | | | | | | | |
| SCHEDULE FACILITIES | | X | | | | | | | |
| FINALIZE DATE | | X | | | | | | | |
| TELECONFERENCE TO SET OBJECTIVES | | X | | | | | | | |
| GET P.R. INPUT | | X | | | | | | | |
| MAIL ANNOUNCEMENTS | | X | | | | | | | |
| RECEIVE VISUAL & HANDOUTS FROM RESOURCE | | | X | | | | | | |
| PREPARE VISUALS | | | X | | | | | | |
| MAIL MATERIAL | | | | X | | | | | |
| REVIEW CONTENT WITH RESOURCE | | | | X | | | | | |
| VERIFY MATERIALS RECEIVED | | | | | X | | | | |
| VERIFY EQUIPMENT WORKING | | | | | X | | | | |
| VERIFY SITE MODERATOR | | | | | X | | | | |
| FINAL MEETING WITH RESOURCE | | | | | | X | | | |
| EQUIPMENT CHECK OUT WITH SITE MODERATOR | | | | | | X | | | |
| RECORD CONFERENCE | | | | | | X | | | |
| TELECONFERENCE | | | | | | X | | | |
| "THANK YOU" TO RESOURCE | | | | | | | X | | |
| MEMO TO MGT. ON PROGRAM | | | | | | | X | | |
| NAMES TO WORD PROCESSING FOR CERTIFICATES | | | | | | | X | | |
| DUPLICATE RECORDING | | | | | | | X | | |
| RECEIVE EVALUATIONS | | | | | | | | X | |
| EVALUATIONS TO DATA PROCESSING | | | | | | | | X | |
| UPDATE PARTICIPANT DATA BASE | | | | | | | | X | |
| RECEIVE EVALUATION ANALYSIS | | | | | | | | | X |
| UPDATE RECORDING LIBRARY | | | | | | | | | X |
| WRITE FINAL SESSION REPORT | | | | | | | | | X |

**FIGURE 5-1**

outside of Fairbanks. I was amazed to see two individuals checking every single control setting. First, one person would go through the reams of paper, setting the controls to the desired positions, then the second person would repeat the same process, checking each setting. Then they would send the commands to a device that simulated the satellite to triple check their command sequence. After they told me how many thousands of dollars per second a mistake would cost, I became a believer in checking out systems. Naturally, the more complex the system, the more important the checkout of equipment becomes prior to the program. However, the responsibility is on the implementer of teleconferencing to estimate the potential impact of a failure on not only the organization, but the teleconferencing effort as well. In one of the full-motion video systems I designed, the network was checked out each morning at least one hour before the first program. This would give an engineer sufficient time to correct any problem and get the system fully operational. Even with audio conferencing systems I recommend that each site call the originating location to make sure the telephone connection is good and that the equipment works correctly. All it takes is a few minutes, and the peace of mind is certainly worth the effort.

## User Friendliness

This term has become so popular that it may be losing its meaning. "User friendly" generally means that equipment is easy to use, with a touch of warmth thrown in to compensate for our tendency to view machines as cold, unforgiving devices. It can also apply to the content of the program as well. For example, in the computer world user friendliness depends not only on the layout of the various controls, but also on how well the program is written to emulate an actual person with some degree of compassion and warmth.

At the present time, the teleconferencing industry is vendor-driven. That means that it is the vendors who are controlling how a product operates and they are the ones who are determining what the users want. A user-driven environment is a condition in which the competition is high and the level of user awareness of their own needs is such that the users dictate how a product is to operate. The microcomputer industry is a good example. Initially, the units were designed by engineers with little concern about the average person using the equipment. Now, with the personal computer industry becoming increasingly competitive, the users are beginning to demand that equipment become easier to use, with easier programming languages that more closely approximate English.

One of the criteria discussed in the current literature is "habitability," or the capability of the electronic device to learn some of the habits of the individual communicating. Such a capacity enables a regular user to have the system learn and then automatically perform certain activities. Memorizing regular camera settings and enabling the user to form his or her own commands makes communication easier and is an important quality in a user-friendly device. Unfortunately, few vendors have developed equipment with sufficient sophistication to handle the natural variations between users. It is possible for the operator of a teleconferencing system to assist users by watching them closely, taking notes, and then discussing the problems with equipment engineers.

## The Encounter

After ten years in teleconferencing, I still do not have a good, descriptive name for a teleconference that conveys the unusual set of dynamics that are involved in each teleconferencing mode. For example, people in the industry use "teleconference," "program," "going live," "going on the air," "going on-line," and a host of other terms almost interchangeably. Those in the teleconferencing business tend to be refugees from commercial and educational television and use broadcast terms to describe the actual event ("program," "going on-the-air," "going live"), and computer-oriented people talk about going "on-line." For some, meetings become "teleconferences" or "electronic meetings." To educators, a class becomes a "telelecture." While there may be a need for some special term to set teleconferencing apart from the kinds of face-to-face events we are used to, new terms also set the stage for a formality and anxiety level not found in a more traditional setting.

### Participation Anxiety

If the teleconferencing room appears to be too much like a radio or television studio, something happens to the way certain people communicate; they become more rigid, less relaxed. The users might have been warm and friendly people before the conference, but as soon as the camera goes or the audio system becomes active, they change. Generally, that is because they have no role models for teleconferencing. It is important that new users listen to audio tapes of an audio conference or see videotapes of a visual presentation to understand that teleconferencing is not necessarily like radio and television. Learning aides, such as audio tapes or videotapes, can provide the necessary role models for new users to follow. Material written on a piece of paper may be adequate for computer conferencing, in which the information transfer is paper- or computer screen-based, but for the other forms of teleconferencing, the role model should reflect the medium that is to be used. The same is true for other participants as well. There is just as much anxiety on the part of the participants as there is for the person leading the discussion. It is amazing to talk to participants just prior to a teleconference and see their anxiety—it is something new for them and the unknown always makes people anxious.

### One- Vs. Two-Way Systems

First is the distinction between one-way and two-way systems. In some circles these are called noninteractive and interactive systems. In order to explain them more fully, we will take one at a time. One-way systems closely approximate programs that are broadcast. In other words, one location to many. Another term that is being used to indicate that the transmissions are going to a much smaller audience than if the same program were aired over a regular radio or television station is "narrowcasting." A major factor in the one-to-many approach is that those viewing or listening to the event cannot interact with the individual or individuals presenting information. Education was one of the first industries to use this form of information transmission. With special transmission facilities, lectures were delivered from one location and heard in many other locations. The inability of persons in remote locations to interact with the presenter is what makes the program noninteractive and nonparticipative. It is simply an announcement given over a very sophisticated public address system.

Two-way systems, by their very nature, have been designed for the *exchange* of information. The materials presented in an interactive teleconference are not announcements, but rather are discussions or dialogs. In this form of communication the focus is on sharing of thoughts. Generally speaking, whether a program is one- or two-way is a function of the technology used. However, through poor program planning it is possible to render a two-way capable system into a one-way event. It is unfortunate, but it is all too easy for beginning users of teleconferencing to shift the nature of a teleconference through poor handling.

For satellite users, a hybrid approach to the interactive process when using satellite transmission systems is used. The cost of transmitting information to a satellite has remained quite high, while the cost of satellite receivers has decreased significantly over the past ten years. Since it is not economically feasible to equip every participating location with satellite transmission facilities, interaction is achieved in another way. This form is called one-way video/two-way audio. In this setting, the program presenter transmits visual and audio information via the satellite, and participants use the telephone for questions and discussion. It should be remembered that these programs remain primarily one-way events, since telephone interaction is really secondary to the primary program.

### "Us Vs. Them" Syndrome

In this form of reaction, the response by site participants will be "That's not the way *we* do it. What do *they* know about *our* problems?" If there is no moderator at the site who can control the extent of off-microphone discussions, the problem is extremely difficult to control. If the originating location feels that the information being presented is dramatically different than current practices in the various sites, a high level of interaction will be necessary to decrease the information/action gulf between the site participants and those presenting the information. Originating location participants must be extremely diplomatic in this environment or the gulf will increase significantly. To be avoided *at all costs* are negative comments about a method used at a site or comments about an individual asking questions or making comments about the topic. Any form of attack will result in the members of the group banding together to protect the group member, even though they may not know the attacked individual at all. The fact that he or she is at the same location is cause enough!

It is common for site participants in a teleconference to begin to think of themselves as a unified group, rather than individuals. There will be discussions that take place within the group as the presentation is being made. If the speaker telephone's microphone has been turned off to keep extraneous teleconference noise to a minimum, the asides will increase in frequency. The resulting discussion will result in two observable events: possible hostility, especially if a group member has been attacked, and local communication, making it difficult to get concepts across.

If unchecked, the discussions at the site can become quite extensive, resulting in portions of the content not being heard—much as people talking in a conference or classroom creates problems for those around them. This site-based discussion may have another unusual effect, however. Comments among the site participants may lead the group to topics tangential to the discussion. There have been a number of occasions when I have seen a presenter stop for questions and hear comments from a site that do not seem to be relevant to the material discussed. Upon follow-up with participants at the site, it was learned that several members had entered into their own discussion of the material which took the group in an entirely different direction. Frequent interaction and presenter knowledge of this phenomenon can lessen the problem. When a presenter begins to hear comments or questions that seem "off the wall," it is important to stop and ask questions that might lead the presenter to understand the kind of on-site discussion that has taken place while the presentation was being given.

In either case, the greater the amount of interaction between the originating location and the sites, the lower the probability that problems will develop. It is almost universal that on-site conversations immediately stop when a question is asked of another location or a comment is made. The interaction process, then, can be used to control the attention span of the participants.

## Unannounced Questions

NEVER call on an individual or site without some warning! The exception to this rule is in teleconferences with very few participants at a site, with the participants knowing one another fairly well. For example, let's say that the chairman of the conference has made several comments concerning a new policy. There are five locations with five to ten people at each location. Out of the blue, the chairman says, "O.K. That's the new direction. Detroit . . . any questions?" The chairman will be surprised when there is no immediate response and may believe that Detroit is no longer in the conference or did not hear the question. "Detroit? Are you still there? Any questions?" The chairman is now anxious.

What happened? The chairman did not give the location enough time to respond. Often in a teleconference we expect a response from a location as if there were just one person at the location on the telephone. In addition, after years of exposure to radio and television, we all become uncomfortable when there is a prolonged period of silence. In radio and television it is called "dead air" and is avoided like the plague. Just listen to a radio station and see how little dead air there is between songs, commercials or whatever. We have become conditioned to constant sound. Let's take a look at what happened in Detroit when the chairman asked for questions.

1. The question was unexpected, so there is some delay on the part of the local moderator.
2. The moderator asks the group if there are any questions.
3. The group members look around to see who is going to go first, or the moderator may look at each person in turn.
4. If a group member has a question, then either:
   a. The speaker telephone microphone has to be passed to the person with the question.
   b. The question has to be relayed to the moderator to ask.
   c. The question has to be jotted down.
   d. The person with the question leaves his seat and moves closer to the speaker telephone.

If you think out the process, you will find that it takes more than a few seconds to happen. The people in Detroit will not be too sensitive to the passage of time. After all, they are busy trying to get their act together. However, the passage of time will be very noticeable to the chairman and to the other sites.

The best way to handle any question or comment session is to prepare the group ahead of time by saying that a question period is coming up and who will be asked the questions. For example:

> CHAIRMAN: Well, those are some of the details of the policy change. What I want to do now is summarize some of the major points and get some reactions from you. Let's see . . . I'll check first with Detroit and then L.A. and the other offices after that. O.K. The policy will go into effect . . .

Now there is considerable activity going on at each site. Detroit and Los Angeles know they will be on the list first, and the group members are probably listening to the summary with interest so that they can make an intelligent response. Everyone has been warned. The moderator will probably be checking around the table to see if there are any questions and passing the microphone to the first individual, or at least he or she knows enough about the reaction of the group to say "We have two questions here. Just a minute." or "No questions here." Advance warning can significantly improve the speed of communication and reduce the anxiety level of the chairman and the participating sites.

## Communication Equality

Whether intentional or otherwise, giving either one location or a specific set of users more advanced communications capabilities indicates to all users that there is something special or more important about those that have more capability than the rest. This is normally not a problem, *unless* the program developer is trying to generate equal participation from all locations. For in interactive communications, those with lesser facilities both will be perceived and will perceive themselves as "second class communications citizens." While this may seem insignificant to the director of a corporate communications center, you can be certain that those in the field will attach more significance to the difference than one would casually think. Although difficult to quantify, there have been a number of situations which lead me to include it as a potential problem area.

Communication inequality exists when there is a significant difference between the levels of sophistication used by the various participants. For example, one location has a well-outfitted studio, and another location has minimal equipment. Satellite broadcasts, for example, generally use a fairly sophisticated studio complex, while the receiving sites can only receive the visual image, cannot send their image back, and must use a telephone to ask questions. In a specific case I saw, one location was equipped with fairly expensive color equipment, while the others had basic black-and-white equipment. There was a perception that the more sophisticated location was "showing off" and was flaunting its technical capabilities. While this may seem to be a small difference, it is worth discussion *because it impeded effective communication.*

No matter how silly a user attitude might seem to be, the critical element is communication. So it is certainly worth considering any unusual comments heard by other users that may be indicators of something inhibiting communication effectiveness. After all, teleconferencing systems are supposed to improve communications, not add new barriers between groups or create new corporate communication problems. Audio systems can be affected by the same type of elitism. For example, equipping some locations with state-of-the-art studio conferencing equipment, while giving others $29.95 Brand X units that sound like a tin can and string will not endear you to the hearts of the low-cost hardware users. Computer conferencing users may have their own reactions to those with more sophisticated terminal devices that permit the user to edit text prior to transmission, while the poorer users of "dumb" terminals that have no storage or editing capability curse the fact that their messages always look like the electronic equivalent of crayon writing on Big Chief tablet paper.

Communication inequality can also apply to the material being presented in the teleconference. A conference implies interaction, but there are many instances where interaction is given little more than lip service. This seems to be due to a lack of role models on how to use teleconferencing. When a participant or moderator arrives at anything that begins to look like a studio (radio or television), he or she seems to adopt the belief that it is not a conference but a broadcast. To many, a broadcast is where one person talks and that is it. Educators have the most difficult time with this problem. Instead of a give-and-take between the educator and the students, the encounter becomes a lecture that could have just as easily been recorded and mailed out.

If the various sites have the capability to discuss items, then that feature should be used. When interactive capability is available and promoted, the participants rightfully assume that it will be used—that they will have the opportunity to interact with someone else. When that capability is not used, there is a "violation of expectations" that may adversely affect future teleconferencing efforts. How you get interaction started varies between each medium and will be discussed in more detail later.

### Need To Visualize Others

There are few teleconferencing systems that really permit all the participants to see one another. Those installations are few and far between. The majority of the teleconferencing population uses technologies that do not permit participants at the various locations to develop a solid mental image of the others involved. There are many in the teleconferencing field who feel that the ability to "see" someone is not critical to the effectiveness of the communication event. In fact, some have indicated that the lack of social contact may speed the communication process, and I would agree.

I have seen any number of meetings between relative "strangers," and they tend to focus on the task at hand much quicker. But there is something to be said for having a mental image of those at the other end. Believe me, I have heard all the arguments and examples given by those in audio and computer conferencing that seem to support the assertion that the visualization aspect is not important, but I firmly believe that knowing what someone else looks like assists in the communication process. I also believe that initial users of teleconferencing want to know what someone else looks like as well. Whether the system is slow-scan television, audio, or text-based, I go out of my way to make sure that there are plenty of pictures passed around—pictures of those at the various locations, pictures of the buildings where they work, pictures of the room where the conferences originate, descriptions of the towns, and maps showing the site locations. The pictures may be Polaroid$^{TM}$* group shots, photocopies, or black-and-white prints, but there are plenty of them that go out to the various participants. My experience has been that when newcomers do not have any visual image of the person on the other end, it is one more item that increases the anxiety level—one more potential barrier.

---

* Polaroid$^{TM}$ is a trademark of Polaroid Corporation.

One computer conferencing system that I will be discussing in depth in the chapter on computer conferencing has the right idea. They have a directory feature in the system which lets users look up the names of other participants. When a user first begins to use the computer conferencing system he or she is encouraged to write a few lines about his or her interests—those human qualities that set us all apart. Although there does not seem to be enough room to write all the things that you might like to write about yourself so that people can get to know you, it does serve a very useful function in opening the door to future interaction.

## The Aftermath

The event has ended. There is a sigh of relief from the first-time teleconference user. But the job is not finished. There are a number of other details that need to be reviewed before one can consider a teleconference "finished." In this section, we will review debriefings, evaluation, feedback, and the exploration process for future programs.

### The Debriefing

Immediately following the teleconferencing event, it is important to discuss the conference with the major participants involved. In the initial stages, this should be a personal discussion of the problems, the positive aspects, and the new applications seen by the participants. As the users gain experience with the medium, the debriefing can be reduced to a telephone call and, eventually, an evaluation form. In the beginning, however, personal contact is important. During the debriefing it is important to first focus on how the user "felt" about the experience. It may have been many years since the user had a formal exposure to interpersonal communication, and he or she may be unable to articulate some of the personal problems experienced without some help. In this stage, positive support is important. Reinforce the skills that the user remembered and point out just one or two additional items the user might try the next time to improve the encounter. At the same time, attempt to determine the usefulness of the introductory training. By listening to the first-time users, you will be able to refine your training programs to more directly address the situations encountered in those critical first sessions.

User comments about the "friendliness" of the teleconferencing equipment are also important to note. While it may be easy to pass over initial operational problems by saying "Oh, you'll get used to it," always make a note of the comment and seek to improve the technology so that the difficulty does not continue to give first-time users a problem. If it is apparent that the users are complaining about problems that were addressed in the training literature, it may be wise to describe the problem to a public relations person and have him or her make suggestions on how the introductory text might be modified to more clearly communicate the information. Frankly, it is always a good idea to let someone totally unfamiliar with teleconferencing review your descriptive materials to make sure they make sense. Above all, do not attempt to explain what you have written to the reviewer. Just make a note of the interpretation problem in the margin and see if others stumble on the same part. Then critically look at the passage and see if it can be written more clearly. If any user has a problem with your explanation, then YOU have a problem.

## Evaluation

The bottom line of a teleconferencing system is how it supports the organization: how it furthers the mission statement and objectives of the corporation or educational institution. Benefit is generally thought of in terms of:

1. Dollars saved.
2. Dollars gained.
3. Increased value per dollar spent.
4. Long-term potential, even though there are limited short-term benefits.

Whatever the firm decides are the objectives, it is important that the system be evaluated according to *predetermined and agreed-upon objectives.*

The evaluation should be made from several perspectives. First, the entire evaluation process should provide management with a method for determining how successfully the system meets the initial objectives. These initial objectives should be as realistic as possible to avoid "violated expectations." Prior to the start-up of the system, attention should be paid to the data collection process so that it will provide the information necessary to determine if the concept is appropriate. Second, since teleconferencing may be new to the organization, predicting success based on the success of others is problematic.

Managers understand the volatile nature of new projects—that there will be unforeseen problems. However, management expects the implementer to understand those uncertainties and, as much as possible, to prepare contingency plans ahead of time. This includes sufficient dollars to remedy problems as they arise. Third, evaluation on a rapid turn around basis is absolutely necessary to identify problems so that corrections can be initiated immediately. The use of monthly, quarterly, and yearly reports are also good evaluation vehicles. Explaining the system's strengths, weaknesses, and corrective actions to management and the user community opens the communication lines. After all, this is a method to increase communication, and if there are problems that do not have an appropriate communciation channel to reach you, there will be significant difficulties.

The participants will also evaluate the teleconferencing effort. The participants will form opinions according to the following:

1. An internal, personal assessment of the program.

2. An assessment based on interaction with other participants at their site.

3. An assessment based on the comments from other sites.

4. An assessment of the teleconference as it compares with the experience of other users.

All of these factors make up an overall impression of the teleconference. There is a great deal of flexibility in each of the areas, and an individual participant's impression is more easily changed when the internal assessment is fairly neutral. If the internal assessment is very positive or negative, there is increasing resistance to change via the other exposures. These assessment factors are combined with the following:

1. Emotional state coming into the meeting based on work and home life.

2. Emotional reactions to those who are present at the site location.

3. Emotional reactions to the person leading the teleconference, or factors associated with the originating location, e.g., corporate headquarters, the university.

4. Attitudes toward the topic based on previous encounters, advanced publicity, and word of mouth.

5. Attitudes toward the teleconferencing process, or anxiety resulting from a lack of experience.

All these factors add up to a preconceived attitude toward the teleconference. It may be impossible to determine the impact of these efforts, and there may be nothing you can do about the user who had a bad day just prior to using the system. But you need to realize that evaluation questionnaires and other instruments will never fully communicate all the attitudes which lead up to a particular response. An evaluation questionnaire should, therefore, be treated as an indicator of some of the reactions and not as absolute fact.

## Questionnaires

A questionnaire which accurately obtains the necessary information is difficult to construct. In the majority of the questionnaires developed by teleconferencing users, the questions fall into several basic categories.

*"Yes/no" questions.* Probably the simplest approach of all. Questions are asked so that participants either agree or disagree with a statement. The beauty of the "yes/no" questions is that they force the participant to make a choice, the responses can be easily tabulated, and the results are easy for management to understand. In reality, there are three possible responses: "yes," "no," and "no response."

*Scale questions.* Sometimes called "Lickert" or "Semantic Differential" scales, these questions allow the participants to check a response within a range. Most of the time, there will be five possible responses: strongly agree, agree, neutral, disagree, strongly disagree. The questions are strongly worded positive or negative statements, and the participant checks or circles the most appropriate answer. For example:

1. The program quality was excellent.      SA A N D SD
2. The program met my expectations.      SA A N D SD

The Semantic Differential scales use a slightly different approach in that a topic is defined by the question, the scale uses polarized terms, and the participants check their assessment. For example,

1. Program quality      Excellent __ __ __ __ __ Poor
2. Content relevance      High      __ __ __ __ __ Low

As you can see, there are a number of ways in which a question can be asked. Probably the Lickert-type scales are most commonly used. These scales permit those responsible for teleconferencing to have more of a "flavor" of the participant's feelings about the event than the "yes/no" questions. In many cases, the information collected is converted from scales to a "yes/no" format for presentation to management.

*Questions.* There are as many different questions asked of participants as there are systems and applications. The questions that are appropriate for educational programs make no sense when a meeting is involved, so it may be necessary to develop more than one questionnaire. Here are some sample questions that could be included in an evaluation form. Some are "yes/no" and others are "scale" questions. Select some questions that are appropriate and rewrite them to fit the type of response that you would like to use.

1. Was the information presented relevant to your profession?
2. Could you have easily obtained the information elsewhere?
3. Were the visual materials easy to see?
4. Could you hear everyone easily?
5. Overall, how would you rate the program?
6. In how many teleconferences have you participated?
7. Would you attend another teleconference?
8. Were the handout materials adequate?
9. Were your personal objectives met in the teleconference?
10. How valuable was the interactive capability?
11. Did the teleconference save you time and travel?
12. Did the equipment function correctly?

13. Was the equipment easy to operate?

14. Did the program meet your needs?

15. Did the instructor appear to know the material?

16. Was the material presented in an understandable manner?

17. Was the program well organized?

18. Were the objectives clear?

19. Were the audiovisuals clear and understandable?

20. How well prepared was the instructor?

21. Was the program worth attending?

22. How satisfied were you with the interaction that took place?

23. How valuable were the handouts?

24. If you were able to travel, how much travel time did the teleconference save you?

25. If the program or meeting had been held elsewhere, could you have attended?

26. How long was the teleconference?

27. What is your title?

28. Who was your moderator?

29. What was the title of the program?

30. What was the nature of the teleconference (meeting, educational session, etc.)?

31. How many people attended at your location?

32. What is your location?

There are two basic approaches to the length of the questionnaire. First, if you are interested in keeping track of each encounter, then keep the number of questions short—ten or less. If more questions are asked, then you will begin to see participants avoid completing the questionnaire. Second, use a more complete questionnaire for courses that consist of a number of teleconferences. I would strongly recommend the use of a short questionnaire for completion after each encounter because it can help to identify problems before they become serious enough to reduce the overall evaluation of a program series. But keep the encounter questionnaire very brief.

*Analysis.* There is no question that the analysis of scale questions is more difficult and time consuming. If there are to be a fairly large number of participants using the system over a period of time, by all means computerize the questionnaire evaluation. It is possible to have the evaluation questionnaires printed on sheets that can be optically scanned by the computer, thus eliminating the time required to convert the information from the evaluation form to a computer format. However, *always* start with a draft form so you can determine whether or not the information collected is useful before taking the next step and having expensive forms produced. There are many computer programs available which can provide you with analysis information. One of the most common programs found in data processing centers is the Statistical Package for the Social Sciences (SPSS). The program is powerful and easy to use. Check with your data processing department for their suggestions.

### Feedback

Evaluations are one mechanism whereby those responsible for teleconferencing can assess the level and quality of activity on the system. There is an additional need to feed back information to the participants who completed the evaluation and to those involved in the presentation of information. If the homework was done on the front end of the event, then the probability of the evaluation being positive is quite high. By sharing evaluation information with presenters, you further reinforce positive statements you may have made in the debriefing. If there are negative ones, they will probably be linked to the constructive suggestions that were made in the debriefing as well. It is recommended that either the raw evaluation results or a summary be forwarded to the presenters.

If there is a large variation between your personal observations and the evaluation data, it is critical to immediately learn why the difference exists. In this case, it may not be wise to share the raw evaluation data. Instead, determine the cause of the variation and then forward a summary to the presenter stressing the positive aspects of the evaluation data, but make sure you make note of any unusual findings and offer a few suggestions on how they can be approached the next time. I try to forward a summary rather than the raw data. The reason is based primarily on a tendency of presenters to focus on negative comments. A number of times a presenter has been given evaluations which show that the presentation was superior, BUT one or two participants have some negative comments. It may be our nature, but presenters seem to attribute undue importance to those few remarks. The result can be discouragement when none is warranted. So be a little careful about circulating raw evaluation data.

In several cases when a continuing series is involved, I have had a presenter respond to participant comments from the last teleconference at the beginning of the presentation. This process gives the participants the feeling that their comments are being read and considered. Feeding back to the participants is an important part of making sure they understand the system is responsive to their needs and observations. If any improvements in the presentation format or equipment have been made, credit is given to the appropriate participants. This can have a tremendously positive impact on the participants. When a specific individual is not known, make it clear that the improvement was a result of suggestions made by one or more of the participants.

### Further Exploration

Following the first encounter with teleconferencing, the debriefing, and the summary of the evaluations, I recommend getting together with the presenters and/or participants in the teleconference to see how they view the potential for teleconferencing in their area. I have NEVER had an individual or group fail to follow up the first encounter with future teleconferences. By approaching them in this manner, you are allowing the users to determine the level of their participation, rather than pushing teleconferencing on them. I have seen very few ''hard-sell'' approaches succeed in getting people to communicate with others—they have to want to do it. When approached from a ''soft-sell'' perspective, the users continue to use the system, but in a slightly different manner than you may have originally envisioned. Their frequency of use may be greater or less than initially predicted. Again, you are dealing with individual personalities. What one group does may have little correlation with other similar groups.

A hard-sell approach may produce some initial increases in intensity of use, but utilization falls off over time. However, when an implementer acts more like a facilitator use will *increase* over time. Naturally, a little creativity on how teleconferencing may be used to address a user's problem may be in order, but the nature of the relationship between the user and the implementer determines much of the future direction. So do not push teleconferencing too hard in the beginning. In one case, an audio teleconferencing system set up by a large company had encountered some resistance at one location. When I visited the site to show them how they were to use the audio conferencing equipment, we discussed some of their resistance, and the conversation turned to some of the institutional problems they were having. I discovered that they were having difficulty reaching some of their employees with in-house education because many lived too far away to drive in especially for the sessions. I showed them how they could use their audio conferencing equipment and a local conference call to bring those people into the meetings so that the employees did not have to travel. Immediately they became excited about the concept of audio conferencing and, subsequently, became strong supporters of the larger corporate network. The key element in achieving success in that case was (a) listening to their problems and (b) suggesting ways that they could address some of their unique problems. Simply trying to get them more involved in the network probably would have paid off at a later time, but the fact that we focused on *their* problems, instead of the larger network problems, created a better interpersonal relationship which led to a creative solution which satisfied both needs.

**Promotion**

Making the results visible may be the name of the game in some organizations. If anyone has taken a risk in bringing teleconferencing on board, it may be worthwhile to see that the successes are publicized so that they receive some positive strokes for their risk. Do not be too slick about the whole process; it is possible to go overboard with promotion. As a result of intelligent promotion, people may be more willing to try to use teleconferencing, additional funds may be available for subsequent modifications, and some clients may view your organization as one that is ''on the leading edge.'' It may be a small step , but it does help your organization's competitive advantage. Good publicity can make the people who have particpated in teleconferencing feel good about their initial efforts. You may find that even with good evaluation data, management may use informal communication lines to determine the success or failure of the teleconferencing system. They will probably ask some of those who participated in teleconferences for input. Keep in touch with your users. Make sure the system works well for their needs, and if it does not perform well—fix it! Remember: if you do not correct the problems, there is every likelihood that there will be no teleconferencing system to correct in the near future.

When budget reductions are made in the executive offices, they are made on the basis of both factual and ''gut level'' feelings. Unless teleconferencing is seen as a resource that assists a number of areas in the organization, then there will be reductions in the teleconferencing budget. Diversity of users is one mechanism that will increase the probability of success. By viewing teleconferencing as a corporate-wide resource and seeing to it that a number of areas are receiving the benefit of greater communication, you are ensuring the future of teleconferencing in your organization. When was the last time you saw a company remove its telephone system in a cost containment effort? Too many areas would be negatively impacted. The telephone serves everyone and everyone depends on the telephone. Much in the same way, the more people using teleconferencing systems, the more difficult it is to remove the system.

## Educational Factors

Educational use of teleconferencing in business and education is on the increase for many reasons. Fundamentally, there is an increased need to reach learners who cannot travel to the traditional classroom setting. A significant shift in the philosophy of educational institutions was seen as the ''baby boom'' students passed through the schools and colleges; enrollments began a slow and steady decline. Suddenly it became a question of survival for the Ivory Towers. New buzz words like ''Lifelong Learning'' began to appear in the major journals. Probably the latest twist has been the idea that degrees should have to be ''renewed'' every few years. Although there is something to be said for the fact that our knowledge base is changing so rapidly that periodic updates may be of value, institutions of higher learning would certainly benefit from the potential income such a move would generate. But many of the baby boom generation are now in management or middle-management roles, and their ability to leave the company to make that journey to the nearest educational Mecca for the latest update is limited. Small extension centers, courses offered through computer conferencing, audio conferences and communication satellites are all developing as colleges and universities make the move to market their educational wares.

This is a difficult transition for some educational centers. For many years the demand for education has been high, and there was little incentive for innovative programs that extended beyond the walls of the campus. However, more and more are trying innovative programs to reach out to the student. This is new territory for both the schools and the instructors. I am sure that there are many corporate education directors who quietly smile as the local school announces an "innovative" outreach program that has been a part of the corporate education environment for decades. Many larger businesses have never had the luxury of a central classroom area; they have been on the road for years dealing with adult learners.

Adult learners . . . These are not the 19-year-olds sitting in a classroom groaning at the assignment of a five-page paper on some abstract concept. These are people who know a thing or two and, in many cases, have more expertise in certain areas than the instructor! Adult learners let a teacher know, in no uncertain terms, when they perceive an assignment as "busy work." Adult learners have opinions on every subject and can make those opinions known with unusual force. Some instructors that are used to rather docile college students may view an adult class as a pack of wolves just waiting for the instructor to show a weakness and then going in for the attack. The instructors have a right to be concerned, because adult students have the knowledge and capability to challenge an instructor. In this section, we will discuss some of the factors in adult education as they relate to teleconferencing.

**The Socratic Method**

We have come a long way since Socrates sat at one end of a log and asked questions of his single student which, through the student's self-discovery, led to knowledge. Over the past thirty years we have seen the rise of the mass lecture—several hundred learners crowded into a large auditorium listening to a small speck in the front of the room. What was missing was the opportunity for interaction and discussion with the instructor. While teleconferencing makes it possible to reach large, geographically separated groups with educational material, it would be a mistake to see teleconferencing used as a new form of electronic mass lecture in which the interactive component is cosmetic rather than functional. Educators today are just as concerned with the learner's integration of information as the pure dissemination of information, and teleconferencing offers a unique capacity for group discussion oriented toward the application of information and its subsequent conversion to knowledge.

In a teleconferencing environment, the instructor's role is that of facilitator rather than all-knowing expert. Education is replete with a variety of self-paced learning systems that make sure that the facts presented can be repeated by the student, but the internalization and application of that information may best be accomplished through intense discussion. This is where teleconferencing can serve to supplement traditional information delivery systems. In addition, there is a trend toward capitalizing on the experience and knowledge of the other learners by using teleconferencing as a method of linking, or "networking," those individuals into application study groups. These group members both apply their new knowledge to realistic problems and at the same time share among themselves their real-world experiences. The instructor participates by guiding the discussions rather than pontificating academic facts—it is the discovery of knowledge in a group setting. The use of satellite systems for the mass distribution component, followed by more economical audio and computer conferencing for small group discussions, is a major departure from traditional approaches and the results will be interesting to watch.

### The Teleconferencing Instructor

The type of individual who performs well in a teleconferencing environment needs to be flexible as the newer educational challenges emerge. Since the instructor cannot physically be in every location and demand attention, the electronic teacher needs to have more refined persuasive and group process skills than his or her traditional classroom counterpart. An important psychological component for an electronic instructor is an understanding that there is no "right" way to solve a problem; there are multiple solutions depending on environmental factors. An instructor who believes that his or her way is the correct way is not the type of instructor who does well in teleconferencing.

A number of years ago, psychologists developed a variety of scales to rate an individual's degree of flexibility in handling divergent ideas. The more inflexible the individual, the more dogmatic is the individual's personality. These so-called "dogmatism scales" have been used by such groups as police departments for selecting the types of officers who would function best in highly sensitive interactions with the public.

My observations have shown that a similar scaling system can be used to determine the probability of instructor success in dealing with students via electronic systems. The more dogmatic the instructor, the lower the probability of teleconferencing success. Although the research has been around for a number of years, Milton Rokeach's discussion of dogmatic personalities in *The Open And Closed Mind* provides some interesting food for thought as we seek to locate those individuals who will do well in the new electronic environment.

### Participation and Interaction

The problem with delivery of material does not stop with the instructor, but extends to how to involve participants in the discussion of the information presented. In a teleconference it is very difficult to quickly glance around the room and see if there are any puzzled looks on the faces of those in the class. Other methods must be used to assess the degree of understanding. The only form of teleconferencing which comes close to providing the same kinds of visual cues one would see in a classroom is a two-site, full-motion video teleconference. Even in that setting there are limitations. Since the camera is the eyes of the instructor, somehow the camera must be commanded to scan the various participants, and the result is a scan that is significantly more lengthy than a quick glance. Multi-site video teleconferences are even more involved, since only one location may be seen at a time. The responsibility becomes twofold. First, the instructor must spend more time in seeking out questions and, second, the learner must be more aggressive in asking questions. All too often, learners adopt a puzzled look on their faces in the hope that the instructor will call upon them. That learned behavior has no value in an electronic education setting.

While some learners seem to have no problem with jumping right in with a question, they are a very small minority. The rest of the individuals fail to overcome their fears about asking spontaneous questions when they are not familiar with the medium. Let's look at audio and video systems first. We have all experienced the flush of "stage fright" as we prepare to ask a question, those feelings about how we will be perceived by the group and the instructor. In a teleconference there are even more potential stress inducers:

1. "What will the people here think of my question?"

2. "What will those unseen people 'out there' think of my question?"

3. "What opinion will the people out there form of my group if I ask the question?"

4. "What will the lecturer think of my question?"

Normally, people in a class setting only concern themselves with questions one and four. So the mental concerns double in a teleconference. There are several ways to approach the problem.

The first method is the directed question. With that method a specific individual or location is asked a question. As was mentioned earlier, it is critical to give some advance warning that a question is to be asked; otherwise the anxiety level will go sky high and the time delay between the question and the response may be too long to be comfortable. I have seen adults actually become speechless when surprised with a question—so flustered that they simply cannot provide a response. There is a high probability that the person who has been put on the spot in this fashion will not return to the class, and the local group may blame the instructor for embarrassing one of their fellow workers. Always try to give advance notice!

A second method is to get everyone to say something early in the teleconferencing process: their name, their department, their occupation, the number of their children, what the weather is like. The problem with this approach is that when you have three or more locations and a number of people at each location the time consumed is quite high. Very probably the evaluations will indicate that the initial discussion process was a "waste of time." Although you may feel the exercise is important, it is the participants' perceptions of value that need to be considered. The same kind of approach is often used in a classroom, but remember that the size of the class is limited to 25 to 30 and that we can see each individual; in a nonvisual teleconference those same visual-attention factors are not present, which can make time seem to pass much more slowly if you at a location that is just listening.

A modified approach that I believe works quite well involves a little more time, but the payoff is higher. Prior to the first formal session, the instructor meets with each individual location via teleconferencing. During that session the participants introduce themselves to the instructor, and the group discusses some of their personal objectives from the course. This approach has several advantages. First, it demonstrates that the instructor cares about the group because he or she is taking the time to get to know them a little bit better. Second, the instructor learns more about the objectives of the students and can modify the lecture material to better meet those stated objectives. Third, each one of the participants uses the teleconferencing equipment, which helps to overcome some of the fears associated with the technology. The major disadvantage of this approach is that it does little to break down the intergroup barriers. However, I have seen instructors do wonders by having individuals in one group answer questions raised by members of another group. Let me give you an example:

> JOAN . . . anyway, we have been looking at this equipment for our community and I wonder if you have had any experience with it?
> INSTRUCTOR: That's a good question, Joan. If my memory serves me correctly, I think that Phil in Chicago has had some experience with that and maybe he can give us some of his ideas. First, let me mention that there is a growing trend in the industry toward this kind of outreach activity, and I expect we are going to see a number of new products on the market over the next year. Phil, Joan Jones in Denver might be interested in what you folks in Chicago have done. Any comments?
> PHIL: I think what we're doing is a little different than what Joan wants to do, but let me tell you what we did . . .

The instructor has stepped out of the role as expert on everything, acknowledged a group member as having important and useful experience, and has opened the door for future intergroup communication.

In teleconferencing, much the same as the classroom, interaction is much easier with smaller groups. However, more attention must be paid to involving participants than is needed in the traditional classroom. In long-term teleconferencing efforts it is wise, therefore, to keep group size fairly limited if a high level of interaction is desired. As the instructor gains experience with teleconferencing, the size of the group can be gradually expanded.

## The Teleconferenced Core

Many people initiate teleconferencing with the mistaken belief that *all* travel will be replaced—that all the course material must now be taught via this medium. It is important to avoid this trap. Start by looking at course work in terms of "core" material that can be delivered in a teleconference and "customized" material that can be handled locally at each site. I have had many say initially that to convert XYZ course to teleconferencing would be impossible because of the need for hands-on demonstrations or lab-type sessions. My response has been to look for the common factors first and then for ways to handle the material which requires more direct supervision. This approach has been far more successful in involving instructors who have some initial reluctance to teleconferencing. For example, if one-third of a course can be handled by teleconferencing, it does mean, after all, a reduction in travel by one-third. The value of teleconferencing should be viewed from a cumulative perspective (macro viewpoint), rather than on an individual scale (micro viewpoint).

In one specific case, there was a need for nurses in several hospitals to receive a course in anatomy and physiology. At first, the instructor thought it would be impossible to conduct a telecourse since the course required physical demonstrations with the students participating. Our approach was to use the instructor to deliver the core content material and to use lab assistants at each location to supervise the hands-on aspect of the course. Prior to each lab session, the instructor would meet via the system with all of the lab assistants to review the objectives for the lab session and discuss any potential problem areas that might arise. The instructor would also review some of the material covered in the last lecture so that the lab assistants would have the opportunity to informally quiz some of the students on the content material. So when considering a course, first start by focusing on the aspects that would lend themselves to the medium, then turn to the other aspects and concentrate on creative solutions to the problems by using the individuals with experience at each location to assist the instructor.

## Shared Instructional Responsibility

One of the problems your organization may face has little to do with the standard course to be offered over a system. You may find that there are competent individuals at the remote locations who are conducting excellent classes but are finding their time becoming increasingly limited. In this case, it may be worth considering a team teaching approach that uses those currently delivering education at their respective locations. A few years ago during a teleconference, a director of a pharmacy department complained about his inability to train his new pharmacy aides to the level he wanted. He went on to say that the first group he trained was excellent, the second group received a little less information, and the third group even less. His need for high quality aides remained the same, but his available time was decreasing. Other pharmacists on the teleconference said they also were teaching similar programs and were finding the same problem. The solution to the problem was simple and straightforward. Since there were five pharmacists involved, we took the total course work and divided it into five modules, with each pharmacist responsible for the development and delivery of a complete instructional module. Once a week, the pharmacy aides from all the locations met and heard the lectures from the different pharmacists. The result was a tremendous time savings for each of the pharmacists and an increase in the quality of the education provided, since the individual pharmacists could focus on the complete development of one module instead of worrying about developing the entire course.

## Participative Goal Setting

Prior to the implementation of one teleconferencing system, I surveyed over 800 of the potential participants and asked them questions concerning their impressions of the quality of current educational efforts. I was surprised to find that only about 50 percent felt the material they received was relevant to the work. Upon further discussion, I learned that in most cases a lecturer would present information he or she felt the group should know. Many of the lecturers felt that their information was relevant but that the participants just were not able to make the connection. There was little or no communication between the participants, whom I call "end users" of information, and the instructor. There is certainly nothing unusual about this approach; it is the traditional method of operation by educators. Unfortunately, the participants felt it was the instructor's fault, and the instructor felt it was the participants' fault. The end result was wasted time.

I decided that a different approach was necessary to increase the relevance of the information presented. When an information need was identified by the end users and an instructor was located, a draft course outline was circulated to an end user at each site. After the representatives had an opportunity to review the outline and objectives with the other end users, the representatives and the instructor met via teleconferencing to discuss the draft outline. At that time, the representatives were able to state their own location's problems more clearly for the instructor so that the course objectives could be modified. When unsolicited information was to be presented, a similar procedure was followed to ensure that the outline addressed some of the concerns that would be raised at each individual location. Armed with this feedback, the lecturer could customize the information for the audience. A subsequent evaluation asked the same relevance question of those that had participated in the teleconferences, and the relevance level increased from 50 percent to over 90 percent. Of course, additional communication and time is necessary for the draft process, but the prelecture discussion generally lasted less than 30 minutes—which is a small price to pay for increasing the relevance and utility of the information presented.

This approach is merely an extension of what is taught in public speaking courses—know your audience! The more knowledge you have about the audience members with whom you will be communicating, the better you communicate. In the case of participative goal setting, we are using the medium to assist in the development of the content to be delivered via the medium. Teleconferencing enables users to communicate quickly with one another and should be used as a means to achieve better overall communication.

## Handouts

Generally speaking, many adults who attend educational sessions tend to assess the quality of the program in terms of the weight of the handouts they receive. Of course, there are exceptions, but all things being equal, the amount of handouts does impact the participant's rating of the program's quality. Unlike the typical high school or college student, adult learners tend to hold onto their handouts and use them as reference material. The preference is for typed materials rather than notes in their own handwriting. For this reason, I recommend that a complete set of handouts accompany a lecture. Companies that provide national workshops recognize this need and always provide those that attend with large, loose-leaf binders with articles and other tidbits. The handouts should include an outline of the program (with ample room for notes in the margin), several relevant articles, telephone numbers and addresses of the participants for networking purposes, and the names and addresses of major equipment/service providers (if necessary).

### The Abstract Vs. The Concrete

Whether it is a correct assessment or not, many other users of teleconferencing have noted that as you move down the organizational ladder, the content interest shifts from the abstract to the concrete. For example, supervisors attending a supervisory training course tend to be far more interested in specific things they can do, rather than a discussion of Theory X, Y, or Z. Managers tolerate abstract discussions better, but they are interested in a condensed approach that zeroes in on the ''pearls'' of wisdom that they can easily remember and apply.

When I sit down with those who are about to make a presentation, we first try to narrow the objectives to five or less and to develop the necessary pearls to support those objectives. The body of the lecture then fills out to support and reinforce the objectives. In addition, I recommend that lecturers try to subdivide material into distinct categories, such as ''The five steps to . . .'' and ''The three things to remember are . . .'' This telegraphs to the listeners that several key items are forthcoming and they should begin to write them down in their notebooks. When statements are hidden in a narrative style, it is difficult for participants to pick out the important details without guidance from the instructor.

## Meeting Factors

While meetings are just as varied as the individuals involved, there are a few considerations that should be kept in mind when setting up a meeting.

### Preparation

As long as there are meetings, there will be participants who will have not prepared in advance for the material to be discussed. Circulating the material ahead of time is just as critical in a teleconference as in a face-to-face meeting. An important component of a teleconference is determining ahead of time the specific outcomes desired. An agenda has been one mechanism for preparing the participants for the discussion, but the leader should have a very concrete idea of which items will require (a) agreement from each location, (b) a vote, (c) task assignments, and (d) reports. Meetings via an interactive communications system should be used for interaction, rather than one location giving a lengthy report on what has been happening; so be sure to identify areas in which participation and idea sharing is desired.

### Concurrence

The biggest problem in teleconferencing is agreement and concurrence. Since it is not possible to easily look each of the participants in the eye to see if there are any concerns, some other approach is required. The most basic, but effective, method is the roll call. In the roll call, each location is called upon in turn to react to the information presented. Do not rely on the "Are there any questions?" approach. Only after participants have been involved in a number of teleconferences will they readily respond to such a query. A roll call is recommended every time a major statement is made that will require the participants to perform some action at their end. This may seem like a waste of time, but it saves time in the long run. The last thing you want is miscommunication and misunderstanding—a roll call reduces the probability that problems will arise.

The stages in a roll call might be: (a) description of the problem and tentative solution; (b) roll call of the various locations for their reactions; (c) summary of the reactions by group leader and modified recommendation; (d) open-ended call for further comments; (e) final roll call to ensure that everyone agrees with the final recommended action; (f) next item of business. After the first roll call when everyone has an opportunity to state their position and the summary, the open-ended request for further questions does work—if people have comments, they will respond. The final roll call serves the purpose of putting everyone "on the record" as agreeing with the final decision. If you follow this approach, you are protected from someone coming back later and saying that you did not give them a chance to respond. Build this approach into your meetings.

A similar approach is useful when performing task assignment. Make sure that you touch base with each individual so that you will be satisfied that they understand the task components and the deadlines involved. When summarizing the meeting at the end, specifically review all the decisions, task assignments, and any other items on which group agreement was reached. Provide one final roll call to see if anyone has departing comments before closing the meeting. If a future meeting is required, the end of the teleconference is a good time for everyone to pull out their calendars and set the next day and time. This will save someone's secretary a day in calling all of the participants trying to find the best time.

### Brainstorming

Originally developed in the 1930s by Alex Osborn, brainstorming has been an integral part of the idea development process. The new Nominal Group Technique (NGT) is beginning to be used more frequently and lends itself more to a teleconferencing environment than the older brainstorming style in which ideas flowed in like a flood, generally overwhelming a teleconferencing system.

Developed by Andrew Van de Ven and Andre Delbecq, the NGT works like this:

1. A group of five to ten is assembled.

2. A specific problem is presented, along with the necessary background information for newcomers to the organization.

3. Each participant writes down as many ideas or potential solutions as possible in 10-15 minutes.

4. Each participant, in turn, reads off their list of solutions. The solutions are written down on a flip chart at each location.

5. After the last solution has been read, each idea is discussed in sequence. New ideas are added onto the list during discussion.

6. Following the discussion, each participant writes down and prioritizes the top five solutions to the problem.

At this point, the face-to-face NGT group would hand their written choices to the group leader who would tally the results. In the teleconferencing environment, only computer conferencing offers the capability of the secret ballot. If you are using a bridging service, it is possible for the leader to connect with each location individually so that a site's group vote can be collected. After all the information is collected from each location, the entire group is reconnected for the results. The critical question is the extent to which the secret ballot is necessary. The reason for the secret ballot is reduced ego destruction when a participant's idea does not make it to the top five. Only you can determine how much of a problem ego involvement might become.

The key advantage of NGT for teleconferencing is that it is very structured, from a communication standpoint, and enables the leader to go from one location to another in a very directed manner. The "free for all" brainstorming session does not work well in a multisite teleconference when speaker telephone quality or other technical considerations inhibit the communication between participant and leader. Again, like any other meeting aspects of teleconferencing, the objectives must be clear and communicated to the participants.

## Ad Hoc Program Factors

An *ad hoc* teleconference is one that generally occurs infrequently. *Ad hoc* conferences also require that teleconferencing services be established to enable the program to take place. This is to differentiate an *ad hoc* event from the occasional use of an existing teleconferencing system by individuals. The *ad hoc* teleconference is the equivalent of the commercial television network's "Special." Generally, big dollars and big audiences are involved. The content can range from an annual stockholders' meeting to the announcement of a new product to the press to an "educational" session which promotes consumption or to show potential buyers how to use a new product. Considering the mass of logistical details which must be dealt with, the *ad hoc* teleconference is a major undertaking which has its own unique set of human factors.

## Preparation

Because of the potential mass audience and the number of participants with no previous knowledge of teleconferencing, more preparation work is necessary than with any other teleconference. It must be remembered that an *ad hoc* teleconference itself is a media event—people will be attracted to the event because of both the content and the media—so efforts should be made to maximize both. The expectation level will be quite high, and there is a greater need for higher quality production value than there would be for routine teleconferences.

One of the best ways to prepare participants is with a blow-by-blow account of what will happen during the teleconference, especially from a technology standpoint. The ''gee whiz'' factor can be used in your favor if you are trying to indicate to the participants that your company is familiar with the state-of-the-art and on the leading edge when it comes to new innovations. People like to feel that they are a part of something new and exciting, and they will tell their friends about it. However, do not make the technology the center piece of your publicity; after all it is the message you want to communicate. Use the newness of the technology to further your image.

## Marketing Support

While an *ad hoc* program may include some two-way interaction, the size of the audience will limit the extent to which people can actually ask specific questions. Therefore, support the teleconference with on-site personnel to complete the communication. Like the educator looking for the core material to present, a marketing teleconference should be the centerpiece, followed by personal customizing of the message to suit the participants at the various locations. It is also a good idea to use the event as a method of collecting information about the participants. Name and address information can be used to send follow-up information or ''thanks for participating'' letters to the individuals that attended.

## Contingency Plans

What if something goes wrong? The bigger the teleconference and the more sophisticated the technology, the higher the probability that something will not go as planned. You need to have a specific back-up plan that can be brought into action when the unexpected happens. One teleconference I was watching lost the sound portion of the program for over an hour. The reaction of the audience was amazing. People were making comments out loud about the way those in the teleconference looked. Some attempted to read the lips of those talking and repeated what they thought was being said so the rest could understand the nature of the discussion. Needless to say, the planners had no contingency plans.

In a video teleconference, if the picture goes away, then continue to provide the group with the sound. If the sound vanishes, turn the whole thing off and have someone at the location that has been filled in on the content make an informal presentation and answer questions. Television without the picture is acceptable—without sound it is useless. Large-scale audio conferences are less complex than their video counterparts, and the loss of audio can be corrected within a few minutes, but satellite programs are more difficult to correct and some local activity is advised. With computer conferencing there can be problems. In one demonstration I was conducting, the computer communications network decided to "go on vacation" (malfunctioned) in the middle of the presentation. There were other numbers that I could call to connect directly to the computer, bypassing the network, but they were sitting safely in a file folder on my desk many miles away. Try to plan for the unexpected.

However, it is sometimes impossible to predict some events. For example, during one audio conference I called on a location for questions and heard nothing. I called again. Nothing. The bridging company conference coordinator came on the line and noted that the line was still connected. Then, out of nowhere, the sounds of sirens and klaxon horns blasted the silence . . . loud voices were shouting directions . . . the crackle of two-way radios punctuated the shouts. Then a woman's voice was heard as she picked up the microphone, "Sorry, Bob. We're in the middle of a fire alarm here. Would you mind asking another location the question?" What would you have done? Naturally, I went ahead and thanked the woman for letting us know what was going on, asked her to let us know when the situation was back to normal, and proceeded to ask the question of the next location. Those circumstances simply cannot be predicted.

In one satellite teleconference not too long ago, hundreds of viewers were watching a round-table discussion of the impact of new regulations on the health care industry. The four-man, one-woman group opened up the discussion for call-in questions, and the session was proceeding normally. Then one caller said he had a question for the woman panelist. The television director at the satellite origination site had his cameraman zoom in on her. The caller then said, "I just wanted to say that you have the most beautiful-looking breasts I have ever seen!" CLICK. You could have heard a pin drop. Then you could hear a few chuckles from the audience members at the originating site. I think it was the first obscene satellite teleconference call in history, and it stunned the other panel members, the director, the audience, and the woman. The discussion went on, but the damage had been done. For hundreds of viewers, the caller set video teleconferencing back 20 years. The next year the same firm overreacted, and callers dictated their questions to a secretary, who passed them to the group. The interactive process was significantly reduced.

## Writing Prepared Comments

When I was teaching public speaking, I always used to tell my students "DON'T WRITE OUT YOUR SPEECH! MAKE AN OUTLINE. TALK FROM THE OUTLINE. DON'T READ YOUR SPEECH!" So what happened? Someone would always get up in front of the group and read his or her speech. Generally, you want to avoid a scripted speech because (a) you lose contact with your audience, (b) you cannot easily deviate from your script if the audience does not seem to understand what you are saying, and (c) the written style is far more complex than an oral style and more difficult to understand. Naturally, if the fate of the Western world depended on the accuracy of the statement, then a written speech would be appropriate.

### Hints For Visual And Audio Systems

In the real world, there are many who will read their remarks, so at least try to follow the following suggestions:

1. Use short sentences. One complete thought per sentence. In fact, some of the most effective sentences are not sentences, but descriptive phrases.

2. Use contractions, except when making a point or when they do not seem appropriate.

3. Since you are writing for the ear and not the eye, read your material out loud to yourself to hear how it sounds. Also remember that when the time comes, you will be reading much faster than when you practice.

4. DOUBLE SPACE EVERYTHING.

5. Do not start with an unfamiliar name. Delay the name until you have the audience's attention. Always put someone's title *before* the name for listener identification.

6. DO NOT USE PRONOUNS. He, she, his, him, this, those, they, and it can become confusing since the audience cannot re-hear what you have said.

7. If you have to take a breath in the middle of a sentence, it is too long!

8. Avoid clauses that separate the subject from the predicate.

9. Use action-oriented words. Teleconferencing is immediate, so use words that relate to the here and now—today, this afternoon, this morning, a few minutes ago. Avoid exact time unless it is critical.

10. Use an active sentence structure: noun, verb, object.

### Hints For Visual Systems

Adding a visual component creates some additional complexity. Remember that the audience member has three primary problems: (a) seeing the visual information, (b) hearing the words, and (c) combining the visual and audio information to form an understanding of the material. To guide you further, keep the following in mind:

1. Look at the visual information BEFORE you write your text so that you can capitalize on what the visual information is saying to your audience.

2. When the camera is on the individual, the text information should be strong, active, aggressive, and colorful. Place your text on large poster boards and have someone keep them next to the camera. If you keep your nose buried in your notes you will look like you do not know what you are talking about.

3. When the camera is on a visual, the text should not dominate. The text should explain and supplement the visual information. Do not make any startling statements when a visual is being shown. The President certainly would not say "We are going to war!" while the visual was a picture of the world.

4. Always write a summary of what is said on a film or videotape that you are using. This will enable you to relate important points should the equipment malfunction.

If you follow some of these guidelines when preparing your manuscript, your message will be communicated more clearly.

## Summary

In this chapter we have covered some of the human factors that apply to many teleconferencing modalities. In each subsequent chapter, we will delve into these factors in more depth. It is important that you realize that in teleconferencing the HUMAN factors are more critical than the TECHNICAL factors. All too often we tend to concentrate on the technical side and fail to realize that it is the people issues that need more attention. Naturally, we want to develop the technologies to help solve some of the human barriers to communication. If you approach the hardware as only a means to support better communication, rather than an end in itself, you will be on the right path. There is much about the new technology that can detract you from the overall objective. The flashing lights and command center atmosphere of a teleconferencing room has a certain appeal to some, but the goal is a communications system that is transparent to the users. The system should permit rapid communication without creating additional barriers.

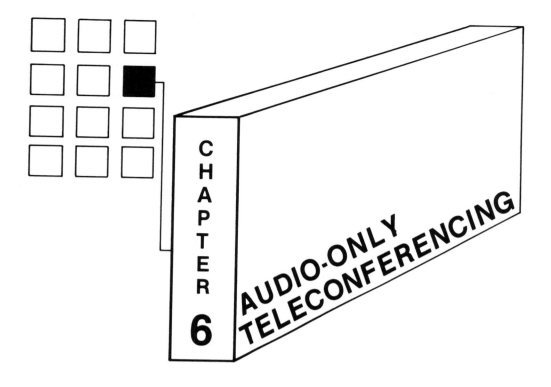

CHAPTER 6

AUDIO-ONLY TELECONFERENCING

Audio-only is one of the most basic forms of teleconferencing. The backbone of audio conferencing is the vast telephone network that reaches almost all corners of the world. The level of sophistication can range all the way from several telephone instruments interconnected to sophisticated conference rooms wired with the latest in conference microphones and interconnected via a high-fidelity dedicated line network. Audio systems provide the easiest way to begin regular teleconferencing. The cost is low and the potential applications are great. The ELRA Group estimates that 90 percent of the 2.5 million teleconferences in 1983–1984 are audio teleconferences.[1] Reports from users indicate that audio-only systems can replace up to 50 percent of our normal face-to-face meetings. However, I would suggest that you treat this figure lightly, because the degree to which audio can be effective depends on your needs for visual information. For example, 50 percent certainly would not apply to radiologists and others who deal with extremely visual media. Those topic areas that deal primarily in words—general discussions of strategy, procedures, some elements of education—can utilize audio systems quite successfully. When visual information is required, audio systems do work quite well when there is sufficient time to mail copies of the visual information ahead of time to the participating sites.

One of the disadvantages of audio-only systems is that they are not seen as "sexy" (a low "pheromone factor") by those who are interested in using teleconferencing as a major component in marketing efforts. In selected marketing areas, the payback can be great. Audio systems can provide competitive advantage, but more on the tactical marketing side rather than with "flashy" effects because of the potential perception that audio is a fairly primitive form of technology. The common statement that one will hear is "What's so special about audio conferencing? It sounds like a conference call to me." The statement is true, but those who use audio systems prefer to call it "audio conferencing" for a good reason. What sets audio conferencing apart from the conference call is the way the medium is used. It may be elitist, but one old hand at teleconferencing put it this way:

> Someone who holds a conference call thinks there is nothing really different between (a) a group of people all on the same telephone line and (b) just two people on a telephone line. Someone who holds an audio conference understands the subtle changes in the group dynamics associated with electronic group communications.

For a variety of reasons, many businessmen attach a negative connotation to the term "conference call." In all probability, it is because those who have participated in a conference call have not had very good experiences with the event. Before we take a look at some of the specifics of audio conferencing, let's take a look at some of the applications and advantages/disadvantages:

A. Applications

1. When multisite operational/tactical communication is necessary.

2. Where low cost is a critical element.

3. When individuals know one another.

4. Where ease of operation is necessary.

5. When participating locations change so that a dedicated system is not indicated.

6. Where the majority of the information to be discussed is not visual.

7. Where there is sufficient lead time to send out visual materials for review prior to the program.

8. Where the low "sex appeal" of the communications modality will not impede marketing.

9. Where geographic considerations dictate the use of telephone grade lines.

B. Advantages

1. Inexpensive communication charges.

2. Inexpensive user equipment.

3. Able to fit many applications.

4. Networking is relative easy.

5. Equipment easy to use.

6. Able to involve any telephone anywhere in the world.

C. Disadvantages

1. Requires visual materials to be sent out ahead of time.

2. Nonverbal communication impossible.

3. Due to use of telephone as basic communications element, limited "sex appeal."

4. Unable to address *ad hoc* needs for communication of visual information.

5. Some user resistence to audio due to poor past experiences.

Now let's take a look at some of the specifics of audio conferencing. In the following material, we will cover the technology, the methods of interconnecting locations, and some of the specific audio conferencing skills.

## The Technology

The telephone is one of the most basic communication technologies. In this section we will look at attachments to the regular telephone to improve its utility and devices that link telephones together.

### Telephone Headsets

If the regular participants in your teleconferences will be the only ones in their office involved, it may be worth considering the addition of some of the newer telephone headsets to replace the handsets. The advantages of a headset are:

1. You have both hands free to shuffle papers and take notes.

2. You don't end up a one and one-half hour teleconference with a stiff neck as you try to hold the handset between your ear and shoulder so that you can have both hands free.

3. The single user is provided with the advantages of a speaker telephone, but with privacy of communication.

There are two types. First, there is the traditional operator-type headset. I would recommend the Plantronics StarSet® *, which sells for less than $200. This type of headset is comfortable to wear, the audio quality (what you hear and how others hear you) is very good, it does not mess up your hair (since it hangs quite comfortably over your ear), it is extremely lightweight, and it plugs right into your existing telephone without the need to have a telephone installer hook

---

*StarSet® is a registered trademark of Plantronics, 345 Encinal Street, Santa Cruz, CA 95060.

the unit up. It also permits the users to easily alternate between the headset and the standard handset. When not in use, the unit can be unplugged and stored.

The second type has just recently entered the market. This device is *wireless*; there is no physical connection between the headset and the telephone instrument. This means that you have maximum freedom to move from your desk to a file cabinet without having the cord spill your cup of coffee. The wireless unit consists of three components: the headset itself, a small transmitter/receiver that clips to a belt, and a table-top transmitter/receiver/charger that hooks into the telephone line. The wireless headset has many of the advantages of the Plantronics unit, but it does have a headband that may create problems for those who wish not to mess up their hair, and it may require a telephone installer to hook the unit up if you have a multiline set (a telephone with buttons for several lines and a hold button). The range is normally about fifty feet, but count on ten to fifteen feet as a more reliable range if you are in a building with quite a bit of metal in the walls. Wireless telephones generally cost about $150. However, I would strongly suggest that you try it out in your setting before purchase to determine if the quality and range are adequate for your needs.

### Speaker Telephones

So far in this chapter we have talked about teleconferencing where there is just one participant at each telephone. However, to get the most out of teleconferencing, a method of letting several in the room hear and be heard should be explored. The most common complaint of speaker telephones is that the users sound like "they're in a barrel." Absolutely! There is no question about it—many speaker telephones sound *terrible*. The speaker telephone has to perform some pretty amazing work to sound as good as it does. Try this experiment: find a reasonably good cassette recorder, place it on a desk, get back about three feet (the distance most people stay from their speaker telephones), and talk in a normal voice. Now, play the tape back. It will probably sound pretty bad. There will be considerable echo as the microphone picks up your voice and the reflections of your voice off the walls and the desk top. To add to the speaker telephone's problems, it must also amplify the sound of the person on the other end so that you can hear it, but not pick up that sound on its microphone. A tough job.

One concern that callers have (those on the other end) is that their comments are going all over a room—no privacy. This can be a major problem and should not be overlooked. Those with speaker telephones tend to turn up the volume so that the sound is much louder than if the person were in the same room. Due to the fact that the telephone system concentrates all its energy in the narrow-frequency range that is most understandable under poor conditions, the information coming from a speaker phone penetrates doors and walls much more easily than if there were just two people in a room. Those that work in an open office environment will have real problems with speaker telephones being heard by everyone. This is one situation where a speaker telephone should be limited to closed offices and conference rooms.

The speaker telephone is very much like a small public address system; it consists of a microphone to pick up the person talking and a loudspeaker so that conversations on the telephone can be heard by others. But unlike a public address system, speaker telephones have a built-in switching system to avoid feedback when the microphone is placed too close to the loud speaker. When someone in the room is speaking, the microphone is turned on and the loudspeaker is turned off. When no one is speaking, the loudspeaker is on and the microphone is turned off. The garden variety speaker telephones are in either the microphone on/speaker off or the microphone off/speaker on mode. So, we have a "simplex" operation—you are either in a listening mode or talking mode. This means that if someone says something while you are talking, you will not hear it. In order to avoid the device turning on and off too rapidly, the speaker telephone's circuit has a slight delay built into it to permit you to move from sentence to sentence without the device changing modes. Due to this delay, a listener must wait a brief amount of time before saying anything, otherwise the beginning words will not be heard. This delay, coupled with the barrel effect, is one of the things that turns off some users about speaker telephones. In addition, the circuit in some units is more sensitive to lower male voices than higher female voices, which can create some problems for women users.

Why do people sound like they are in a barrel? Simply because the further away you are from the microphone, the more the sound reflections from the room are picked up by the speaker telephone's microphone and the less the actual voice is picked up. The same thing would happen if a network news reporter took the microphone in from of his or her mouth and moved it five or ten feet away. Microphones work best when they are as close as possible to the mouth of the person speaking. Given those limitations, speaker telephones do a pretty good job.

This leads me to the kind of setting in which the speaker telephone is used. The poorer the acoustic treatment in the room, the poorer the speaker telephone's quality. A room with bare walls and a wood or tile floor reflects sound around the room without absorbing much. This is called a "live" room. The opposite type of room would have carpet on the floor, an acoustic ceiling, and drapes. A room that absorbs sound and reflects little is called a "dead" room by acoustic engineers. If the speaker phone microphone is to be far away from the users, a room that is somewhat dead would result in a better sound quality for those on the other end of the telephone conversation. In a live room, the microphone would be picking up more reflections than actual direct voice and would result in the barrel effect noted earlier.

One final word: IF YOU ARE SERIOUS ABOUT AUDIO CONFERENCING, AVOID INEXPENSIVE SPEAKER TELEPHONES. In the lower-quality devices, the switching between microphone and speaker is very apparent and distracting.

*4A Speakerphone.* This is the most common speaker telephone seen in businesses and is an excellent device. See Figure 6-1. Provided the user realizes that the microphone is located in the separate on/off switch and not in the speaker

**FIGURE 6-1**
4A Speakerphone

*Credit: Reproduced with permission of AT&T.*

enclosure—which is where most people think the microphone is located. A natural assumption on their part, but wrong. I surveyed 100 users of the 4A and found that only two knew where the microphone was located. The result is that people place the on/off switch containing the microphone far away from where they sit and talk. I spoke with one user who said that people he called had a horrible time hearing him and, as a result, he rarely used it. I looked around his desk and did not see the on/off switch. When I asked him about it, he said "I have enough clutter on my desk already without all those wires." He opened his desk drawer and continued, "I keep the darn thing in here." Sure enough, sandwiched between a telephone directory and a box containing his business cards, there was the small microphone—hidden away from sight. No wonder people could not hear him!

My only major criticism of the 4A is that it is not possible to manually turn off the microphone. In many teleconferences it helps the quality tremendously to turn off your own microphone if someone else is giving a lengthy presentation. This defeats your speaker telephone's internal switching equipment and prohibits sounds in your room (dropping a pencil, someone laughing, a public address speaker) from switching your speakerphone into the talk mode. The 4A does have an off position (marked "quiet") on the on/off switch, but a small spring in the unit forces the user to keep pressure on the switch to keep the microphone off. The only way that you can defeat the microphone in a 4A for a lengthy period of time is to lean a heavy book on the switch, or to hold the switch in the quiet mode all the time. The monthly rental for the 4A varies from state to state, but is generally less than $20 a month. The installation charge is less than $100.

***Panasonic Easa-Phone*™ \* *KX-T1020*.** The quality of the Easa-Phone™ is as good as the 4A in most settings and does allow the user to turn the microphone on or off manually. By the way, the microphone is clearly marked! It does not have enough volume for a large gathering, but does a pretty good all around job. The Easa-Phone™, however, seems to be more sensitive to a poor environment (a "live" room) than the 4A. The price for the Easa-Phone™ is in the $150 range.

***Darome Model 610 Convener*™ \*\*.** For larger groups, a more sophisticated speaker telephone attachment is recommended. In the $600 range, the Darome 610 Convener™ has been THE standard. This unit uses separate microphones that are placed around the table to be used by the participants. A new low-profile version has been introduced called the Model 710 Convener™. See Figure 6-2. Those on the other end of the conversation will hear excellent audio, provided the participants do not get too far away from the microphone.

---

\*Easa-Phone™ is a trademark of Panasonic.
\*\*Convener™ is a trademark of Darome, Inc., 5725 East River Road, Suite 780, Chicago, IL 60631.

**FIGURE 6-2**
Darome Model 710 Convener™

The unit comes with a speaker enclosure that houses the speaker, the switching electronics, and the hardware to connect directly to the telephone line. Connection to a multiple-line telephone will require the assistance of a telephone installer. The Darome product has the following advantages:

1. Built-in direct connection for any standard modular telephone jack—the standard single-telephone instrument jack used by the telephone company.

2. A built-in speaker and amplifier. It can be plugged into a public address system for even larger presentations.

3. The ability to connect any number of microphones. While one is supplied, I would recommend a minimum of four for most conferences.

4. The ability to connect almost any type of professional quality microphone to the unit.

5. The ability to plug in a tape machine to record the conference.

6. The ability to plug in a tape machine and playback a prerecorded tape to others.

7. If used for larger groups, it will serve as a local public address system so that the comments made by users into their individual microphones can be heard by everyone else at the location.

8. The unit uses a press-to-talk button on each microphone. Microphones are not active unless the button is pressed to avoid aside comments and room noise from being overheard. A special lecturer microphone, provided with the unit, can be locked in the "on" position so that the push-to-talk button does not have to be held down all the time.

9. Extra-long power and telephone cables. The extra-long cables may seem minor, but when you are faced with day-to-day operation, not having to haul around extension cords is certainly a big help.

The device is very portable, which lets users move it from location to location easily.

*Darome 630 Convener™*. In the $1,200 range, the Darome 630 is a full-duplex device, meaning that there is no switching back and forth between microphone and speaker. Listening to a duplex device is a pure pleasure. Naturally, if the other party is using a lower-cost, switching speaker telephone the advantages of the duplex model are reduced.

## Microphones

With the higher quality audio conferencing equipment, it is possible to use separate microphones to fit your unique situation.

*Shure® \* SM-10A headset microphone.* If you plan to use your audio conferencing equipment for educational application, in which a lecturer will be making longer presentations, I would recommend that you purchase a special-purpose microphone. One of the problems I have noticed is that during longer presentations lecturers move further and further away from the desk top microphone, thus reducing the quality. To avoid this problem, and to give the lecturer maximum flexibility to move notes, I use a Shure® Model SM-10A headset. See Figure 6-3.

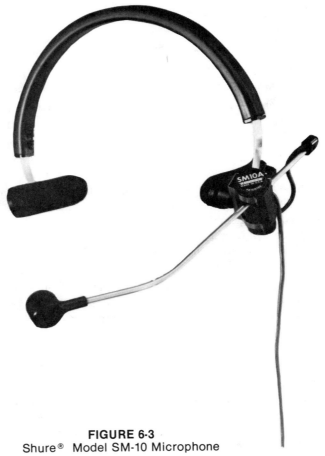

**FIGURE 6-3**
Shure® Model SM-10 Microphone

*Credit: Courtesy of Shure Brothers, Inc.*

---

*Shure® is a registered trademark of Shure Brothers, Inc., 222 Hartrey Avenue, Evanston, IL 60204.

The SM-10A microphone is the one used by the astronauts in the space shuttle, it has excellent audio quality and is comfortable to wear. Since the microphone is worn on the head, it always remains the same distance from the mouth, so the quality is consistent. Lecturers love it! After a few minutes they forget they have it on due to its light weight, and they become much more informal and spontaneous than with the regular desk microphone.

*QUORUM$^{TM}$ * linear-array microphone.* Probably the most sophisticated microphone system for teleconferencing applications, the QUORUM$^{TM}$ microphone is a superb device. See Figure 6-4. Renting for less than $100 per month, the microphone can easily pick up larger groups within a 12-foot radius. An unusual characteristic of the microphone is that someone two feet away sounds almost the same as someone ten feet away: a desirable feature. You can also set the microphone on a matching speaker so that the sound from the other locations comes from the direction of the microphone. Since participants normally talk toward the speaker, by co-locating the microphone and the speaker, the participants are always talking in the correct direction. In order for the QUORUM$^{TM}$ to work best, it needs to be in a fairly good acoustic environment; it does not like rooms with bare walls reflecting sound all around.

### Bridging Systems

There are a number of problems which occur when more than two telephones are connected to the same line at one time. The telephone system in our country is optimized for two telephones on a line at one time. When additional telephones are added two things begin to happen: (a) the volume of the participant's voice decreases and (b) the noise on the telephone line increases. Telephone bridges use electronic systems to compensate for these problems. Each telephone bridge uses slightly different techniques to accomplish the goal of returning the quality of the conference to the level of only two telephones on the telephone line at the same time, and each manufacturer has its own opinion of what constitutes a good teleconference.

In order to reduce the accumulation of noise each time a new telephone participant is added to the conference, the most common method of maintaining high quality audio is to turn down the volume of all the telephone lines except for the one associated with the person currently speaking. The noise level drops dramatically, and the quality of sound for the person speaking is enhanced. While this is an excellent approach, it does create a new set of problems. In our everyday use of the telephone, we are constantly interrupting each other, inserting comments like ''I agree'' in the middle of an individual's statement. When you have turned down all the telephone lines coming into the bridge except one, it is not easy to insert these statements. As a result, we perceive that the telephones are not working normally and our frustration level increases.

---

*QUORUM$^{TM}$ is a trademark of American Telephone and Telegraph.

**FIGURE 6-4**
QUORUM™ Teleconferencing Microphone and Loudspeaker
*Credit: Reproduced with permission of AT&T.*

As with speaker telephones, some bridges are simplex, while others are duplex and permit many participants to talk at one time. Simplex bridges permit only one voice to be heard on the system at one time, and there is a slight time delay between when a participant finishes speaking and when the bridge will permit others to talk. Unfortunately, since bridges cannot recognize speech *per se*, they will react to loud noises (a car passing, someone laughing or coughing) and will keep the volume up on that line until the noise goes away; only the bridge operator can override the bridge's switching electronics. For example, a long-winded speaker on a simplex bridge cannot be interrupted until he or she finishes talking. However, once you understand the principle behind the bridge, you learn to (a) pause as you speak so that others may interrupt, and (b) delay agreement or disagreement until someone is finished speaking.

There have been some recent advances that provide bridge quality close to that of a full-duplex system. In these new systems, the methods used to keep the noise down and give the participants the illusion that they can talk and be heard any time are complex, but work quite well. Remember, though, that if a participant is using a simplex speaker telephone the advantages of such sophisticated equipment may be lost. If a number of the participants are using their regular telephones or full-duplex speaker telephones, then the effect is very pleasing.

*PBX equipment.* Probably one of the least known and understood features of today's current business telephone systems (called a Private Branch Exchange, or PBX) are the teleconferencing capabilities that may already be in place. Telephone systems that are in many businesses may already have the capability to bridge three or more telephones. In some instances there may be some limitations. For example, a six-party teleconferencing feature may only have the capability of including two outside parties in the conference, while the other four parties must be inside the company. Since the majority of the parties are using the same switching equipment, there is normally no problem with noise and volume levels, so the equipment is fairly simple in design and may incorporate only very basic volume-controlling circuits. If a participant is calling in long-distance, there may be some noticeable reduction in the quality associated with the distant participant. Since the number of participants is very limited and there is no sophisticated switching equipment to keep noise levels low, the conferencing will be full-duplex, permitting the parties to interrupt each other.

A PBX equipped with a conference call option may use either the operator to connect the calls or may permit users to establish their own teleconference. In the operator-assisted mode, the PBX operator calls the various extensions or outside numbers, much as a telephone company conference operator might do, and then interconnects the various participants. In all likelihood the operator will not monitor the conference to inform the participants of an accidental disconnection, but the probability of an extension becoming accidently disconnected is extremely small.

In the "meet-me" form of operation, each person who dials an appropriate extension number automatically becomes part of the conference. There is no operator required. Of course, the problem is that several people may already be holding a conference or someone may accidently become part of your conference;

there are few or no controls over access. On the advantage side, since your equipment may already provide this feature it is very inexpensive. The only cost would be the long-distance costs associated with the distant party. If you have a PBX, it would certainly be worthwhile checking to see how the conferencing capability is initiated. In addition, request information from the telephone equipment vendor on options that might increase the conferencing capability. You might find a rather rapid pay-back period.

*Stand-alone equipment.* Now we come to the stand-alone bridges. They can be installed anywhere, even if you do not have a PBX, and are specifically designed for teleconferencing and the problems associated with multiple long-distance participants. While there are a number of manufacturers of bridges, I want to talk in detail about one manufactured by CEAC® *.

CEAC® is a major manufacturer of telephone hardware in Alabama. The CEAC® bridge is used by several of the major independent companies that provide teleconferencing services, which will be described in the next section. In addition, the Bell system has offered the CEAC® device (under the Bell name) for those wishing to rent a bridging system from Bell. The CEAC® product is reliable and offers a number of interesting features. It is a full duplex device that can permit a number of participants to be heard at the same time, but it does turn down the volume on lines that are not in use to avoid line noise. Here are some of the features of the CEAC® bridge:

1. The ability to break a teleconference into several smaller groups. This feature enables the moderator to assign tasks to groups and to permit those groups to conference among themselves. When the subgroups have finished they can rejoin the larger group.

2. The unit automatically adjusts individual telephone line volume levels.

3. The bridge can operate in either an operator-assisted or meet-me mode. That means that callers can be first intercepted by the operator and then placed into the conference, or that callers can dial a telephone number and join the conference directly.

4. The ability to easily record a conference.

5. The ability to play back prerecorded material into the conference.

6. The operator (or moderator) can see which participant is speaking by looking at blinking lights on a small indicator box which correspond with each telephone line.

7. The system switches fast enough so that several individuals can engage in a duplex-like conversation.

---

*CEAC® is a registered trademark of Peripheral Switching Division, CEAC, Inc., 1500 East Conecuh, Union Springs, AL 36089.

8. The ability to handle all audio-based communication devices: telephone, facsimile, electronic blackboard, slow-scan television.

9. The bridge can be activated 24 hours a day through a sophisticated remote control system. If necessary, all functions can be controlled from a Touch Tone™ * telephone anywhere in the world.

The CEAC® bridge can handle up to 32 telephone lines at one time and can be purchased in multiples of eight lines (8, 16, 24, etc.). The basic cost is about $2,000 per bridge telephone line.

*Line problems.* There is one problem facing potential purchasers of a bridge. It relates to the quality of the telephone lines between the telephone company's nearest telephone switching center (called the "central office") and the bridge itself. If the lines are in poor shape, then ALL the participants in a teleconference will notice a lower quality. The potential for problem lines increases with the distance from the central office to the bridge. Those that have had some experience with this problem recommend the following:

1. Specify to the telephone company that you will not accept poor-quality lines.

2. Request assistance from the manufacturer of the bridge in dealing with the telephone company.

3. Find someone in the telephone company who is familiar with telephone line noise problems and get him or her assigned to your order. Since most customers are not as picky as you will want to be, most installers are not prepared to deal with your demands.

Do not pay for telephone lines that are poor quality! Be aggressive and require that everything be in top shape.

*Your bridge operator.* If you install your own bridging equipment, it will be necessary to assign someone to assist callers when the system is not operating in the "meet me" mode. Although you may operate in the "meet-me" mode most of the time, more important teleconferences need someone to greet the participants as they call in and monitor the telephone lines for any problems. Nothing will reduce the value of your investment more than a poor operator. An operator who does not understand what is going on, has little understanding of the group dynamics in an audio conference, or (the worst possible case) is rude can be a significant liability. It just makes good sense to find an operator who is friendly, helpful and knows what he or she is doing. It is best to train several individuals so that a backup is always available in case of illness or vacation.

*Maintenance.* Although reliable, every piece of electronic equipment will malfunction. Be prepared. For example, the CEAC® bridge places its electronic

---

*Touch Tone™ is a trademark of American Telephone and Telegraph.

components on cards which slide out of the unit and provides spare cards so that a problem can be corrected very quickly. However, it would be a good idea to contract with a local telephone service company to provide support service. It is important to have someone that can assist with such items as moving the equipment, repairing the system, and dealing with the telephone company on local lines.

## The Connection

Rather than purchasing your own equipment, there are firms that have the necessary hardware to combine all the telephone lines for a teleconference. The charge for this service varies between the providers.

### The Conference Call

The conference call, a service provided by the telephone company, is the most widely known method of establishing a teleconference. You just call the telephone company operator and request that a conference call be established. In some of the larger cities, there is a separate "conference operator" who does nothing else but establish conference calls. The conference operator will request the following information from you:

1. The person responsible for the conference call. Generally, that is the moderator or chairman of the event.
2. The time, date, and length of time for the conference call. Make sure you indicate the time zone when referring to the start time. There are a number of variations (cities that do not participate in daylight savings time, for example), so be careful about the time.
3. The names of the participants and their telephone numbers. In a conference call, the operator needs the information to call each participant.

Here are some of the questions you may wish to ask the conference operator when setting up your conference call:

1. The cost. For exploratory purposes, you can call the conference operator at any time and request this information. All the conference operator needs is:
   a. The anticipated length of time for the conference call.
   b. The area code and *the first three digits* of the telephone number. These three numbers designate the central office involved, which is used for billing purposes.
2. The procedure to be followed in case of accidental disconnection. During the course of an hour teleconference, it is possible that some of the lines will be disconnected for a variety of reasons. The conference operator will probably respond by saying that they monitor

the participants' lines and will call them back if they are accidently disconnected. It is critical that both you and the lecturer know the procedure by heart—you can well imagine the problems that will develop when your lecturer is disconnected during an important presentation! My personal experience has shown that they may not notice that a line has been disconnected. In several cases, it has taken me between 10 and 20 minutes to rejoin a conference. Just to be on the safe side, get the following information:

   a. Obtain information from the conference operator on how much time should pass before a participant tries to rejoin the conference by calling an operator.
   b. Obtain the *exact* procedure a participant in another city, that might be served by a non-Bell telephone company, would use to rejoin the conference call.

The telephone company conference call is pretty straightforward. At the appointed time, the following actions will take place:

   1. The conference operator will call each participant one at a time to establish the connections.
   2. The conference operator will call the conference originator or moderator last.
   3. Once all the parties have been contacted, the conference operator will bridge all the parties together so the conference call can begin.

Based on my experience and the experience of others, here are some of the problems with a telephone company conference call:

   1. The quality of the standard telephone conference call bridging equipment tends to be poorer than if a more sophisticated, stand-alone audio conferencing bridge is used.
   2. Special features, such as the ability to record a conference or play back prerecorded tapes, are not generally available.
   3. Depending on the size of the group, the length of time to connect all the parties to the teleconference can be significant. A substantial amount of time may pass between when the first party is contacted and when the last member joins the conference so it can actually begin.
   4. If disconnected and the conference operator fails to notice the problem, it may take a participant from several minutes to as long as 15 to 20 minutes to rejoin the conference call.

In spite of some of the problems, I use the conference call for conferencing small, task-oriented groups within a 200-mile radius of my location. For larger conferences where I want to make sure the quality is high, I use a teleconferencing bridging service bureau.

**FIGURE 6-5**
Connex Coordinators Working With Audio Teleconferencing
Groups in their Danbury, Conn., center

Credit: *Courtesy of Connex International, Inc.*

## Bridging Service Bureaus

Over the past few years, a number of private firms have emerged that provide teleconferencing bridge services which go beyond the services provided by the telephone company conference calls. Generally, these services will call themselves "audio teleconferencing companies" to set themselves apart from the conference call system associated with the telephone company. Some are free-standing companies, while others are services provided by manufacturers of bridging equipment.

One bridging service company is Connex International in Danbury, Connecticut.* An aggressive audio teleconferencing firm not owned by a particular vendor, Connex specializes in personal service, which to me, is an *extremely* important consideration for many first-time audio teleconferencing users (see Figure 6-5). Some of the benefits offered by Connex are:

1. An "800" number for reservations, which can also be used by participants to check out their speaker telephones and other equipment before the teleconference.

2. The ability to record a teleconference. Tapes can be used for archival purposes or can be sent to those who were not able to join in the discussion.

3. A telephone number that participants dial to join the conference. This speeds up the initial process since each participant does not have to be called by a conference operator.

4. In the event of a disconnection, a participant simply redials the same telephone number initially dialed to join the conference. This will connect the caller with the bridge coordinator who will reconnect the participant with the conference.

5. Since the bridge coordinator is dedicated to your conference, he or she will immediately notify the group if a participant was disconnected and will announce to the group that a participant is rejoining the conference.

6. The ability to play back prerecorded material. This can be a presentation by the president of the organization, radio commercials, or other elements that will serve as the basis for discussion.

7. Helpful personnel! This is one feature I cannot stress enough. The Connex people are a pure delight to work with and are committed to providing you with *any* assistance to make your audio teleconference a success. Believe me, having someone who you can talk to about your plans and problems is of real value.

8. Connex can call participants who are late in joining the conference to remind them of the event.

10. Connex will send out mail reminders of the teleconference, if you so desire.

---

*Connex International, Inc., 12 West Street, Danbury, CT 06810.

11. Since participants call the bridge service from their own locations, they can make use of WATS lines, MCI, or other low-cost communications channels to reduce costs.

12. Connex will make all the necessary connections for international calls.

13. Up to 200 telephone lines may be bridged together at one time.

14. A larger conference may be subdivided into a number of smaller discussion groups which can rejoin all the participants later in the program.

15. Not only telephone conversations, but facsimile, slow-scan television and other audiographic systems may also be linked by the bridge.

Connex offers three different services that are worth mentioning. The ConnexCall™* is the domestic version of the telephone company conference call that we have discussed. The Sat/Call™** service provides those using one-way video satellite transmissions with the capability of connecting all the video reception locations for a live, interactive audio discussion. This is an alternative to supporting a series of "800" numbers for the participants to call with questions. The WorldCall™*** service will connect as many non-U.S. sites as you want for a conference. The audio quality of an international call is generally poorer than for domestic service, and the electronic circuitry in the bridge can help the quality of those *long* distance participants.

In addition to the technical assistance provided in the WorldCall™, Connex offers multinational corporations access to translators to assist with language barrier problems. This service is called InterpretTel™****. Frankly, I believe InterpretTel™ to be one of the most creative services offered by a commercial bridging company. Two forms of the service are offered. First, the consecutive translation. In this case, the remarks are made and then translated. In the second case, simultaneous translation; translations are made at the same time as the presentation (*à la* United Nations style). The simultaneous-translation feature is much more technically complex, and Connex requires additional notice so that arrangements can be made to make sure that the more specialized translators are available for the conference.

One of the other features offered by Connex is its "Instant Reservation Service." At the end of the session, while all the participants are on-line, the group can decide on the best time for the next teleconference, and the reservation can be made on the spot. This avoids the countless telephone calls associated with trying to find common times for the next session. Naturally, keeping everyone on-line in-

---

*ConnexCall™ is a trademark of Connex International, Inc.
**Sat/Call™ is a trademark of Connex International, Inc.
***WorldCall™ is a trademark of Connex International, Inc.
****InterpretTel™ is a trademark of Connex International, Inc.

creases the total cost, but the additional expense is more than recovered in the savings of individual telephone calls and postage associated with the traditional method of setting up meetings.

From a user standpoint, Connex offers a number of educational programs. In order to introduce others to audio teleconferencing, Connex offers the Connex "Hotline." Offered twice monthly, the "Hotline" lets perspective users call in and discuss audio teleconferencing with coordinators and other users. There is no cost for this service, except for your telephone call. Since there will probably be several others on-line at the same time, it is a good way to get a feel for teleconferencing at low expense. For those who are more experienced, Connex offers a teleconferencing workshop called "Meetings by Teleconference." Held on demand, but generally on a quarterly basis, the workshop covers some of the specifics related to conducting meetings via audio teleconferencing. There is a nominal charge for the workshop. I would suggest that a potential user first join the Connex "Hotline," conduct one small teleconference, and then join the workshop. You will find your list of questions much longer after you have had some first-hand experience before joining the workshop. Connex also offers a program entitled, "How To Train By Teleconference." This program specializes in the unique problems associated with the presentation of educational material via an audio-only system. Finally, Connex will provide educational programs on-site on how to effectively use audio teleconferencing.

The single disadvantage is that the service may be more expensive than the conference call. Only you can determine if the services I have listed above are worth the increased cost. From a user standpoint, there are two costs associated with using a audio teleconference service bureau: (a) the communication costs associated with the long-distance call to the bridge and (b) the cost of the bridge time itself. By giving any operator the area code and central office numbers of the calling location and the bridge, it is fairly easy to get the per minute direct dial "1-plus" costs associated with each participant. If you will be using WATS lines, the individual in your firm who pays the telephone bills can give you the hourly cost for using those lines. Bridge costs run about $20 per caller per hour, and discounts are normally available if you plan to be a regular user. The "meter" starts running with the time the first caller checks in and terminates when the last caller hangs up. So, you want to request that participants call into the bridge within five minutes prior to the meeting, rather than fifteen or twenty minutes ahead of time.

If you are going to use Connex International or another bridge firm, here is some of the information you will want to have ready:

1. The date and time of the program. To avoid mistakes, convert the meeting time *to the bridging company's time zone*. This is to avoid confusion in future discussions. Remember that they will note the time of the conference on their schedules in their time zone. By the way, do not assume the bridge personnel automatically know the time zone you are in—*always be very specific about the time and zone.* I try to

give Connex at least two weeks' notice. In some cases, I have scheduled as much as a year in advance for very important meetings.

2. The *maximum* length of time for your conference. It can create problems for their schedules if you say you will be finished in an hour and run one and a half hours instead. You are not the only one who uses their facility. Since you are billed only for the time that you use, not the time you indicate you will use, play it safe and request a little more time than you think you will need.

3. The number of locations that will be calling in, including your own. Do *not* give them the total number of participants. They are only concerned with the number of telephone lines that will be coming in and not the fact that there will be ten to twenty at each location.

4. A listing of the locations that will be calling, including their telephone numbers. This is so the coordinator will be able to check off the locations as the callers check in and so that telephone numbers will be available for the coordinator to call should there be some problem.

5. Any special requirements. This includes:

   a. Connex recording the conference for you. I might add that the quality of the Connex recording is much better than it would be if you attempt to record the conference from your location. Remember that your recording will pick up any telephone line noise from the participant's telephone line to Connex and from Connex to your location. The Connex recording will just have the noise from the participant to their location.

   b. Connex playing a prerecorded audio tape for you. You may wish to have the same message (or lecture) delivered in several conferences. Playing a recording of the material saves the lecturer repeating the information, but the lecturer can still be on-line for the question-and-answer period.

   c. Mailings or other methods of reminding the participating locations of the teleconference.

   d. Any special configurations that you would like to have. Included in this category would be breaking a teleconference into several small groups. If you are thinking about this option, have a pretty good idea of the timing involved and which locations will be divided into which groups. Then discuss the idea with the Connex coordinator.

6. The Connex coordinator will then provide you with the telephone number that is to be used by the calling locations. If there are quite a few locations involved, Connex may ask you to assign the par-

ticipants specific numbers. Make sure that you inform Connex the locations that you assign to each telephone number.

7. *Repeat the telephone number to make sure you have it right!* Be sure to *personally* check all correspondence to make sure that the phone numbers are correct. There is nothing more embarrassing than to realize the day of the conference that the numbers you sent out were incorrect!

8. Advise the coordinator of the equipment the various sites will be using. If the locations are using speaker telephones without the ability to turn off the microphone, the coordinator will be prepared for some additional quality problems that may result.

The day of the teleconference, the sequence of events is:

1. Approximately five minutes prior to the scheduled start of the teleconference, you and the other participants call the number provided by Connex staff.

2. The Connex coordinator will ask the location to identify itself (city, name, or other information so that the coordinator can keep track of those that check in against the list the moderator has provided for Connex ahead of time).

3. The coordinator will then place you and the other callers on hold (with music) to take care of the other locations checking in.

4. If you are the moderator, the coordinator will periodically come on your line and update you as to the sites that have checked in.

5. At the scheduled start of the meeting, the coordinator will provide you (the moderator) with the current status and ask whether or not you wish to start the conference, wait for the late check ins, or have Connex call those that have not checked in.

6. If you want to start, the coordinator will advise you that those checking in late will be announced to the group.

7. The coordinator will then perform a roll call of the participants. The coordinator will call each location by name and ask the participant to respond with some form of geographic location information. This serves two functions:

   a. Provides the listeners with some idea of the geographic make-up of the group. This helps the participants develop in their own "mind's eye" a map of the participating locations.
   b. Enables the moderator and the coordinator to perform one final check of the audio quality of each location. If one or more sites have called in on a poor telephone line, the sites will be asked to replace their call, since there is a significant probability that the site's quality will improve with the next call.

8. The coordinator will then check with the moderator to see if the moderator was able to hear all locations adequately. Since it is possible for one-half of a long-distance call to go one route across our country and the other half to take an entirely different route, making sure the moderator can hear and be heard is important.

9. The coordinator will then formally turn the teleconference over to the moderator, and the conference begins.

10. In the event that a location joins the conference late or is accidentally disconnected, the coordinator will interrupt the conference and advise the moderator.

This information is good to share with those who will be speaking or addressing the group. This reduces some anxiety because the lecturer will know exactly what will happen every step of the way.

Whenever you are dealing with a commercial conference bridge and are attempting to call the bridge using an operator-assisted call, *never* mention to a telephone operator that you are attempting to connect with a conference bridge! The operator will automatically assume that you are trying to join a telephone company conference call and try to locate your conference, and the operator may NOT inform you of the attempt. The net result will be considerable confusion, wasted time, and an anger level that may be very noticeable when you finally do join the conference. So do not indicate to a telephone company operator that you are attempting to join a audio conference. The same is true when attempting to rejoin a conference in the case of a disconnection.

I remember being disconnected and dialing our PBX operator to get a WATS line to call the conference bridge service. All the WATS lines were tied up, so I requested a direct-dial line and explained that it was important I get the line so I could rejoin the teleconference. In an attempt to be helpful, the switchboard operator put me on hold and starting calling telephone company operators to find my conference. She returned to my line, after ten minutes, confused because she could not find my conference, and I was upset that she did not just give me the line. Although she was just trying to be helpful, the meeting was a complete disaster—I was supposed to be the moderator. After waiting a few minutes, the other participants hung up and went about their business. Who needs that kind of stress? Just give people the number you want to call and say nothing about a teleconference.

## The Skills

Audio teleconferencing requires its own set of group process skills. In this section we will review some of them in more depth.

### Objectives

At the outset, you want to have it very clear in your own mind what you expect the meeting to accomplish. Especially in terms of *outcome*. If you begin to think about the specific actions that you want people to take following the meeting, you are (a) developing a mission statement for the program and (b) providing a solid set of objectives that can be evaluated. Educators were some of the first to talk about the educational lecture in terms of "behavioral objectives," and the concept lends itself quite well to a teleconference.

To say that you want the participants "to have an appreciation" for something is NOT a behavioral objective. For example, if it was a marketing program to introduce a new product, you might say that you want the participants to perform the following: (a) be able to say the name of the new product, (b) spell the product name, (c) list five of its ten best features, (d) give three reasons why the product is superior to the products manufactured by other vendors, (e) be able to state the product's price, and (f) sign an order for the product based on the presentation. These are quantifiable items that can be evaluated. Writing down the objectives forces the person getting ready to present the information to think about what is really important in some form of prioritized order. Once this has been done, the rest of the program will follow fairly easily because you have identified those things that you want to accomplish.

Programs that are designed to create a more positive "feeling" about the product or the company also need to be made more concrete. For example, an "institutional" program that promotes the image of a company rather than a product should attempt to focus on those things which create positive feeling on the part of the participants, to list what they are, and then to measure how successfully you were able to get the point across. After the program, the participants should be able to answer questions like these:

☐ In what three ways does the company show that it is interested in the consumer?

☐ What has the company done to speed the handling of customer complaints?

## Shorter Meetings

There has been a fair amount of observation that audio conferences tend to take a shorter amount of time to accomplish the same tasks. The research has been vague in this area, but I would agree that audio meetings do *seem* to take less time. The current speculation is that audio meetings, without the face-to-face component and having a slightly more rigid structure, tend to skip the idle chat that takes place in face-to-face meetings. This does seem to change, however, over time. As soon as the participants become more at ease with the medium, jokes and idle discussion do return to the meeting, but they continue to be fairly short in duration. It also seems that audio conferences that have duplex equipment at the various locations tend to become more informal than simplex systems. The switching continues to remind participants that there is an intermediary technology present and continues to hold down informal discussions.

It is possible for a meeting moderator to capitalize on the structure of the medium and maintain a controlled environment more easily. Audio meetings seem to work best if one views the meeting according to *Robert's Rules of Order*—a participant asks for permission to speak, and the chairman becomes the focal point of communication switching. As the originator of the teleconference, you are in charge. Because you have initiated the teleconference, there is a certain amount of power that goes with the control of the communications system. The other participants will unconsciously grant you a certain amount of credibility because you have arranged the session. It is possible for you to capitalize on that impression. Remember that the other participants will be looking to you for examples on how to use the medium effectively. If you do not have a good grasp on how to structure the meeting and achieve closure, your credibility will rapidly diminish.

### One-Way Use

There is a tendency for lecturers and other resource participants to treat the audio conference as a radio broadcast. Remember that first-time users bring into the session stereotypes of what they think might happen and, generally, the closest approximation is a radio broadcast. Microphones and loud speakers simply reinforce the misconceptions.

First, there is nothing wrong with using teleconferencing equipment as a form of broadcasting to small audiences (''narrowcasting''). One of the questions to consider is in what circumstances would anyone want an audio teleconference to operate or sound like an audio tape? When would you want no interaction? Let's look at some examples:

1.  When information needs to get to participants quickly, and audio tape systems are either too expensive or will not get to the participants in time.

2.  When participants may only want to listen in on certain portions. For example, presentations at an all-day conference can be piped to the teleconference bridge and participants can dial in to hear only the portions of the program in which they are interested. In this case, access to the presentation is more important than the potential interaction with the presenter.

3.  When, for a variety of political or organizational reasons, interaction with the presenter is *not* desired. An example would be a live statement from a president concerning a major policy change, to be followed up with discussions at each one of the sites concerning the details of the announcement. In this case, there may have been a teleconference between the site leaders prior to the larger teleconference to discuss local presentation details.

### Interaction

The most common mistake that beginning users of audio conferencing make is asking the nondirected, open-ended question, such as ''Does anyone have any questions?'' When everyone is in the same room, a quick look around gives a participant a good idea about the timing of the question. Some people like to give others a chance before they jump in, but the nonvisual nature of audio conferencing makes that behavior impossible. What happens is that the audience sits at their respective sites waiting for someone else to ask the first question.

A much better approach is the "directed question," a question directed to a specific individual or site. The lack of spontaneous participation on the part of some group members is one reason why audio conferencing people have noted a problem in closure. By that I mean, when a moderator asks "Does anyone have any problems with that approach?" and hears nothing, the moderator assumes that everyone agrees. Generally, that is not the case. If it is important, it is worth a full roll call of the participating sites asking for specific agreement or questions. There seems to be another psychological benefit from this approach in that the participants feel that they have been involved in the process. The open-ended question, and lack of response, seems to create a feeling of isolation on the part of the participants which can be counterproductive. Therefore, it is a good idea to actively seek consensus when moving on to another item on the agenda. Do not leave anything to chance! Do not assume that simply because someone did not raise an objection, that a problem does not exist!

After a directed question is asked, there may be a delay. The delay can be due to the need for the participant to collect his or her thoughts. Remember that the passage of time is always longer for the person who has asked the question and the other listeners than for the person preparing to respond. In a number of cases, when asked whether or not the question was heard, the response may be "Yes, I heard the question. I was just thinking of a response!" The same type of delay occurs in meetings everyday, but our visual clues tell us that the question was heard and a response is forthcoming. In an audio conference, those clues are not present, so we do not know if we have been understood.

The degree of interaction is dependent in large part on the person in charge of the teleconference and the opportunities presented for participants to interact. If a program follows a radio broadcast style, then interaction is generally included almost as an afterthought. If one develops a mental picture of a conference room or classroom, it is apparent that interaction exists in irregular intervals, generally tied to information blocks or information packets. An outline, for example, contains irregular detail as it pertains to topical areas. It is important to recognize these information packets and to schedule interaction to occur during or directly following the presentation of a packet.

### Getting Started

The biggest complaint about audio-only systems is the lack of visual cues. No matter what the researchers indicate can be accomplished via audio, the participants miss the ability to see the various individuals involved. For those interested in audio systems, it is comforting to note, however, that this tendency to perceive audio systems as inferior is transitory. After several sessions the participants adapt quite readily to the lack of direct visual contact. Here are some suggestions on how to speed the process of user acceptance:

1. Provide all sites with a picture of the main presenter and those involved in the presentation of the program. If possible, the picture should be taken at the location from where the program is to be delivered. Since any picture of the table, microphones, and people involved will be looked at by participants during the program, having the visual information in its proper setting will permit easier acceptance by the participants. Even pictures of those at the other location is valuable visual information.

2. Provide the sites with a map and/or pictures showing the various participating locations. This helps with what I call "spatial dislocation"—the disorientation participants feel when they do not have a good idea where the questions or comments are coming from (geographically, that is).

3. Do not attempt to present highly visual material at the very beginning. Discussions about procedures, policies, and other items that can be presented in typed, outline form serve as the best way to get started. Once the participants begin to realize that they do not have to "see" everything live, they can progress to more complex visual information.

4. The first program should be very strongly task-oriented, not a "show and tell." The focus of the program should be not a demonstration of the technology; instead it should fulfill a need and let the participants feel a sense of accomplishment. Get the participants' minds off the technology and on to the business at hand. Any introductory remarks should not be apologetic (e.g., "I know this is not the same as a face-to-face meeting, but . . ."), but rather they should be straightforward and matter-of-fact.

5. Introduce all those in the room at the origination site and briefly describe the origination setting. Again, give the participants some information for their "mind's eye."

6. During the program, strive to give the participants at least two or three "pearls" that they can apply to their own daily tasks as soon as they leave the meeting. You want to make absolutely sure that they walk away from the session feeling "I really got something out of that!" The more they feel they received from the meeting, the more they will accept nonvisual communication.

7. Provide each of the participants with some information on audio conferencing so that they will know what is going on.

8. Provide a detailed agenda with plenty of writing room.

In the case of larger gatherings, have the local moderator give the number of participants at each location. Write this information down. You will have a much better idea of the size of the audience, which in most cases is significantly greater than just the number of participating locations. In the case of very large gatherings (40 or more), the conference bridge coordinator can simply read off the list of those that have checked in and are part of the conference. Please make sure that you have the copy of the participants' names in the same order as the conference coordinator so that you do not have to jump back and forth between listings trying to figure out who is in the conference.

If you have a small number of sites, you may wish to have the participants at each location give their names. I have had very poor luck with this approach. The advantage is that it does break down some initial participant anxiety. The chief disadvantage is (a) that it takes quite a bit of time (assuming five locations and five people at each location); (b) often the participants are too far away from the speaker telephone's microphone, along with the switching of the sound (both by the bridge and their speaker telephones), which can make it difficult to hear everyone's name; and (c) even though you state otherwise, some will believe that the name-after-name roll call will be part of each and every teleconference and will walk away thinking that the first 15 minutes of introductions was a real waste of time. With medium-sized groups, I recommend using a moderator at each location who can poll the group for questions and comments. In addition, you can provide the moderators with additional training on how to best promote interaction in their groups.

Some time ago, I listened to one group discuss how they were going to get everyone involved in the first program by having everyone give his or her name. They opened up the teleconference and started to go from site to site. Unfortunately, they did not realize that the number of participants was much larger than expected. They were expecting about 30 individuals and over 70 gave their names. A full 30 minutes of the one-hour program was spent on the roll call. It is important to have some idea of the size of the audience before the start of the teleconference.

As you perform your roll call, listen carefully for the quality of the audio. It may take some practice to determine whether or not poor audio is a function of a bad telephone line or of people being too far away from the microphone. A bad line will have a static-like or waterfall sound in the background, while poor audio will have a hollow and weak sound. One of the more common problems in audio conferencing is that people seem to believe that everyone will be able to hear them just as easily as they can hear others. If the quality is perceived as good, then other participants believe that the good-sounding audio must be coming from a setting similar to their own. They assume the same kind of setting and the same kind of equipment. So they expect that even though they may be sitting seven feet away from the microphone, they will be heard as well as someone six inches from a microphone. It just does not work that way.

### Information Needs

Let's look at some of the specific information about teleconferencing that should be distributed or gathered.

*Packet for participants.* By way of an introduction to audio teleconferencing, the material handed out should include:

1. Date of the program.
2. Title of the program.
3. A listing of the participants and the moderator at the other sites listed, or sufficient room for the listener to write in the name of the moderator and any other information concerning names and questions asked from that location. The name of the facility, city and state are also helpful pieces of information.
4. The telephone numbers associated with the various sites. Often listeners will hear comments from another location and would like to discuss a topic of mutual interest following the teleconference. This fosters the concept of "networking" individuals.
5. The objectives of the program.
6. The speaker(s) involved.
7. Plenty of room for notes.
8. The procedure to follow is case of a disconnection.
9. The participant reminders.

Take the above information and type it up in a format that fits your particular situation, and you will be gathering much of the necessary planning information.

*Participant reminders.* Specifically, the basic reminders should include the following statements:

1. If you are going to ask a question or make a comment, try to get as close as possible to the speaker telephone's microphone.
2. *Always* start with your name and location.
3. If practical, make notes to yourself so that you are more at ease when stating a question or making a comment.
4. Wait until a pause in the conversation before asking a question. It is recommended that you say the moderator or presenter's name and then wait to be recognized. Thus, you will avoid asking an entire question only to learn that someone else was asking a question at the same time and no one heard you.
5. Be friendly! Be just as courteous as if you were in the same room as the presenter.

Again, by retyping the above information, you can assist the participants with their teleconferencing effectiveness.

*Originator information required.* Items the program originator should develop and follow are:

1. What are the objectives of the program?
2. What materials should the participants have in front of them?
3. What materials should the participants receive so that they will have plenty of time to read them?
4. What is the name of the moderator at each location and the telephone numbers?
5. Has each site's equipment been checked out prior to the program?
6. Are you absolutely certain that each site has the correct telephone number to call (in the case of a conference bridge)?

The suggestions lend themselves to duplication and circulation prior to the teleconference. After you review the statements made, add additional notations which fit your particular setting.

*Graphic material.* With the proper planning, it is possible to significantly reduce the problems associated with the lack of direct visual contact. By following these steps, you can ensure good graphic communication:

1. Review the presentation for possible graphics. Charts, financial tables, illustrations, drawings, and sketches should be developed to support the presentation.
2. Number all visuals in sequence in the upper right hand corner so that participants can find them easily. DO NOT rely on the title of the graph; it takes participants too much time to read the information.
3. Place letters (A through Z) beside the points in the visual that you will be discussing. Again, fast and easy identification of critical points is the objective. Circle the letters to set them apart from the other visual material. Remember that reproductions will be in black and white, so obvious contrast and easy identification are key elements. See Figure 6-6.

When dealing with visual materials, identify critical areas if there is any potential for confusion or wasted time in describing locations on the graphic. When in doubt, mark the graphic.

## Personal Experience

Finally, if at all possible, try to get some initial experience with audio conferencing before a major program. Set up a conference call with four or five individuals in your company to discuss a subject. Even though there will be a cost, the charges for several local connections will not be significant. By trying the medium out on a ''friendly audience'' you are creating a minimum exposure/risk situation for yourself. I know of one individual who decided to test conference calling on his own before a major program for his corporation. Since his father's birth-

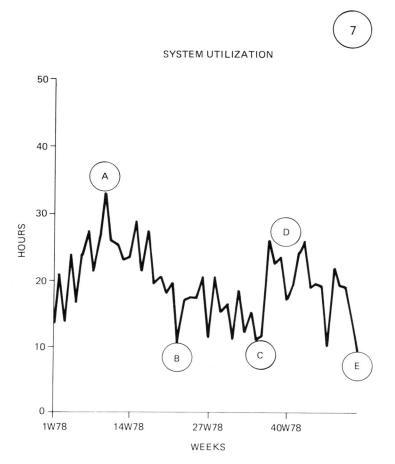

SYSTEM UTILIZATION

7

FIGURE 6-6
Sample Audio Teleconferencing Graphic Marked For
Easy Participant Use

day was coming up shortly, he arranged for a conference call between his home, his father, and several of the children. While it was not possible to test all of the protocols that he had read, it did offer an opportunity to get a feel for the situation.

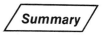

**/ Summary /**

Without a doubt, audio teleconferencing is the easiest form of conferencing you can initiate. The costs are low and the payoff can be significant. Fancy equipment is not required and if you follow some of the simple guidelines outlined, basic audio conferencing will substantially increase productivity.

## Chapter 6 Notes

1. "Survey for public television station predicts growth in teleconferencing." *TeleSpan Newsletter*, June 15, 1983, 3.

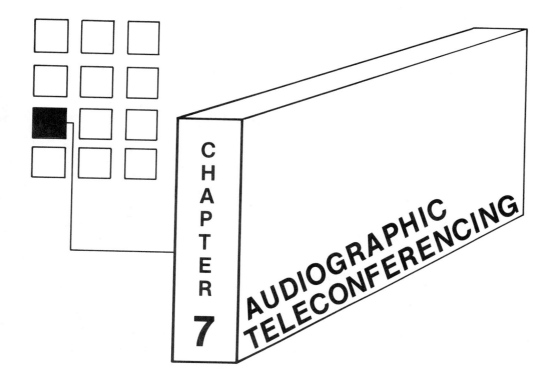

CHAPTER 7

AUDIOGRAPHIC TELECONFERENCING

**W**hen users need something more than audio-only communication, it is generally because they have some form of graphic material that they need to share with the various participating sites. Several methods are available, some which require mailing and others that send visual images electronically. Audiographic equipment is a little more complex than many of the audio-only devices and is, therefore, not as portable. The audiographic equipment is more costly than basic audio, but certainly less expensive than full-motion video. Let's look at some indicators for audiographic teleconferencing:

1. When fairly low cost is important.
2. When the number of locations to be involved does not vary considerably and the amount of communication is consistent.
3. When ease of operation is essential.
4. When a more ''flashy'' teleconferencing environment is necessary for marketing reasons.
5. When visual communication is required.

There are many that believe that this next step up from audio-only communication adds much to teleconferencing. As was mentioned earlier, Bell Telephone estimated that of the 16 percent of international travel that could be replaced by teleconferencing, audiographic systems would be used in 52 percent of the cases.[1]

In this chapter we will discuss three basic approaches to audiographics: remote control projectors, facsimile, and telewriting systems.

## Remote Control Projectors

One of the easiest methods of providing some visual or graphic communication is to remotely control slide projectors located at the various participating sites. In this situation, a presenter has all of his material copied onto slides, duplicates are made, and these copies are then sent to each of the sites to be involved in the teleconference. During the teleconference the presenter presses a button and all the slide projectors change at the same time. This approach to handling visuals has been around quite a while, but has been more extensively used in recent years.

From a technical standpoint, many of the users of this approach build their own control equipment or acquire one of the control units on the market. A basic design has the following features:

1. The lecturer presses a button when a new image is to be seen, many times with one of the buttons on a Touch Tone™ telephone.

2. A simple electronic device at each participating location listens to the incoming telephone line. When it detects the right tone combination, it turns off the speaker so the listeners do not have to sit through two or three seconds of loud tone.

3. To make sure that the tone received is a *bona fide* request to change slides, the device will change the slides only if the tone is present for a predetermined length of time. If the command is determined to be valid, the slide change is initiated.

4. After the tone has disappeared, the electronic circuit will turn on the loud speaker so that participants can hear the lecturer.

Daystar Audio Visual* and Mast Development Company** both offer random-access remote-control devices in the $1,000 to 1,500 range. With random-access equipment a presenter can dial in the number of the slide to be seen by the audience, so it is not necessary to go through each slide in sequence. This is a tremendous advantage if it is necessary to go back to a slide presented earlier in order to answer a question. Revox*** Systems even has a projector for microfiche films costing less than $3,000. This projector may be of interest to those firms that receive much of their computer financial statistics on microfiche instead of com-

---

*Daystar Audio Visual, Inc., 3 Inverness Drive East, Englewood, CO 80112.
**Mast Development Company, 2212 East 12th Street, Davenport, IA 52803.
***Revox Systems, Inc., 2224 Hewlett Avenue, Merrick, NY 11566.

puter printout. Microfiche duplication is extremely inexpensive and can be valuable in educational settings as well. There are many companies that have their own microfilm/microfiche cameras which can be used to produce good quality microfiche originals which then can be copied for distribution.

There are a number of applications in which this approach is very appropriate and not costly. There are, however, some disadvantages to using remote control projection equipment that should be considered:

1. The slides or fiche may not arrive in time.

2. Someone may put the slides in upside down, backward, out of sequence, or all three. This possibility can be reduced by sending out the slides already in their carrier.

3. Slide projectors have been known to change in the wrong direction, creating some local problems.

4. Slide projector bulbs have been known to fail in the middle of a lecture, or (and even more frequently) when they are first turned on.

These problems notwithstanding, this approach has been very heavily used in education, especially in the medical profession. In this case, illustrations and charts are sent to the various participating locations ahead of time. Pictures of artwork, X-rays, charts, graphs, and listings of major points to be covered in the lecture lend themselves to slide reproduction and distribution. With the proper safeguards, it can be very effective.

## Facsimile

A technology that has been around as long as television, facsimile (or "FAX" as some call it) is similar to television in that an image is scanned by an electronic device and the resultant signals are sent via a transmission system to a receiving location, where the signals are recreated on paper rather than a television screen. The major advantages of FAX are its speed and the fact that a paper record ("hard copy") is created. With the increasing need to move information faster than the mail system will allow, FAX is a good way to get information there NOW. The fact that the information appears as a paper clone of the original is certainly attractive because it reduces the possibility of human error that exists when the same information is transferred by word-of-mouth. In all, there are over 350,000 FAX machines in the United States.[2] Some of the more common applications are:

1. Financial reports, orders, and invoices.

2. Engineering and architectural diagrams.

3. Advertising copy and layouts.

4. Photographs.

5. Maps and other similar information.

6. Library and reference data.

A number of teleconferencing facilities have a FAX machine in the room so that information to be discussed can be distributed quickly to all locations. While many use FAX to transmit information just prior to the conference, FAX can be used during a conference as well. For example, a copy of an ad layout could be sent to the participating sites. Then, during the conference, the participants could circulate their modifications for additional review. Modifications to an engineering design can be handled in the same manner as well.

There are some disadvantages to facsimile, however. A potential user might want to consider the following:

1. The equipment is generally not portable.

2. Only one copy is transmitted, so additional photocopy work at each site may be necessary.

3. Unless a sub-minute FAX is used, transmission time may be too long for some users.

4. The resolution may be too low to show the necessary detail.

5. The communication costs will double if all facsimile machines are linked together.

6. Three-dimensional items are difficult to transmit. It is possible to take photographs ahead of time, but there may be some time lag involved.

7. *Ad hoc* pictures of participants is normally impossible.

For some users, the disadvantages are minimal. However, it is important that you assess the type of visual images that will be used by your company before acquiring facsimile equipment.

The three factors to consider in the purchase of facsimile equipment are *speed, resolution, and compatibility.* As you might expect, cost increases as the transmission time declines and/or the ability to resolve small detail increases. By the mid- to late-1970s, there were almost as many "standards" as there were vendors. To address the problem, the International Telegraph and Telephone Consultative Committee (CCITT) of the International Telecommunications Union established standards, called "groups." Group 1 standards were for FAX machines that transmitted a page in either four or six minutes via analog signals over voice grade lines. The longer transmission time provides increased resolution. Group 2 machines are also analog, with transmission times of two and three minutes. Group 3 facsimile machines are digital in nature, but also use voice grade lines. The transmission times for Group 3 are under one minute and are called "sub-minute" devices. There is a Group 4 reserved for very fast digital machines (under 15 seconds), but no standards have been set yet.

There are many manufacturers of facsimile machines on the market, each with its own "bells and whistles." While the Rapicom® is considered by many as an excellent vendor, I hesitate to recommend any specific company due to the wide variation in features. Some will communicate with word processors, some will automatically dial distant FAX units during the night when the communication costs are the lowest, some will enlarge or reduce documents, and some will even automatically imprint date and transmitting location information. Others can call predetermined units and "poll" them to see if they have any information to be sent. If there is nothing to be sent, the connection will be terminated, but if there is information to be sent, the polling unit will command the polled device to begin transmitting. Other aspects to consider include: (a) whether the unit can automatically answer the telephone (autoanswer) and receive incoming information; and (b) whether the unit can automatically transmit many pages of information without attention, thereby saving considerable operator time.

I would recommend that you first determine whether your company already has any facsimile machines and if so, the CCITT group. Then estimate the number of pages of information that will be sent in conjunction with your teleconferencing effort, the required resolution, and the extent to which users may wish to use facsimile *during* a teleconference. If the number of copies to be transmitted is low, resolution is not a critical issue, and few are to be sent during a teleconference, then you may be able to use a facsimile machine in the under-$3,000 range. If your assessment indicates otherwise, then you should take a serious look at one of the faster, more expensive models. You may find that once you take communication costs into account, a $15,000 sub-minute machine may save you more money than a low-cost four-minute device.

## Telewriters

Telewriters enable users to physically write on a surface and have that written material appear on receivers throughout the teleconference as it is being written; in other words, the handwriting appears in real-time. The chief advantages are that hand-directed graphics can be communicated immediately and that there is an increased sense of "being there" on the part of the participants. A number of users say that watching the writing appear as it is being written is almost like having a full-motion television camera pointed at a blackboard. The device's advantages are:

1. Easy to use. No major manipulation of the technology is involved.

2. Easily integrated into settings where frequent use of blackboards, flip charts, transparencies, and paper sketches are used.

3. Well suited to "chalk talk" kinds of presentations.

---

*Rapicom, Inc., 2475 Augustine Drive, Santa Clara, CA 95050.

While the devices are not inexpensive, users of audio plus telewriting have indicated that their people have found no pressing need for full-motion video. It should be noted, however, that their applications have been well suited to this form of communication (primarily educational or technical). An important caution: MAKE SURE THE PRESENTER HAS LEGIBLE HANDWRITING! There have been many lectures that were less than successful simply because those at the remote locations could not read the handwriting. It would be a good idea to have the potential presenter practice so that he or she could see precisely how his or her handwriting will be seen by others.

### Tablet Systems

Tablet systems generally use a fairly small writing and viewing surface (5 " by 7 ") and sell for under $10,000. By using a pressure-sensitive writing area or manipulating a writing device, the horizontal and vertical movements are translated into tones, which are sent over the telephone lines. On the receiving end, the tones operate motor devices which move a pen or similar stylus which writes the information on a piece of paper. One device, manufactured by Talos Systems*, writes on overhead projector acetate film so that a larger group can see the writing. A series of new products have been introduced that will permit the writing to appear on a television screen.

### Electronic Blackboard

Bell Telephone's Gemini® 100 electronic blackboard is easy to use. From all outward appearances it looks exactly like any 51 "-by-65 " blackboard. See Figure 7-1. Behind the blackboard are sensors that detect the location of the chalk while the presenter is writing. This position information is converted to audio tones and sent over the telephone lines to receivers at each of the participating locations. The viewers see the presenter's writing appear on a 23-inch television monitor as the presenter writes. To erase the information, the presenter picks up the eraser from a holder on the blackboard. Sensors in the eraser holder note that the eraser had been picked up and send an erase command to the receivers to blank the areas where the eraser cleans the board. Two telephone lines are required for the Gemini® system: one for the presenter's voice and one for the blackboard tones.

From a technical standpoint, the Gemini® is practically fool-proof. From an operational perspective, the only problem is the presenter who insists on erasing lines with his or her hand rather than the eraser. Since the eraser has not been lifted, the system still believes someone is using the chalk. As a result, the palm of the hand or finger rubbing out a misspelling creates quite a block of white on the receivers' screens! For group participation, a number of Gemini® units can be linked so that the television screen will show everyone's comments. It is also possible to record a presentation with a stereo cassette recorder. Since the

---

*Talos Systems, Inc., 7419 East Helm Drive, Scottsdale, AZ 85260.

**FIGURE 7-1**
GEMINI® Electronic Blackboard

*Credit: Reproduced with permission of AT&T*

133

Gemini® generates audio tones, one channel of the stereo recorder is used for the blackboard material and the other is used for the voice information. In this manner, it is possible to record material at each location so that those that could not attend the session can view it at a later date.

The Gemini® can really turn an audio-only teleconference into a live, participative session. After about 30 minutes of use, I have noticed a strange phenomenon. If the audio quality from the presenter is good and there is extensive use of the board, people actually begin to feel that the person is in the same room with them! Interaction increases and the participants become more animated in their gestures. It is almost as if the participants believe that the presenter can see them. The system has cost about $500 per month, but price reductions are being considered.

## Summary

Audiographic devices are beginning to come into their own as users seek more economical methods of handling graphically oriented material. The critical issue is whether the information passed between locations lends itself to these technological options. If it does, then I would certainly get some hands-on experience. If immediacy is important, facsimile and telewriting offer attractive options. I must comment, however, that the teleconferencing market is still missing units that integrate the advantages of facsimile and telewriting. I am sure that as the market matures, there will be significant increases in the flexibility of these devices.

## Chapter 7 Notes

1. "AT&T discusses survey of international teleconferencing needs." *The TeleSpan Newsletter,* October 15, 1982, 3.

2. J. Seaman, "Electronic mail: Coming at you." *Computer Decisions,* October 1982, 128–160.

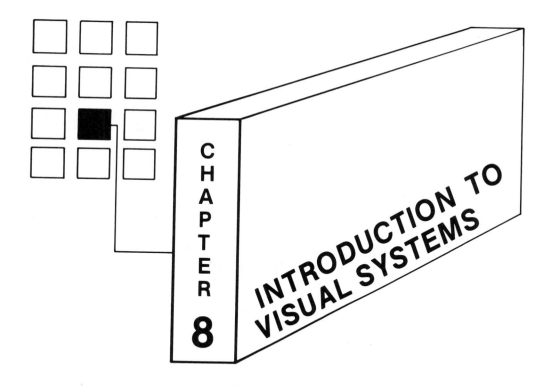

# CHAPTER 8

# INTRODUCTION TO VISUAL SYSTEMS

The systems that have been getting the most attention these days are the visual systems. For the purpose of this discussion, visual systems are those primarily used for the presentation of information picked up via a television camera and presented on some form of television set or monitor. In this section we will look at some of the common factors which include:

1. Captured-frame or slow-scan television.
2. Television with the addition of overlay graphics (the so-called "videographic" systems).
3. Full-motion television.

There will be some information from the discussion of audio systems repeated in this section, because some readers may have skimmed past the audio section and right to the visual chapter. For those of you who have already read some of the information, it will be worthwhile review.

More so than any of the other teleconferencing systems, the visual systems are being used for routine meetings, special marketing purposes, and reaching large audiences. The marketing applications seem to be receiving the greatest attention, as are some of the larger mass communication efforts. These efforts are very different than the types of teleconferences we have been discussing thus far, so the unique problems and group dynamics associated with large teleconferences will be discussed separately.

Why visual systems? The answer is similar to some of the discussions of audio—basically because of the need to reach people fast and to show visually oriented information in a timely fashion. There is one additional feature that should be taken into account when evaluating visual systems: APPEAL! Even though the research has indicated that audio systems are extremely effective for a host of teleconferencing needs, visual systems have more user appeal. A visual system *seems* far more impressive to new users than audio systems—more "state of the art," more "progressive." That may be a faddish way to look at teleconferencing, but it is a reality that must be considered. What that appeal is worth to the organization in dollars and cents must be determined on a case-by-case basis. That is one reason why it is so critical to develop a *complete* set of objectives for the teleconferencing efforts. Those objectives should take into account other elements than whether it reduces travel costs, because, much like advertising, large-scale visual teleconferencing has a psychological impact. It will be one set of rose-colored glasses through which clients and employees will view the organization.

From the perspective of some of those who use teleconferencing systems, an audio or computer approach might be the most cost effective. However, management may view your approach as "unimaginative" or "ordinary." Unfortunately, I can offer no concrete recommendations on how the situation should be handled. Cost, obviously, will be one major factor. If one were to conduct a survey of potential teleconferencing users, full-motion video is often considered the ideal. So anything less than full-motion may be considered a compromise. However, always keep in mind that teleconferencing is to support the mission statement of the company and that the form of teleconferencing used should support the underlying goals and objectives.

## Visual Human Factors

The way that people react to visual images is worth noting. We all have traditional television habits which we bring into the visual teleconferencing setting. In this section we look at a few of those factors.

### Vanity

First, there is considerable resistance on the part of most participants to actually being in front of a television camera. With many this resistance decreases over time, but for a significant portion there is no reduction in their feeling that they do not want to be seen on television. A basic concern on the part of televised presenters is that they will look foolish or unsophisticated. It is extremely important that adequate time be devoted to on-camera training and rehearsals prior to the actual event. This will prepare those that will be assisting with the presentation to anticipate the need for visuals, as well as significantly reducing the presenter's anxiety—which is primarily due to not knowing what will take place. One frequently cited complaint relates to an interesting phenomonon; people on television look as if they had gained weight. Exactly how much depends on the viewer, but figures seem to range from ten to twenty pounds. It must be remembered that this is the perception of the person in front of the camera; others will see little or no difference. When the conversion from three-dimensions to two-dimensions takes place, there is a visual widening of any object and this is perceived by many as weight gain. Television seems to promote greater attention to appearance in general prior to the session. Women and men are equally vain when it comes to stepping in front of the television camera.

There have been several individuals with whom I have worked who were very sensitive to some facial feature that THEY perceived as unattractive. While their appearance did not present any problems for others, there was a good deal of self-conscious behavior, such as selecting seats in the teleconferencing room so that the camera would always show their "good side" or constantly watching the television monitor to make sure they looked good. Normally, these intense reactions are rare, but it is important to watch for such behavior and take corrective steps so that the behavior does not get in the way of effective communication. In teleconferences where there are equipment operators, make sure the participants cannot see a television monitor of their picture, or the on-camera participants will constantly look at their image. In dedicated teleconferencing rooms, it may be a good idea to make the local image monitor smaller than the incoming image, so that attention is drawn to the larger television set. As an alternative, the local monitor could be situated near the equipment control unit so that only one or two individuals could see the local image.

For those who are seeking to maximize their image on television, here are a few hints:

1. Do not wear white. White creates problems for television cameras. Light blue is preferred.

2. Stay away from close-knit plaid. A garment with close vertical or horizontal lines will appear to be moving and distract the viewer. Wear solids or wide stripes. The same is true for ties.

3. Look at the camera. The camera represents the group with whom you wish to communicate, not someone off camera.

4. Do not read from a paper or note cards. Looking down will give the impression you do not know what you are talking about. Use cue cards or electronic prompters mounted on the camera. If you have never used a prompter, *ALWAYS* practice with the equipment first.

5. Have someone check your appearance. Do NOT rely on yourself to make sure your hair is in place, etc.—you have better things to think about.

Follow these few suggestions and you will improve your video impression.

### Frame Tension

Make sure that all participants in a teleconference are shown to the other location(s). This is not a major problem in teleconferences where there are directors and camera operators, but it can be a significant problem in teleconferencing rooms where the participants manipulate their own equipment. There is nothing more disconcerting to participants than to find that there has been someone relatively important sitting just outside the view of the camera. When that person jumps in with a comment or two, participants may feel that the confidentiality of the communication has been violated. From that moment on, there will be a constant concern on the part of the participants as to whether someone else is in the room, just out of sight. In film, this is called "frame tension." The old horror movies are the best example . . .

> VISUAL: The heroine slowly walks down the dark alley toward the camera. A slight mist is falling. Thin clouds of fog diffuse the street light at the end of the alley. She looks slowly around as she walks. She is afraid.
> AUDIO: The music builds. (We know something is going to happen.)
> VISUAL: She walks toward the camera until her face almost fills the screen. She looks off to one side. Then, suddenly, from the other side of the screen comes a hand that covers her mouth!

Now we all know that if she had been looking around, there is no way that she could have missed the man standing to one side of the screen. However, even before she reached the camera, we knew that there was *something* lurking off to one side. We feel tension because we cannot see more than what is on the screen (frame). Our field of vision is both directed and limited by the camera.

While a visual teleconference is certainly not a horror show, the concept of frame tension still exists. It pertains to the simple fact that we cannot see more than what the camera is presenting. Unless some effort is made to show the complete environment in the room, the participants will have a feeling that there is someone else in the room that is not being shown. This feeling is increased if we see one or more of the participants looking off camera with regularity, as if there were someone else in the room with whom the participant was making eye contact. When that hidden person speaks, the effects on the distant participants can be significant. The voice from nowhere! If no attempt is made to move the camera to show the hidden participant, the quality of teleconference communications can be seriously affected.

The bottom line is: *Always* go to great lengths to introduce everyone who is at a location, and show them if possible. If someone comes into the room, announce that fact. It is important to the participants' mental health that they know exactly who is listening and viewing them. I do not know how many times I have been in a teleconference, seen the participants look off camera at someone, smile, and return to the camera as if nothing had happened. From then on, I wonder who else is in the room. Even if everyone is looking at a slide or some other visual piece of information, always stop the communication in process and announce that someone has joined the discussion. In addition, announce when someone has left a teleconference. It really makes a lecturer feel quite foolish when he or she asks a question of someone who is not currently on the screen, but who was there just a few minutes ago, just to learn "Oh, they left to go to another meeting."

## Visual Conference Manners

This brings up an interesting point. What would have happened if all the participants were in the same room? The person who was about ready to leave would excuse him or herself! But, for some reason, in a teleconferencing environment there is a general disregard for the same common courtesies that we would display if we were all in the same room. I have seen a number of teleconferences when a lecturer had finished a presentation, and the participants at remote locations just walked out of the room without saying a thing—not even "thank you!"

For example, I remember standing with a lecturer at the conclusion of a presentation and watching as participants 45 miles away just got up and walked out. Then one man walked up to the camera and simply turned it off. The image of a large emotionless face fading into black left a rather sick feeling in my stomach. No one had expressed their appreciation for the discussion. I am afraid that my explanations to the lecturer fell on deaf ears in light of what he perceived as insulting behavior. Why do people do these sort of things? All too often we simply cannot get used to the fact that we are involved in *interactive* television, television that we can talk back to. The man who turned off the camera was simply doing what he normally did after seeing a regular television program. When I called the man who turned off the camera the next day, he was mortified by the effect he caused. There was no malice in his action; he was just acting normally based on years of television watching. He was so embarrassed that he called the lecturer, who was then over 2,000 miles away, to apologize. With a little education, these effects can be minimized, but it takes time. Each time a new participant joins a group an overt effort has to be made to educate the participant in common courtesy.

There is something impersonal about television. There is something cold about the two-dimensional screen, no matter how big and life-like it is. If anything, more common courtesy should be extended to the other participants than one would normally assume is necessary in a face-to-face meeting. People introducing themselves when they speak and emphasis on "thank you's" should be stressed. In addition, sometimes people forget that the systems are two-way and that the moderator or lecturer can see the listener located many miles away. I have seen people roll their eyes, assume an extremely informal posture, and exhibit personal hygiene habits that would make anyone embarrassed to watch. There are actions that certainly would not have been made if the participant had been in the same room as the speaker!

How many years have we been watching television? How many years has it taken for us to develop the habit of turning on the television and letting our eyes glaze over as the screen flickers in front of us? Even though a conference may be interactive, we bring into the event a considerable amount of learned behavior that begins to emerge whenever we see a television screen. This is one reason why making use of the interactive capabilities is important to overcome our habitual television viewing behavior. After all, interaction is what sets visual teleconferencing apart from regular television, and it is that distinction that needs to be reinforced. *Developing some form of interaction early and on regular intervals will maintain the distinctiveness of visual teleconferencing and will keep reminding participants that they are involved in a communications environment very different than their past exposures.*

For example, by opening the teleconference with a brief discussion with one or more of the remote locations will indicate more graphically to the participants that the teleconference is capable of interaction. If no initial effort is made to involve the locations, then the participants will revert to a traditional television model in which the viewer is a passive participant, and the probability is great that getting meaningful interaction later in the teleconference will be more difficult. I recommend that after the initial interaction between the presenter and participating locations, the presentation be structured so that requests for questions or comments are scheduled every ten to fifteen minutes.

## Engineering Human Factors

The manner in which visual systems are configured has much to do with user acceptance of the medium and its utility. In this section, we will take a look at some of the unique human factors that are associated with equipment design and the nature of the electronic systems currently on the market, such as interfaces, camera controls, parallax problems, room design, lighting, and audio.

### Interfaces

The process of controlling teleconferencing equipment significantly increases in difficulty as the move to visual communication takes place. The person responsible for the implementation of a system must worry about how to ensure that the system will be operated successfully. More and more the term "user friendly" is being used in the teleconferencing area. Simply put, it means that in order to control the teleconferencing equipment, a user does not have to be a NASA trainee or electrical engineer. Second in importance only to the human support for the teleconferencing area, development of a user-friendly system is critical to the overall success of visual teleconferencing.

One of the issues that continues to plague implementers is the constant mental battle between the desire for professional-looking presentations (like we see on television) and those produced by the users themselves in an effort to keep operational costs reasonable. "Will they be able to do it?" you ask yourself. It is essential that we think of the visual teleconferences as conferences and *not* programs! As soon as an implementer gets the idea that they are programs, the trap is set and the programs become productions. If it is determined that each teleconference is to be a full production requiring engineers, directors, and a cast of thousands, the resultant cost of teleconferencing will be too high to be continued. After all, cost containment is one of the reasons why teleconferencing finds its way into a company. A substantial percentage of teleconferencing use will be by managers and others that are using teleconferencing to get their jobs done. Naturally, they want the conference to go well and so do you. Providing them with easily operated, fairly sophisticated equipment is extremely important.

There is no getting around it: designing a user-friendly visual teleconferencing system takes time and money. More than many realize. In most visual systems, the time and money expended on the human interface aspects are quite low in proportion to the total cost. In fact, the interface is far more important than whether the cameras are black and white or color, the quality of the wood table, or the artwork on the walls. Visual teleconferencing is not like audio teleconferencing; you cannot simply have the telephone company install a speaker telephone and then get on with it. Before you get started on the design phase, whether you custom build your own facility or buy ready-built equipment, there are some important questions that you have to answer:

1. What will the users want to do during a teleconference?
2. How frequently will each user be involved in a teleconference?
3. What special requirements are necessary for the system to fit your business?
4. How many users will be in each teleconferencing facility at the same time?

Let's take each one of these questions and see why the answer is important. First, "What will the users want to do during a teleconference?" This is the most fundamental question. It pertains to the style of the conference and the types of visual modes the users will want to have available. If, for example, the bulk of the teleconferences will be educational, then you can expect greater use of visual materials rather than the camera pointed at the presenter for the duration of the presentation. Determine the kinds of materials that will be used: slides, overheads, illustrations, videotapes, audiotapes. If there are to be many meetings (as opposed to educational uses), there will be more use of people-oriented cameras. Again, find out what kinds of graphic materials will be used: computer printouts on odd-dimension paper, slides, transparencies of typed pages that are in the wrong format for television, etc. The best guide is to observe the current meetings of your potential high-volume users and try to get a feel for how the meetings are conducted and how information is exchanged.

The second question deals with the frequency of utilization by each user. If you determine that there will be quite a bit of use, but a month or two may go by between times when specific individuals use the system, you can expect a significant amount of "skill decay." Skill decay is the natural reduction in the ability to perform certain tasks when there is little regular contact or exposure. Skill decay will not only affect how the participants operate the equipment, there will also be a reduction in the infrequent user's teleconferencing protocol skills as well. If we do not practice certain skills, we lose them. The more infrequent the contact, the more user friendly the system must be. For infrequent users, fewer options in the operation of the system are appropriate. These individuals will not be sophisticated users because their level of contact will not permit them to experiment with the system and learn enough about all the "bells and whistles" to make it all happen the way that you or the vendor indicated. Do *not* be too impressed by the features of a teleconferencing system unless you find it is extremely easy to use. Naturally, the optimum system would permit the infrequent user to operate the system in a credible manner, while the more sophisticated user could utilize the expanded capability of the technology. In either case, the technology *must not be intimidating!*

Third, is there something unusual about some of your users that sets them apart from others? If you are lucky, you may find out the answer to the question after you have participated in some of the traditional meetings held by your potential participants. This is a good time to look at the travel dynamics of the organization. There may be a significant group of travelers that do need some special attention in your teleconferencing design. For example, engineers or architects may have to share a great deal of design information that exists on large sheets of paper which may require the camera to zoom in on certain segments of detailed information. Perhaps a special presentation table is necessary for these users so that they can lay their information flat while the camera moves overhead to the items of interest, rather than the users having to struggle with positioning their drawings over the small graphics area you had considered. These users may care less about the sophisticated people cameras that you have set up; they are interested in their drawings.

Fourth, how many users do you expect to attend each teleconference? The larger the group, the larger the television monitors and the more complex the audio system to handle the participants. The large-screen television monitor is now fairly common in large electronic meeting rooms, but the image can be very poor for those close to the screen. For very large groups, several new television projectors are on the market which present very good images, but the cost is high—$20,000 to 25,000. One thing to avoid is a number of smaller television monitors scattered around the room. Not only is it visually confusing, but participants have no idea where to look in order to maintain eye contact.

**Camera Controls**

Since the camera represents the eyes of the viewers, some attention should be given to the camera and its manipulation. At the present time, it is possible to remotely control all of the functions a camera performs. These functions are:

1. Zoom. By moving the optics within the lens, it is possible to give the impression that the camera is moving closer or further away from a subject. The camera itself does not move, only the glass within the lens.

2. Pan. Motors can swing the camera left or right.

3. Tilt. Motors can point the camera up or down. Generally, both functions are combined into one motorized unit called the "pan and tilt head." A "head" is what the camera sits on.

4. Focus. Motorized rotation of the lens so that objects near or far come into focus.

5. Iris. Motorized opening and closing of the metal petals that control the amount of light entering the camera. Performs the same function as changing the f-stop on a camera.

So we have six different controls that must be manipulated so that the camera can pick up an image correctly. Until recently users have had to play with each control in turn until the image was ready, causing a considerable waste of time and creating a high level of frustration. Trying to "zero in" on one set of financial statements on a sheet of paper would require a complete set of manipulations. How have we handled the simplification of all these controls? Very poorly, I think. Unfortunately, I wish I could point to a system on the market that has addressed the problems, but there is not a single vendor that has cracked the problem. That is not to say that operation of the systems is impossible—only far more difficult than it should be. To date, the approaches have been:

1. Pan and tilt. Combining the pan and tilt control into a single control called a "joy stick." Very much like a video game control, moving the stick to the right or left side caused the camera to pan right or left; movement forward or backward caused the tilt motor to point the camera down or up.

2. Iris. Using more sophisticated electronics in the camera, called an "automatic light compensation" (ALC), to control the camera's electronic iris so that the metal iris in the lens can be preset at a compromise level. Using a photographic analogy, the ALC would change the camera's sensitivity to light, very much like changing the speed of the film used in a camera instead of opening or closing the f-stop.

3. Focus. By using camera image tubes that are extremely sensitive to light or by increasing the amount of light in the room, the iris could be very small (letting in little light). An interesting effect occurs when the iris becomes smaller; the total distance that appears to be in focus increases significantly. Thus, with a very small iris opening, an object either has to be very close or very far away to be out of focus. Recently, some new automatic-focus television cameras have appeared on the market. Their success has yet to be fully documented. Remember: we do not have to worry about the same extremes of distance that confront a photographer; the distances of interest are limited to between 3 and 30 feet from the camera.

**FIGURE 8-1**
Slow Scan Television Wireless Remote Control
Used By Research Health Services, Kansas City, MO.

*Credit: Larry Brown*

Figure 8-1 shows an interface control unit that controls two television cameras and a Colorado Video slow scan unit. The layout is simple and straightforward. To make the operation even easier, there are no wires to clutter the conference table. A beam of infrared light is used to transmit the control signals to a receiver. I expect further advances in the application of wireless technology as designers attempt to make operation of systems less difficult.

One other interesting problem affects both slow scan and full-motion systems when the participants have the capability of controlling their own cameras. This relates to the camera movement when the user presses the control to move the camera left or right. The problem is that there are *two* different lefts and rights! Let's try to see why this is true.

To start, let's look at an analogy from the theatre. In acting there are two lefts and rights: stage left and right, and audience left and right. If I am an actor facing the audience and I want to walk to a chair to my left, I move stage left. If I am in the audience looking at the stage, the actor is moving to my right. To understand the problem in a teleconferencing environment, all we have to do is substitute "participant" for "stage" and "camera" for "audience" and the problem becomes clearer. To clarify the problem even further, let's take a look at a very real situation. I want the camera to point to someone on my left; without giving it much thought I push the camera control to the left and camera swings to my left. I look at the television monitor that is showing the camera's image and stop the camera when the image of the person is about centered. After I look at the monitor (which is showing the picture the camera sees), I decide that the person's face is just a little right of center. I push the control to the right. To my amazement the image swings to the left! What's going on?

When I first moved the camera to my left by pushing the button marked "left," the camera was moving to its right. I was not aware of the difference. When it came to "fine tuning" the image, I concentrated on the television monitor, which was showing the image *from the camera's perspective,* not mine. Now, the left and right directions became confused.

Camera controls can be set up to move according to the camera's left and right OR the participant's left and right—it cannot be both. Which to choose? In almost all cases, the controls should be set up from the camera's perspective. The reason for this is quite simple. For gross movement (swinging the camera over large angles) starting off in the wrong direction can be easily corrected with a minimum of impact, but when the image needs small corrections the participants will be looking at the camera's monitor and will not be aware of the camera's movements to their left or right. A mistake in direction when small movements are being made, especially when the camera is zoomed in on small details, can be substantial and will disorient the person operating the camera more than if large, gross movements are involved.

The bottom line as far as camera control is concerned is that if the users will be spending the vast majority of their time looking at the camera's monitor to adjust the position of the camera, the camera control should be set for the camera's left or right. If there will be little observation of the monitor to set the image, then the control should be set to respond to the user's left or right. You may find that a mix of control movements develops, one set for the camera that looks at large groups of people and one for the camera that is used to present detailed information (blackboard, graphics, etc.), setting it to respond to the camera left and right movements. To decrease the amount of time spent in camera movement, I would recommend the use of the newer camera controls that will "memorize" up to eight camera positions. If a user wishes to move to the blackboard, the push of a single button will cause the camera to pan, tilt, zoom, and focus on the blackboard area. Any fine tuning of the image can be made with the manual controls.

**Parallax**

Another problem to watch out for in visual teleconferencing is the separation between the monitors to be used and the camera. These so-called "parallax" problems can present a confusing image to viewers in other locations. The problems are somewhat different in slow scan and full-motion systems, but both types of problems will be described here. Basically, the problem refers to where the participants are looking during the teleconference. In a full-motion system, the participants will spend most of the time looking at the television monitor that is showing the incoming image from the other location. If there is much distance between the camera and monitor in location #1, viewers at location #2 will have the impression that the people at location #1 are not looking at them.

Remember that much of our western communication is based on eye contact. We assess much from the extent to which others "look us in the eye." At location #1, for example, the camera represents the eyes of those in location #2. The participants at location #1, however, will be attempting to maintain eye contact by looking into the eyes they see on the television monitor. If there is much angular separation between the camera and the monitor, the net effect will be that those in location #2 will have the sensation that the other participants are looking elsewhere, not at them. The secret is to decrease the distance between the camera and the television monitor which is displaying the other participants (the incoming image).

Captured-frame or slow scan television, on the other hand, presents a slightly different problem. Slow scan television, as was discussed earlier, differs from the type of television with which we are most familiar in that it sends still television images over telephone lines. In this case, the participants in location #1 will be looking at the television monitor that shows their *outgoing* image when making a selection of an image to transmit, not the *incoming* monitor. So, it is important for SSTV installations to have the *outgoing* monitor as close to the camera as possible. Nearly all the participants at a SSTV site will be looking at the outgoing monitor while the camera is being adjusted for the "snap shot" that will be sent, not at the incoming image nor at the camera. Once the image has been sent, the attention of the group will return to the incoming image to maintain eye contact.

*Every attempt should be made to place the camera on the same eye level as the participants. When cameras are elevated above the participants, the people look smaller and that impression is increased whenever someone looks down to read his or her notes.* This effect has been used by film makers for years to impress upon the audience a feeling of smallness (camera above, looking down). A larger-than-life impression can be made by placing the camera lower than the participants, looking up. Use of these effects for film is fine, but it should be avoided in a teleconference. Above all, avoid placing the camera above when an important person (president, major expert in an area) is giving a presentation. Their credibility, as assessed by the viewers, will be significantly lower than when the camera is eye level. Again, if the teleconference has a director and camera operators, they will know the basic camera positions. However, an understanding of these concepts is important in installations where users operate their own equipment.

## Room Design

The design of the room can be a critical element in how people relate to each other in a teleconference. In many of the designs the participants are lined up facing one another. This is a simple configuration for technicians. However, it does contribute to the "us vs. them" syndrome—two sides facing one another. After watching a number of such teleconferences, I have noticed another interesting factor: very few of the participants at one location talk between themselves. Almost all communication is from one location to the other; little information is exchanged between participants at the same site. In fact, I have seen situations when intrasite communication has been discouraged. The moderator at one location said that the purpose of the teleconference was to communicate with the other location, not between those at the location. I have often heard the phrase "We can talk about that later . . ." used in this situation. However, *if* all the participants were in the same room, I would wager that the discussion would be fairly interactive, without regard to the participant's city. So the participants all lined up looking only at the other location can add a sense of formality to the communication that closely resembles two sides at a negotiating table. This is the worst possible situation for a "brainstorming" session, for example.

By seating the participants at each location around a "U"-shaped table, the amount of intrasite communication will increase, and there will be some reduction in the "us vs. them" syndrome. *However,* one other problem can develop. Intrasite communication can increase to the point where the participants at the other location are not given their chance to speak. I have not seen this problem develop very often, but I believe it is worth noting. My own personal preference is for the U-shaped table. *Interaction* is the operant word in a teleconference, and every effort should be made to promote both intra- and intersite exchanges. By the way, the same design holds true for slow scan television as well. In fact, I would be more insistent that participants be sitting in a U-shaped configuration when using this modality. Remember that the bulk of slow scan television is audio interaction, with an item of discussion on the screen. In this situation, it is even more important to promote intrasite communication. When there is no movement on the television screen to hold attention, the U-shaped desk can provide participants with the opportunity to look at one another more easily than in a side-by-side configuration. Since the bulk of the activity is aural instead of visual, it seems to be helpful for participants to have something else to look at rather than an inactive television screen.

User access to graphic devices is another area that is worth some discussion. There are several other areas in the teleconference room that may contain images to be presented. For example, the blackboard, slide or movie projection screen, overheads and pieces of paper, videotape recorders, etc. *The issue is not one of controlling other electronic devices, such as videotape machines and slides, but rather ease of participant movement to use such devices.* The blackboard requires someone to physically move to the board. In this case, cameras have to be switched, and a different microphone configuration has to be used to pick up the voice of the person now at the blackboard. The easier all of this is to accomplish, the more user friendly the facility will be and the greater the amount of use of such devices—just as one would expect in a real conference.

### Visual Format

The television screen normally used in teleconferencing is the same as the one used for everyday television; it is wider than it is high. Specifically, it is a ratio of 4 to 3. By that I mean, if the screen is 4 units wide (cubits, hand-widths, meters, feet), the vertical distance is only 3 units high. This is fine when trying to show people sitting side-by-side at a table, but you will have a little trouble with the majority of other visual items in business and education. Information typed on a piece of paper, X-rays, and magazine ads, for example, are all higher than wide and present a problem for the TV camera and monitor. For some firms, the presentation of material that was in a vertical format (higher than wider) was of far more importance. What they have done is tip the TV monitor on its side so that the image seen on the TV screen would be closer to a vertical format. This may seem like an odd suggestion, but remember that your users may be accustomed to looking at images in a certain way and anything that you can do to make teleconferencing easier may make for a smoother transition.

### Creating Visuals

It is very common for a presenter to make an overhead of a typewritten sheet of financials and then attempt to present the information to a large group—*most of whom cannot see the small figures on the sheet.* When it is difficult to get people to modify information for such a common event as a presentation in the Board Room, it is even more difficult to convince presenters that what is easy to see on a piece of paper in front of them cannot be seen by others via a visual communication system. Readability is a function of three variables:

1. The size of the character on the television screen.

2. The resolution of the television set. In other words, the size of the smallest definable unit of light.

3. The distance between the viewer and the television monitor.

Since all these factors are different in each setting, it is difficult to apply a general rule-of-thumb that will work in all situations. After saying that, however, you can achieve pretty good television readability by limiting the text to five lines per image and a maximum of 25 characters per line. If you want to use this guideline, all you have to do is type five lines of 25 characters, draw a 3-by-4 ratio box around the information, and make copies of that box. Then circulate the copies to all those who will be developing information for a presentation and have them either write or type the information so that is all appears within the box. See Figure 8-2.

That's the quick way to do it. If you are interested in maximizing the information to be presented, it is possible to develop your own customized template

1. 20-25 CHARACTERS PER LINE (PICA)

2. 5 LINES PER FRAME

3. DOUBLE SPACE BETWEEN LINES

**FIGURE 8-2**
Typewriter Template For Visual Teleconferences

system which takes into account the size of your rooms and the resolution of your equipment. These are the steps that you go through to design your own template:

1. Determine your worst-case viewing environment. Assuming that all the television monitors are the same size, this would be the location with the greatest distance from the monitor to the furthest viewer.

2. Construct a test transmission page. I would recommend almost a full page of random numbers and letters in the following format: eight characters, two spaces; five numbers, two spaces; eight characters, and so on. Single space between lines. Use the most common type style found on the majority of the typewriters that will be used by those presenting information. For this test, try to use a typewriter that prints ten characters per inch (10-pitch).

3. Determine the resolution of your system. This is done by having an individual sit in the back row at your worst-case site and read information from the television screen. Using a camera with a zoom lens, start by transmitting the entire page. Gradually, zoom in on the page until every character and number can be read by the individual assisting you. Mark the area that can be read. You now know the number of lines (height) and number of characters (width) that can be seen by participants at other locations.

4. Repeat the steps if you want to know the readability when the presenter will be using a typewriter that produces 12-pitch print (12 character per inch).

6. Once you have determined the horizontal and vertical limits, draw a box in the center of a piece of paper using the dimensions arrived at through your experiments above. Users can either type their information within each box or slip the box behind a piece of typing paper and then type the information on the typing paper.

7. Reproduce the template on heavy card stock and cut out the area *within* the template box. Participants can now hold the card over information that they want to present so that they will see what will be transmitted.

If you will be using a blackboard, I would also recommend performing a similar test to help determine readability. In this case, have several people write information on the blackboard, zoom in until the information can be read easily at the remote location, and, finally, mark off the area on the blackboard. Users will then have some assurance that if they write within the marked borders, their written information will be readable at the other locations. This assumes, naturally, that their handwriting can be read! I have a particular problem in creating totally illegible text when I am in a hurry, so having a border in which to work does little to improve communication. Suggest to the users that printing is far more legible. If you will be using a light box for the presentation of transparencies, then I would also recommend that the area to be transmitted be marked on the plastic itself. This will help the users position their information more quickly and accurately.

If you have the option of dictating to users the type of typewriter element that is to be used in presenting informaton over a visual system, use a style similar to the "Orator." This 10-pitch (ten characters per inch) typing element is used by many who are writing speeches. It consists of all capital letters that are extremely easy to read. In order of their readability, I would recommend the following:

1. Orator. A readable 10-pitch, all-capital-letter ball for some IBM typewriters. If your typewriter's typing element can be changed, attempt to locate an element similar to the Orator.

2. Any of the more common 10-pitch styles (Courier, Legal, etc.). Type information in all capital letters.

3. Any of the more common 12-pitch styles (Courier, Legal, etc.). Type information in all capital letters.

   Note: If your typewriters have a "bolding" feature, in which the typewriter strikes the same character several times, use it!

Avoid the following whenever possible:

1. Unusual styles. Included in this group would be script, italics, and any other style which connects the letters. Also included would be handwriting.

2. Fifteen-pitch print (15 characters per inch). Although you can zoom in on the information to make it larger, you will begin to notice problems that are caused by the typewriter: uneven type, poor ribbon, and other problems that would create a poor image upon magnification by the camera.

3. Material typed using proportional spacing. This form of type, found on many word processors and the newer electronic typewriters, packs the letters closer together and can create readability problems.

## Lighting

Lighting is another factor that is given little or no attention in the development of teleconferencing facilities. Television is a two-dimensional medium, and lighting can be used to create a three-dimensional quality. *Many teleconferencing studios, however, use high-intensity ceiling lights that create a very even level of light everywhere. Unfortunately, this creates a very bland image which lacks depth.* I have yet to see a teleconferencing studio with lighting designed to maximize the television image. Lighting should be angled from the front of the room, rather than from overhead. Overhead lighting creates dark faces and very bright shoulders, which confuses the automatic light control in the cameras. I should add that I would consider this as a noncritical area, but one in which more work needs to be done. Again, the priority should be on ease of user operation. If the system is difficult to operate, good lighting will not save the day.

## Audio

The other area that seems to suffer the most in visual teleconferencing is the audio. More attention seems to be paid to the visual element, so that attention to sound becomes secondary. The best sound comes from a facility in which each participant has his or her own microphone. In audio teleconferencing, participants seem to be far more aware of the microphone and the need to be heard than in visual communication. Perhaps this is due to the fact that participants view the visual teleconference as more life-like and expect those on the other end of the teleconference to be able to hear them as if they were sitting across the table instead of many miles distant. There are several possible approaches that can be used.

First, the use of dedicated microphones. These microphones can be lavalier or clip-on types—in other words, small microphones like those used by television anchormen while presenting the news. Getting microphones which produce excellent sound quality for all the participants in a large group conference can be a problem. The other issue is that of the microphone cables themselves. The tangle of wires can present real difficulties for the speaker who decides to walk to the blackboard to jot a few notes down. Another approach to the problem would be the use of wireless microphones. While this does away with the cable problem, the cost is high and the problem of insufficient microphones for larger groups remains.

Some would say that the act of clipping the microphone onto participants presents some user resistance. However, in over 20 years of broadcast news I have never encountered a situation where the process of placing a microphone on an individual has impeded a person's candor once the program started. I am sure that some will disagree, but the psychological problems associated with wearing a microphone is a nonissue in my experience. The potential impact on the teleconference from poor sound, poor system design, and poor attention to organizational problems are far more significant. In addition, the process of *wearing* some sort of device may reinforce the user's opinion that the teleconference is something special and important—that what they have to say is important.

In order to decrease the amount of general noise and inconsequential sound, the use of devices called "voice gates" is common. Often used in public address systems where a large number of microphones are active, the voice gate will automatically turn down the volume on microphones that are not in use.

When the sound rises above a specified level, the volume is turned up. Good voice gates do not clip or cut off the first sounds by a speaker. The quality is quite good and much better than the switching systems found in most audio teleconferencing speaker telephone systems.

Second, the use of teleconferencing microphones. Much of audio teleconferencing and the technologies used in that environment apply to the visual side as well. There are several microphones on the market that have been designed for teleconferencing, and the Quorum™ microphone is a perfect example. Designed to pick up sound over a large circle, it will address many needs. The Quorum™ does have an interesting quality: in a properly designed room a person three feet from the microphone will sound as loud and will have approximately the same quality as a person ten feet away. There is only one cord and no extra cost of wireless microphones—only a single audio source to worry about. In some cases, however, the use of two Quorum™ microphones may be indicated.

An example of a good teleconferencing microphone that incorporates a voice gate is the Shure® AMS8000 (see Figure 8-3). The AMS8000 uses specially designed teleconferencing microphones (see Figure 8-4) which pick up sounds in a very specific direction (see Figure 8-5). Users of the AMS8000 have reported exceptional quality, and the low profile microphones look much better in a television setting than a tall, linear-array microphone. In addition, the Shure® AMS880 video switcher can be attached to the AMS8000 and will automatically switch cameras based on which microphone is being used. This automatic switching is a significant advance for those designing full-motion teleconferencing rooms that require little user manipulation of the equipment.

Third, the use of highly directional microphones to pick up sound from a specific location. These "shotgun" microphones, as they are called, can be effective if the conversation area is limited. These microphones are relatively expensive and, depending upon the acoustics of the room, may be less effective than the teleconferencing microphones.

Fourth, microphones suspended from the ceiling. By using several microphones located over the conference area, it is possible to achieve acceptable audio quality. Sound quality will, however, drop automatically as a speaker moves away from the general pick-up area. My experience with suspended microphones does not lead me to recommend them for most facilities, but they provide another option when the more specialized microphones are deemed too costly.

## System Construction

The question of whether to build your own visual teleconferencing system or purchase a ready-built system (called a "turnkey" system) is a difficult one to answer. At the present time, there is more innovative research taking place in the development of user-friendly interface systems on the full-motion end of the spectrum than in the slow scan television area. Full-motion systems are expensive. The capital outlay and financial exposure are great. This is not an area for the inexperienced; there are too many details that can result in a system that is not

**FIGURE 8-3**
Shure® AMS8000 Automatic Microphone System

*Credit: Courtesy of Shure Brothers, Inc.*

**FIGURE 8-4**
Shure® AMS22 and AMS26 Microphones

*Credit: Courtesy of Shure Brothers, Inc.*

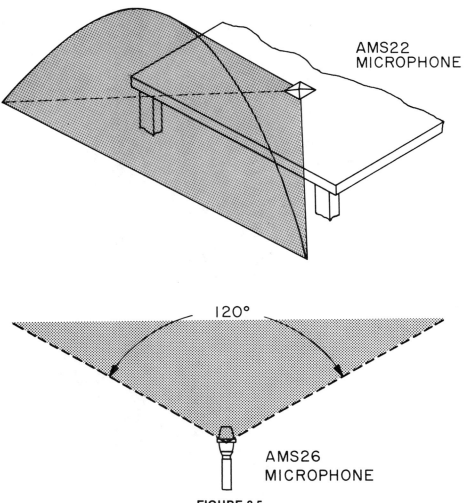

AMS22
MICROPHONE

120°

AMS26
MICROPHONE

**FIGURE 8-5**
Shure® AMS22 and AMS26 Microphone Coverage Area
*Credit: Courtesy of Shure Brothers, Inc.*

reliable, too difficult to operate, and/or too expensive to operate and maintain. Without question, my advice would be to seek assistance from as many experts in the field as the budget will allow! (See Chapter 14.) Consider it insurance. It is a question, however, that only the implementer can answer: What is it worth to ensure the success of a system that may cost between $100,000 and $500,000 and have monthly communication costs of $5,000 to $50,000? It is important to keep in mind that teleconferencing is still a fairly new field, and the ground rules and indicators for success are not well understood as of yet.

Because of the newness of teleconferencing, knowledge concerning potential applications and problems is still fairly limited. If you were installing a computer system or large telephone system, a single consultant might be able to provide most of the answers to your questions. After all, computers and telephone systems have penetrated the market place to such a degree that even the most basic consultant can identify problem areas because he can draw upon the experience of thousands of users. This is not true in teleconferencing. The journals are few, the associations have just recently emerged, and there is some reluctance on the part of corporate users to share experiences. If you look at teleconferencing from a corporation's perspective, you may understand this reluctance. If teleconferencing is a failure, they may not be too enthusiastic to share the information and have articles appear in the journals. On the other hand, if a system is successful it is part of their competitive advantage, so what would they gain by sharing the results of years of work so a competitor could introduce a system in half the time and expense? Naturally, some companies are more than happy to share their experiences, but others are less aggressive.

If you look carefully at the articles in the major journals, you will find that the articles about various corporate systems are (a) authored by the vendor of the hardware selected for the system and (b) appear within a short time of the system's initial installation, which makes meaningful statements about how well the system is operating a little difficult to believe. I can recall a similar situation when videotape recorders were first coming onto the educational market. The articles were written by vendors and promoted the interesting new applicatons XYZ corporation or university used to save thousands of dollars. If you talked to the users themselves, the picture was somewhat different. Thank goodness that phase has passed! If you look at the articles today in the educational technology journals, you will notice fewer articles by vendors and many extremely interesting articles by those that have implemented an approach and have chronicled their struggles. I look forward to the day when the new teleconferencing journals will be replete with solid, usable information gained from hours of real-world experience.

Let me discuss some of the advantages of buying a turnkey system:

Advantages

1. There is no wasted time in integrating all the system components.
2. Maintenance is less of a problem, since one vendor handles the entire product. There is no "finger pointing" between different vendors when things do not work quite right.
3. You are able to capitalize on the experience the vendor has had with other installations—what has worked best, problem areas, etc.
4. You do not support the entire cost of research and development. The cost of new features is spread over several systems.

Disadvantages

1. The systems are expensive. There are still too few systems being built, and the vendor has to recover expenses in the sale of a small number of systems.

2. Vendors may not be willing to make modifications to the system which would make it better suited to your environment. While they want your system to work well so that they can use you for future reference, additional modifications to their systems decrease their profit margins.

3. The advice vendors will give you concerning teleconferencing should be considered biased. Their contact with teleconferencing may be fairly superficial and may not reflect the kinds of operational problems that arise simply because they have little involvement in operational issues.

Now for the "roll your own" systems. From my perspective the advantages and disadvantages are:

Advantages

1. The systems will have lower hardware expenses than turnkey systems.

2. The system will have a greater probability of meeting your individual needs. Again, no one has yet designed the perfect teleconferencing system, although it is getting closer.

3. You will learn a great deal during the process which will benefit the total teleconferencing effort.

Disadvantages

1. Unless you are knowledgeable or have access to others that are very familiar with the technologies, there is a high probability that the system will not operate the way that you want.

2. The total cost, including you and your staff's time during the design phase, may exceed the total cost of a turnkey system.

3. You will have the responsibility of integrating the various components in the system and dealing with multiple vendors.

At the present time, teleconferencing is much like the personal computer industry of a decade ago. The only way that you could get a really good system that met your needs was to learn all you could and then put your own together. That is certainly not the case with personal computers today. The same is true in the teleconferencing field. The vendors have learned much from the early experimenters and have been very successful in integrating much of that early research, but a system that fully meets user requirements and is user friendly does not exist today. As a basic guideline, *IF* your organization has a good electronics support group that is familiar with the technologies in which you are interested, then building your own facility may be a reasonable consideration. However, the more sophisticated the technology, the lower the probability that such expertise is already on the payroll, and a turnkey system is indicated.

Based on the current state of the industry, I still design my own systems, but not to the extent that I once did. My approach has been to purchase all the basic hardware through one vendor and spend my time working with a private engineering company (Selectronics in Hopkinton, Mass.) to design user-friendly interface equipment. Now, I have only two firms to work with and use weekly conference calls to make sure that there is a minimum of finger pointing when the two products are merged. I also pilot-test all of my products first before moving to large systems, and the interface designs are developed with modification in mind. This is because I now know that even the most ignorant users are far smarter than I. Users can create more problems in five minutes than I could ever imagine. One reason why I have selected the particular vendors mentioned in this book is that they have all gone the extra mile for my projects, and I am confident that they would go the extra mile for others as well.

Whether you go with a single vendor or decide to develop your own facility, it is critical that you get consultative input from both the engineering and human factor viewpoints. First, get assistance in looking at needs and applications. Second, match those findings with the various technical options that will not only meet the existing need, but offer flexibility for the future as well.

## Summary

Visual systems are the most complex of teleconferencing modalities. The complexity is not in the raw technology, since much of the current television engineering is used, but it is in user control of the hardware that the problems arise. Participants bring into the visual teleconferencing setting more learned behavior from existing media than into any other electronic conference modality, and interaction is the key to modifying that behavior. The price tags for visual teleconferencing are higher than audio systems, with full motion being significantly higher. Visual systems can work quite well, but they require more needs assessment and consultative input to design a system that fits a company's unique communications structure.

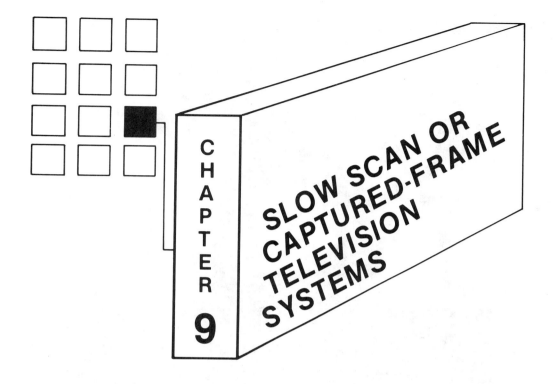

# CHAPTER 9

# SLOW SCAN OR CAPTURED-FRAME TELEVISION SYSTEMS

**D**uring the past several years, there has been quite a bit of discussion in the literature as to what to call the transmission of visual images that provide less than the illusion of full motion. In this category are the visual systems that transmit television camera-based pictures in a time frame of anywhere between 1 and 150 seconds. It seems unfair to place in the same category the whole range of devices with transmission times that range from fast to slow. With recent improvements in speed, the term ''slow'' in slow scan (SSTV) no longer accurately represents the state-of-the-art. Certainly, these systems are not as fast as full-motion systems, but they still capture a frame of television information from a camera and send it on its way—hence another name ''captured-frame television'' (CFTV). There are a number of manufacturers of SSTV equipment. The three major vendors are Colorado Video Inc. (CVI), Nippon Electric Company, and Robot. For discussion of SSTV equipment in this chapter, I will be using the various products made by Colorado Video. CVI, located in Boulder, Colorado, specializes in a variety of video products, with SSTV being one of their major lines. Widely used in the health care industry and in business, the CVI product is rugged and reliable. There are a number of CVI installations all over the world (see Figure 9-1), and it is the one generally used by physicians and others in rural, isolated areas such as Alaska and Canada. While I like the products from all of the vendors, my personal preference is CVI. CVI has been the group most willing to modify their units to meet my specific design requirements.

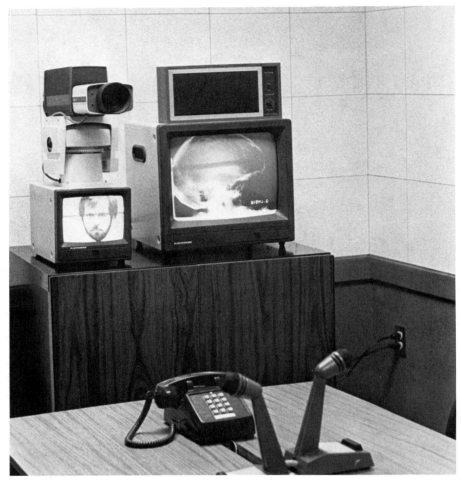

**FIGURE 9-1**
Low Cost Slow Scan Television Installation
at Research Health Services, Kansas City, Mo.

*Credit: Larry Brown*

Their products permit a greater variety of design modifications than some of the other vendors' products. In addition, the company's president, Glenn Southworth, has been a noted expert for many years in the field of SSTV and seems to have a better understanding of user issues than other vendors.

While the physics of transmitting the signals either over the telephone lines or through the air have not changed much since this mode of transmission was pioneered in the late 1950s, the devices that convert the television camera image to a series of tones for transmission have changed dramatically. Today, color is available as well as a number of transmission speeds. The basic SSTV transmitting unit performs the following tasks:

1. A television camera is pointed at an object. The camera converts the visual image to a set of electrical impulses, called "video."

2. The SSTV unit then converts the video information, which is in an analog form, to a digital form. This process is called an "analog to digital conversion," or A-to-D conversion for short.

3. When the user has the proper image positioned, a button is pushed, and the digital information is then stored in the SSTV's computer memory.

4. The SSTV's computer then slowly reads each memory location and converts the digital information into audio tones (D-to-A conversion) that can be sent over the telephone lines.

At the receiving end, the SSTV unit performs the following tasks:

1. The incoming analog information from the telephone lines goes through an analog-to-digital conversion.

2. The digital information is then stored in the receiver unit's computer memory.

3. When the full picture has been stored in memory, the computer then reads the information in the memory and converts the information to an analog form that can be understood by a television monitor, a D-to-A conversion.

4. The TV monitor then converts the analog information to visual images on its screen.

As you can imagine, all the conversions from analog to digital and digital to analog call for a reasonably high level of sophistication on the part of the SSTV units. However, having the information in a digital format within the unit provides considerable flexibility in how the picture information can be stored and manipulated. To give you a better idea how a SSTV image is received, Figure 9-2 shows the development of the video image during a 34 second transmission.

To provide some specific examples, let's look at Colorado Video's Model 290 (see Figure 9-3). In addition to the steps that were just discussed, the CVI 290 has the following features and controls:

1. The "freeze" control initiates the capture process. When the freeze button is pushed, the operator sees the camera image in full motion so that the camera or chart may be moved to the desired location. When the freeze button is released, the camera image then goes through the A-to-D conversion and the resulting

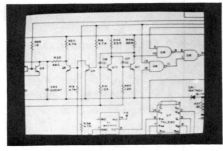

Previous
Image

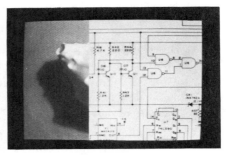

One-third
of Image
Received

Two-thirds of
Image Received

Transmission Completed

**FIGURE 9-2**
Slow-Scan Television Image As Seen At Receiving
Locations During 34-Second Transmission

*Credit: Courtesy of Colorado Video, Inc., Boulder, Colorado.*

"digitized" image is presented on the TV monitor. The operator can then see whether or not the snap shot is exactly what is wanted.

2. A transmit control. When it is pressed, the digitized image then goes through the D-to-A conversion and is sent out via the communication lines.

3. A "reset" control. This is the "stop sending" control and enables the operator to abort the sending process for whatever reason.

4. A speed control. The operator has the choice of two picture transmission speeds. In the fast mode, the time for a complete picture to be transmitted is roughly 34 seconds; in the slow mode, the completion time is 72 seconds. The fast time will result in a picture that is not quite as clear as what we are used to with regular television, but when the image to be sent does not require high resolution

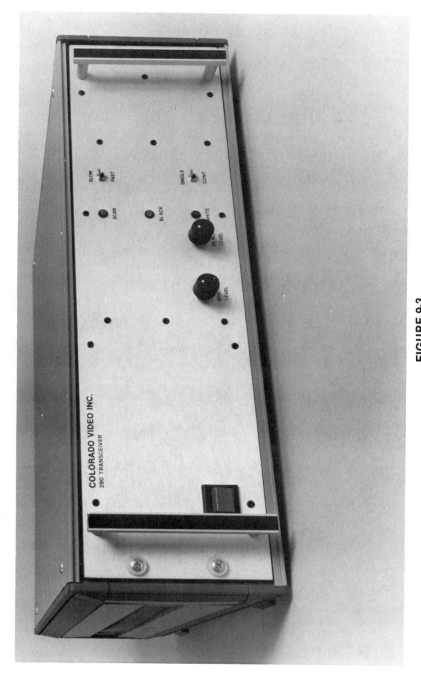

**FIGURE 9-3**

Colorado Video Model 290B-1 Slow-Scan Transceiver

*Credit: Courtesy of Colorado Video, Inc., Boulder, Colorado.*

and speed is more important, the fast time is generally sufficient for most information. The slow mode results in a picture of higher resolution or definition. In this case, the detail is more important than the speed.

5. A continuous- or single-picture mode switch. In the continuous mode the operator does not have to press the freeze and send buttons. After the transmission of one image, the SSTV unit automatically transmits whatever the camera is pointed at. For the vast majority of the meeting and lecture applications, the single mode is used which requires that the freeze and send buttons be used. The continuous mode is more often used in security applications rather than in teleconferencing.

It is easier to operate a SSTV unit than describe the operation. The price range of the Model 290 is $4-9,000, depending on options.

### Transmission Times and Resolution

How fast a SSTV image is transmitted is a function of the available bandwidth and the desired resolution. The bandwidth determines how fast information about each picture element can be sent, while resolution determines the total

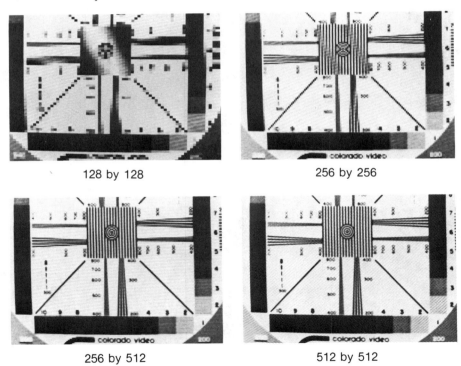

128 by 128         256 by 256

256 by 512         512 by 512

**FIGURE 9-4**
**Slow Scan Image At Several Resolution Levels**

*Credit: Courtesy of Colorado Video, Inc., Boulder, Colorado.*

number of picture elements to be transmitted. In other words, to decrease transmission time it is necessary to *either* increase the bandwidth *or* decrease the number of picture elements (resolution). If you are using regular voice grade telephone lines, the bandwidth is fixed so the alternative is to reduce the resolution. Figure 9-4 shows the effect of the various resolution levels using a television test pattern. The photographs are actually enlargements of a television screen so that you can see the detail of each picture element. Figure 9-5 is a photograph of the full television screen to put the test chart in perspective.

**FIGURE 9-5**
Full View Of Test Pattern At High Resolution
512 x 512 Picture Element Resolution
*Credit: Courtesy of Colorado Video, Inc., Boulder, Colorado.*

## Applications And Indications

SSTV, like the other modalities, fills a specific niche in the teleconferencing picture. Let's look at some of the applications and indications.

A. Applications

1. The health care industry, engineering, and other industries in which discussion of visual material is important.

2. Educational environments where static images are used.

3. Management meetings when moderately fast transmission times are required.

4. When presentation of large or three-dimensional objects is required.

5. When the mail is not fast enough for distribution of slides.

6. When visuals require higher resolution than facsimile can provide.

7. When *ad hoc* discussion of visual information is required.

B. Advantages

1. Portable equipment possible.

2. Has marketing appeal due to visual image and unique transmission qualities (the image "develops" on the screen).

3. Any visual material which can be picked up by a television camera can be sent via SSTV.

4. Some nonverbal communication is possible.

5. *Ad hoc* visual image transmission is possible.

6. Equipment is fairly inexpensive.

7. Uses the dial-up telephone network or dedicated lines.

8. Color transmission is possible.

C. Disadvantages

1. Full motion not possible.

2. Communication costs are twice as high as for audio-only due to separate telephone lines required for audio and visual information.

3. Total cost of end-user equipment higher than audio-only equipment.

4. Operation in certain configurations may require an operator.

5. Transmission time of the image may be too long for some users.

6. Selecting the most appropriate uses of SSTV to maximize utilization may be difficult for users.

Certainly SSTV is not for everyone, but when faced with the need to support an audio-only system with visual information, it is an extremely viable medium. Given the needs of most conferencing environments, I find that the SSTV is a most effective visual medium.

## Human Factors

SSTV offers some rather unique challenges for those involved in teleconferencing. It is very different than what people expect. They are fascinated by the slow scan process and yet are confused by the lack of full motion on the television screen. The delays in picture transmission need to be taken into account, and special attention has to be paid to the images transmitted because of the length of time required to correct a poor transmission.

Determining the visual content may be a problem for users of SSTV. The reaction to SSTV for use in some programs is much like that of audio conferencing: "I just don't see how I can present the information in a series of still images . . ." Frankly, some areas lend themselves better to SSTV than others, but the limitations are very few. If it is *essential* that something must be shown moving to understand it, then SSTV is not the best medium. In this case, distributing a videotape prior to the teleconference is an option.

There is a great deal of similarity between SSTV and photography when viewing an event from a single-image perspective. If you think of a conference in terms of the most salient visual images that communicate the information, then you are on the right track to developing an excellent SSTV teleconference. Many years ago, the noted photographer Henri Cartier-Bresson wrote a book called *The Decisive Moment* and speculated that in each setting there are specific moments in time when an image communicates the essence of the event. He advised photographers that they must have "A velvet hand, a hawk's eye . . ." Cartier-Bresson went on to say, "If the shutter was released at the decisive moment, you have instinctively fixed a geometric pattern without which the photograph would have been both formless and lifeless." When I sit down with potential users of SSTV, I review their program materials in much the same way as I do with those getting ready for an audio teleconference—with one exception. In addition to looking for the "pearls" of content, we also concentrate on the visual "pearls" that will communicate the content in the most effective manner.

SSTV may not have the Pheromone Factor (basic appeal) rating of full-motion television, but its uniqueness can be used to its advantage. The manner in which new images flow across the television screen is very different than what new viewers expect, and it increases attention to the image. From a slightly different perspective, the "unfolding" of the image creates a positive form of frame tension. Viewers continue to watch the screen to see what will appear. Since it may be difficult to predict the exact content of the new image, attention is heightened. By using many images, it is possible to capitalize on the SSTV process to create a much higher Pheromone Factor than if images were changed only occasionally. SSTV may not be as glamourous as full-motion television, but when the costs of SSTV are compared with those of full-motion, SSTV will certainly impress the financial officers!

## Compensating For Transmission Time

The two concerns facing the users of an SSTV system are determining the visual content and compensating for the transmission delays. Both of these issues are interrelated. In a full-motion system, it is easy to "scan" a document with the camera and move the camera from page to page with relative ease. This is not the case with SSTV. Since movement in real time is not practical, the *visual material needs to be organized better than in full-motion television*. Visuals should be selected and developed based on their completeness and the ability to communicate information. However, avoid the tendency to pack too much information onto one visual. I would recommend that users increase the number of visuals, rather than condense the information. By transmitting a number of images, the attention factor will be higher than if a single, high-information-density image was left on the screen for long periods of time.

In order to keep the transmission time fairly short, many users opt for transmission speeds of 34 seconds, which provides a 256-by-256 picture element resolution. A 256-by-256 picture offers sufficient resolution for most applications, but it is slightly less than full-motion television. With this in mind, it is difficult to simply place in front of the camera a full sheet of paper with financial information on it and expect it to transmit well. Viewers at the other end will simply not be able to see all the detail on the page.

If you want to decrease the amount of time it takes to transmit a SSTV image, you must either accept poorer resolution or increase the bandwidth of the transmission system that you are using so that more information per second can be transmitted. In the first case, a decrease in resolution may not be acceptable. In the second case, the communication costs will be higher. What results is a compromise. The two most common transmission times for telephone line transmission of SSTV are 34 and 72 seconds. For many users, the 34-second transmission time provides an acceptable level of resolution in a "just tolerable" time.

Let's assume that we are using a 34-second transmission time for discussion purposes. What does someone do between the time the transmission starts and its completion? *Do NOT cover information that is critical to the understanding of the image.* This may sound difficult, but the reason is fairly straightforward. *People are fascinated by the transmission of a SSTV image, and they will be watching the image unfold before them. They will not be paying as much attention to what is being said.* It is possible, however, to force attention back to the audio by giving the title of the image to be seen within the first five or ten seconds of the transmission. Once the image has started to develop some form, it will be extremely difficult to regain attention until after the transmission. If you talk during the first one-quarter of the transmission, before the image takes shape, there is the potential for passing important information. Another approach would be to pass along some interesting, but noncritical information about the last image that was on the screen. This may be difficult, at best, to accomplish, but it does offer an option. The final approach is to just be quiet and let the image finish transmitting. For many users this may be the best approach of all. If the person talking is not a dynamic individual, then silence is golden. Do not attempt to compete with the unfolding image for the viewer's attention. The best option would be additional memory.

## Memory Options

Since SSTV units store the picture information in a digital memory, by expanding the memory, more picture information can be stored. How additional memory is used is an interesting consideration. Two of the more basic approaches to memory utilization is "continuous presence" and "background transmission."

## Continuous Presence

The term "continuous presence" refers to the ability to always see the images from the locations involved in the teleconference. When two sites are involved, this means that location #1 is able to see that last image received from location #2 and location #2 is able to see the last image received from location #1. Continuous presence requires two memories in the SSTV unit and two television monitors: one memory to store the image that was last transmitted and a television monitor to display that image, and a second memory to continuously store the last image received and a TV set so participants can see that image. In a single-memory configuration, the memory holds the image received or transmitted, whichever is the most recent. *For example, if I send an image from my single-memory system I will continue to see a picture of myself on the screen until someone sends an image to me. Since I would prefer to see the picture of the people with whom I am speaking, rather than myself, a two-memory system is a little more natural.*

## Background Transmission

The "background transmission" mode uses additional memory in a slightly different manner. When a large number of images need to be transmitted, there is a fair amount of wasted time if the person making the presentation has to wait 34 or 72 seconds for a complete image to be transmitted before the discussion can begin. Rather than waiting until the presenter has finished discussing an image before transmitting the next visual, the background mode permits the next image to be transmitted while the presenter discusses the image currently on the screens at each site. In its most common configuration, such a system operates as follows:

1. The first image (image #1) is transmitted, stored in the first memory (memory #1) at the receiving site, and is displayed on a main television at that location.

2. At the conclusion of image #1's transmission, the presenter begins to talk about image #1.

3. An assistant then gets image #2 ready and transmits it, which will take 34 seconds to complete.

4. At the receiving site, image #2 is stored in memory #2 and is not seen by the participants.

5. After the presenter has finished talking about image #1 (40 to 50 seconds, or so), the presenter presses a button which transmits a "change image" tone and the participants now see image #2 on their screens *with no delay.*

6. Whenever the presenter pushes the "change image" button, the system alternates memories. This is beneficial when the presenter wants to compare images and discuss similarities or differences.

7. The process is then started over, with each subsequent image being transmitted while the presenter is talking about the last one received.

Another way that background transmission can be used is with many memories, each with their own television monitor. This way up to four images can be transmitted, stored, and reviewed by participants. Using this type of configuration, a technical group can have a number of detailed images, X-rays of pipe welds, for example, on their screens at the same time. Each new image is transmitted as soon as one is finished.

While the multiple-memory, multiple-screen capabilities are an advantage for some users, for others they can be a grave mistake. Without fixed protocols it would be fairly easy for an educator to become totally confused as to the image in each memory and reduce a well-planned lecture into a disaster. As far as additional memories are concerned, it is my recommendation to keep it simple. Two memories is sufficient for the majority of applications, but there is the potential for problems even with only two memories. Careful attention to training is mandatory, and the system should automatically default to a single memory system when first turned on so that inexperienced users do not get confused.

## Recording SSTV Images

SSTV images can be recorded in several ways. Since the information does appear on a television set, users can record programs on standard video cassette machines. However, users can also record the images on digital storage systems and audio cassette recorders.

### Digital Recording

For those that receive or transmit a number of images, Colorado Video has a device called a Model 930 Digital Image Storage System which can hold up to 400 SSTV images for review or transmission (see Figure 9-6). Since the information in the SSTV's memory is digital, a small microcomputer is used to control a high-speed, rotating magnetic disk storage device. In the receive mode, the Model 930 can receive images transmitted the preceding night, when the communication costs are the lowest. A centralized storage system can accept images from other locations which could be used to review. In addition, the images could be combined and retransmitted during a subsequent teleconference.

In the transmit mode, the images can be prepared in advance. The length of time it takes to store a digitized image onto disk is less than four seconds, so a substantial number of images can be prepared ahead of time quite quickly. Using the Model 930 permits background transmissions to be handled more efficiently,

**FIGURE 9-6**

Colorado Video System 930 Digital Disk Image Storage System

*Credit: Courtesy of Colorado Video, Inc., Boulder, Colorado.*

since there is no need to prepare an image for transmission during the actual presentation. From a manpower standpoint, previously prepared images would not require that an operator be present to assist the presenter at the time of the presentation. The Model 930 can also manipulate the stored images to provide a visual directory so that users can select desired images more quickly (see Figure 9-7). The price for the Model 930 is about $15,000.

### Laser Recording

Panasonic has introduced an optical memory disk recorder which can record and play back still or full-motion images (see Figure 9-8). The TQ-2021FB can store up to 10,000 high-resolution black-and-white images, while the TQ-2020F can store up to 15,000 color still images. There will be considerable growth in the optical storage area over the next few years, which should have a significant effect on all forms of visual teleconferencing. The price range for the recorders is $15,000 to 25,000.

### Audio Recording

Since the SSTV images are nothing more than a series of audio tones when converted for transmission over the telephone lines, it is easy to record the sounds of the images ahead of time on a cassette recorder and play them back when appropriate. Prerecording of any visual information is certainly possible and is recommended when it takes significant time to prepare an image for transmission. The images can be prepared and recorded on the cassette machine without the pressure of a live presentation.

Unfortunately, when a presenter records all of his or her material ahead of time it is very difficult to retransmit a previously transmitted visual in response to a question. Rewinding a cassette recorder to the exact spot of the correct image is not something to try when a program is in progress. Always make sure that the presenter brings along all the raw visual information, even though it has already been recorded. With the visuals in hand, the presenter can switch from the audio recorder to the graphics camera to present an earlier image, then go back to the prerecorded material with only a minimum of delay. Having the originals there in the teleconferencing room also provides a backup should the cassette recorder fail or the recording tape break.

## Transmitting A Live Program

At some point in time, the implementer of an SSTV system is asked if it is possible to "broadcast" a live lecture or presentation over SSTV. There are certainly no technical barriers, since a television camera can easily view the proceedings. However, from a production standpoint such programs leave much to be desired *if* the lecturer uses any graphic material at all. Why? Simply because most lecturers go from graphic to graphic faster than SSTV can transmit the images. For example, the camera operator must first focus on the image, and then

**FIGURE 9-7**
Colorado Video System 930 Monitor Display

*Credit: Courtesy of Colorado Video, Inc., Boulder, Colorado.*

**FIGURE 9-8**
Panasonic Optical Memory Disc Recorder

*Credit: Courtesy of Panasonic.*

there is a 34-second transmission time. Normally, I estimate 45 seconds for each image process. If the number of visual images is small and the lecturer will be spending more than 45 seconds on each item, *then* SSTV coverage of the event is possible. However, I discourage such presentations. Instead, I recommend that the lecturer give a second presentation specifically for the electronic audience. This permits the lecturer to customize his presentation for the medium and concentrate on the interactive process. I have yet to find a lecturer not interested in giving a presentation a second time for the electronic participants.

## Multisite Presentations

The use of SSTV in a multisite situation presents some rather unusual problems. Fast interactions between the various locations do not offer sufficient time for the transmission of individual images from each of the locations while the discussion is in progress. While it is possible to equip each of the participating locations with both reception and transmission equipment (called a "transceiver"), the question of how to use this multisite transmission capability to simulate a meeting environment has yet to be answered. Unfortunately, due to the slow transmission times found in most SSTV applications, high-speed visual interactions are not currently possible.

SSTV does lend itself, however, to transmissions from different locations when the longer-term presentation responsibility shifts from site to site. *An example of this mode of operation would be the team teaching of a course or a "round robin" meeting agenda where each participating city is responsible for updating the others on current activities.* Interaction will be supported by the audio system, but when several more lengthy presentations are necessary, multisite SSTV can be utilized successfully.

I would recommend those using SSTV in larger group settings refrain from beginning programs by having each location transmit a picture of the participants. For example, if ten locations are on-line, then transmissions from each location can easily consume from 10 to 15 minutes (about a half-minute in transmission and another half-minute to view the images, exchange social conversation, and ask the next location for a new transmission). Some would argue that a first meeting should spend some time with the initial socialization process; however, my experience has indicated that this can be counterproductive. Counterproductive not from the socialization standpoint, but because many will perceive the amount of time taken to go through the introductions as a waste of time. A better approach would be to select only one or two locations for the first introductions and then move on to business, or have each location originate more lengthy reports.

## Summary

Slow scan television offers firms interested in the presentation of visual information considerable flexibility. Although lacking some of the stereotypic appeal of full-motion television, SSTV is extremely successful in a meeting environment when the presentation of graphic information, such as charts, tables and illustrations, is common. The equipment and continuing communication costs are much less than for full motion. With adequate attention to the development of good visual images, SSTV can handle most visual demands. If transmission time is critical, the bandwidth of the transmission lines can be increased and multiple memories can be used.

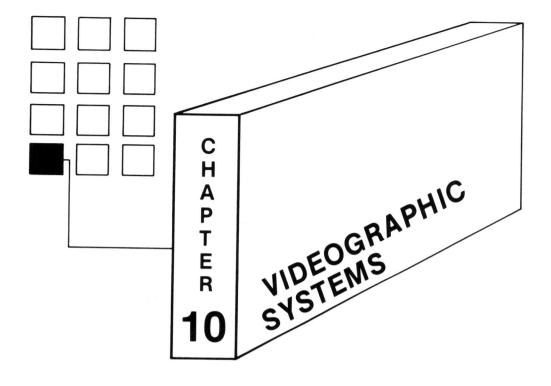

CHAPTER

10

VIDEOGRAPHIC SYSTEMS

**V**ideographic systems combine the advantages of both slow scan television (SSTV) and real-time audiographics. Basically, videographic systems permit users to transmit a SSTV image and then make notations with a pencil-like device which appears superimposed over the transmitted image, and is then transmitted to each of the receiving locations. The best analogy would be a combination of SSTV and the Bell Telephone Gemini™ electronic blackboard sharing the same television screen. While the new videographic systems can also interface with full-motion systems, this chapter will focus on slow scan applications.

Normally, graphics transmitted via SSTV either must be marked ahead of time to ease the process of communicating the new attention points, or presenters have to verbally communicate where they want the participants to direct their attention. With the use of an electronic pencil, videographic systems permit the presenter to circle, underline, or otherwise point out an area of interest—*all in real time.* Since these graphic notations develop on the receiving TV screens as the electronic pencil moves, there is an *illusion* of full motion, and it holds attention better then a pure still image that is being discussed. Frankly, I believe that there will be considerable growth in this technology because it permits the illusion of full motion when discussing basically static graphic information (slides, financial tables, and illustrations), at a cost that is considerably below that of full-motion television.

/ **Problem Focus** /

Both slow scan and videographic systems are problem-oriented modalities in that *the primary use of the visual element is for the display of information that must be analyzed and discussed, rather than presenting images of those in the conference.* As opposed to the emphasis on human interaction in full-motion systems, the focus in SSTV and videographic systems is on the problem. Even with a full-motion teleconferencing system, the presentation of graphic material consumes a substantial amount of transmission time. Those that have installed videographic systems are interested in high-speed problem solving. Examples are engineers cooperatively working on circuit schematics, designers review ad layouts, financial officers reviewing budget projections, product managers looking at a new product design, radiologists reviewing an X-ray, and educators discussing an illustration.

More specifically videographic systems have applications in large automotive, defense, aerospace, pharmaceutical, petroleum, chemical, electronic, and heavy equipment companies. Geoffry Dunbar, president of Interand Corporation, notes that firms are using videographics for:

1. Telemaintenance. Making technical expertise available to remote sites for such purposes as maintenance, repair, or quality control.

2. Document analysis/engineering changes. Linking engineering groups with plants to evaluate documents and discuss potential changes in blueprints, drawings, and parts.

3. Project management. Providing centralized coordination, control, and expertise from headquarters to project offices, construction sites, and subcontractors.

4. Training and education. Transmitting preprogrammed material and "live" events to remote locations to support interactive training of corporate, supplier, and client personnel, as well as educational programs for universities and medical institutions.

5. Crisis control and resource allocation. Responding quickly to crises such as assembly line shut-downs, process plant failures, or military actions.[1]

/ **Presence** /

"Presence" is the sensation that participants are located in the same room and refers to the feeling that the communications system is transparent. Videographic systems offer a great deal of presence in a teleconference, without resorting to full-motion systems. The question of whether participants really need to see full-motion images has yet to be fully answered. To some degree, the answer to the question depends on who is responding. Those that use full motion tend to focus on the nonverbal and nonquantifiable benefits of seeing someone, while users of systems that consume substantially less bandwidth point to cost effectiveness in terms of getting the most "bang for the buck." *The videographic systems seem to take the lead in terms of offering a great deal of presence at a fairly low cost.*

If we take a look at perceived "presence" (the illusion of participants being co-located) versus cost, a plot of system operational costs might look like Figure 10-1.

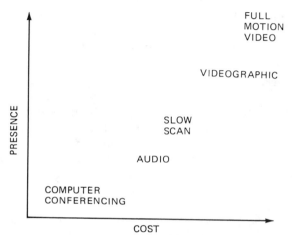

**FIGURE 10-1**
Relative Assessment Of Cost Versus "Presence"
Of Various Teleconferencing Modalities

Not only are initial start-up costs higher with full motion, the continuing communication costs are high as well. When considering any of the teleconferencing modes, it is critical to take a long, hard look at the types of information that is communicated between locations. Then select the modality that has the "best fit" with the needs.

/ *Equipment* /

Probably the most creative approach to videographics is manufactured by Interand Corporation of Chicago.

### DISCON™* 1000

The DISCON™ 1000 is the only fully integrated videographic teleconferencing system which combines a freeze-frame background image with a full-motion, real-time foreground annotation capability. It consists of the following components (see Figure 10-2):

---

*DISCON™ is a trademark of Interand Corporation, Chicago.

1. A Control Center. This terminal is made up of a high-resolution 19-inch color television monitor which shows the SSTV image that was transmitted and an electronic stylus. A user makes his or her graphic notations on the face of the TV monitor. The internal electronics converts the movements of the stylus into information that is not unlike that of the electronic blackboard.

2. A Document Station. The device is used as the input for the graphic information to be discussed. Also attached is a smaller 9-inch color monitor which is used to position the graphic material.

3. Associated electronics. Included are the modems which transmit the graphic information at 9,600 bits per second over regular, voice grade telephone lines, special slow scan television equipment for the transmission of the image from the Document Station, and microprocessors used to control the communication and graphics features. The communications control also includes equipment which corrects for errors due to poor transmission lines.

At each receiving site, the graphics information is converted to video signals that combine with the SSTV image that the participants are seeing on their monitors. So, what they see is an overlay of graphic information on their previously received images.

Some of the capabilities of the DISCON™ 1000 are:

1. The ability to write directly over an existing video image. Viewers see the notations on the same television monitor as the video image.

2. The ability for those at other sites to make their own notations.

3. The ability to make notations in up to 32 colors. This enables users to quickly determine the location which has made notations on the background image.

4. The ability to generate several hundred special user-designed symbols. Examples include commonly used boxes, circles, electronic or engineering symbols, etc.

5. The ability to actually draw on the face of the television image.

6. The ability to erase all notations that have been made, or erase lines selectively.

7. The ability (via error correction software and a ring network architecture) to use voice grade telephone lines for inexpensive visual communication between any number of conferring sites.

8. A comprehensive menu of commands, which can be reviewed by users without changing the notations on the screen, controlled by the stylus.

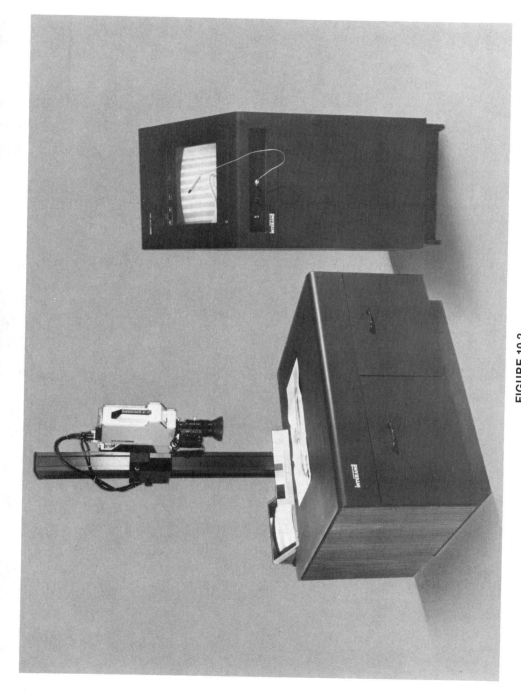

**FIGURE 10-2**
DISCON™ 1000 Control Center And Document Station

*Credit: Courtesy of Interand Corporation.*

9. The ability to obtain a paper copy of the image on the screen in black and white.

10. The ability to make a video recording of the meeting, as well as connect the unit to large-screen projector televisions for group discussion and input.

To operate the system, a user first transmits the background visual information to be discussed. Then, using the electronic pencil, the user touches the desired type of notation to be used (see Figure 10-3). If special types of designs are to be used, by touching the "menu" the user can page through the various options until the desired notation type is located. Once an option is selected, the image on the front of the screen will return to the working image, and when the electronic pencil touches the screen, the new notation is automatically inserted and transmitted to the other locations. The price range for the unit is from $85,000 to $110,000 and includes all the slow scan television equipment, hard copy equipment, color, and additional video monitors and audio facilities.

## DISCON™ 500

For those with existing slow scan equipment, Interand also makes the DISCON™ 500, which performs many of the same functions as the 1000. The 500 is a smaller device, which can fit on the top of a conference table. While it does not have the error correction features of the 1000, the 500 can be used on a stand-alone basis as an electronic blackboard without slow scan equipment. Options include up to 32 colors and hundreds of user-defined symbols and functions. The price range for the DISCON™ 500 is $16,000 to $24,000, depending on options.

## TELESTRATOR™ 100 and 440

For full-motion systems, two models are available. See Figure 10-4. The TELESTRATOR™* 100 is a basic black-and-white model which can be used to annotate motion or still images, while the 440 provides full-color capability similar to the DISCON™ 1000.

/ **Summary** /

Videographic systems offer a tremendous value for those that need to develop a network that permits users to cooperatively work with graphic information. While the transmission of images of the participants is certainly possible for initial socialization, the primary emphasis of videographic devices is the manipulation of image information in real time without the need for retransmitting SSTV images each time a notation is made. The availability of different colors to represent con-

*TELESTRATOR is a trademark of Interand Corporation, Chicago.

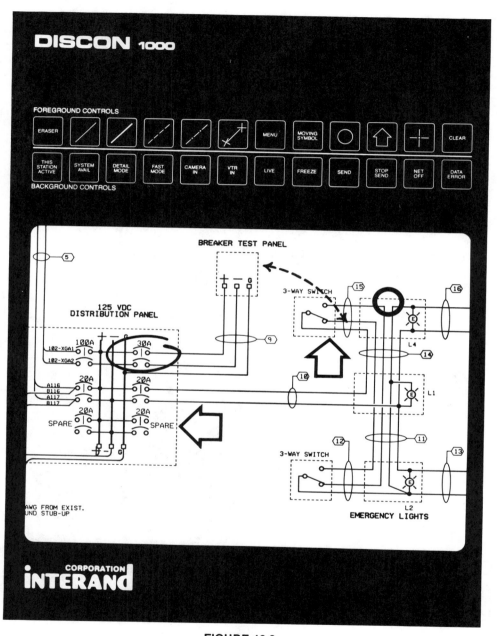

**FIGURE 10-3**
Monitor Display DISCON™ 1000
*Credit: Courtesy of Interand Corporation.*

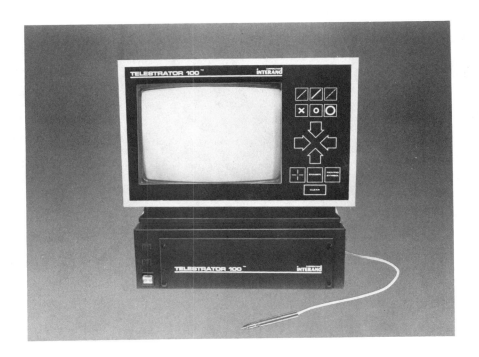

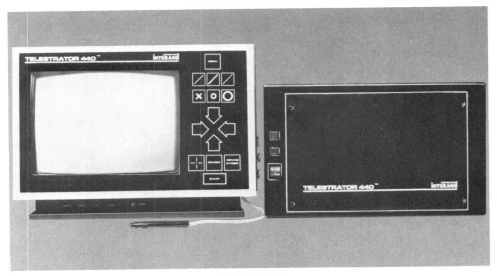

**FIGURE 10-4**
TELESTRATOR™ 100 and 440 Screen and Electronics

*Credit: Courtesy of Interand Corporation.*

tributing sites assists the conference chairman in distinguishing authorship and reduces the potential for a "cluttered" resultant image. Videographic devices warrant serious consideration by firms dealing with graphic information in their teleconferences. While there are other firms that manufacture videographic equipment, the ability to write in color and on the surface of the screen is a strong advantage.

## Chapter 10 Notes

1. G. T. Dunbar, *DISCON*$^{TM}$ *Videographic Teleconferencing Systems*. Chicago: Interand Corporation, 1983.

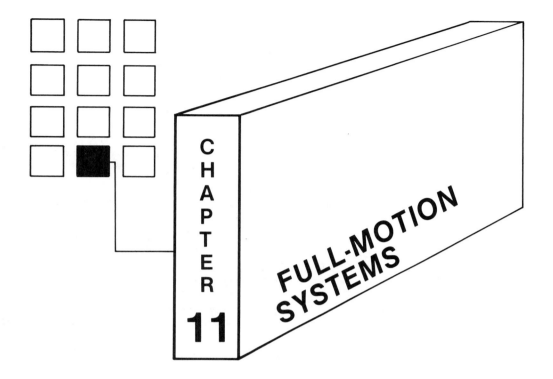

CHAPTER 11

FULL-MOTION SYSTEMS

**F**ull-motion systems look just like regular television, and this form of teleconferencing technology is what most people associate with the word "teleconferencing." Ever since the word Picturephone® was introduced many years ago, the full-motion systems have been touted as the best way of linking individuals as if they were in the same room (high presence). In addition, the cameras, color monitors, and associated trappings of full-motion television create a high Pheromone Factor—a great deal of marketing "sex appeal." So much for the good news. The bad news is that full-motion television is expensive to establish and expensive to operate. In addition, there is growing concern that full-motion video may be less than satisfactory for some dedicated teleconferencing applications due to some simple human factor issues when used on a day-in, day-out basis. In this chapter, we will take a look at some of the general factors associated with using full-motion technology, dedicated systems, and *ad hoc* video teleconferences.

## Viewing Habits And Production Quality

Full-motion video has the distinct advantage of being most like the television we see at home and on training videotapes at work, and it is the one we read about in the marketing journals. After years of experience with television, we are all pretty comfortable with it now—at least watching television. With this familiarity comes a certain amount of negative habit which we bring into the video teleconference from our home viewing. *We expect a certain level of production quality whenever we sit down in front of a television set. In fact, what we see on television today is almost perfect.* Few programs are live anymore, so we rarely see scenes with mistakes unless they are left in the program for comedy effect. The cameras are always on the correct person for that ''head and shoulder'' image while they are speaking. The multiple cameras and planning provide the best visual image for us to see. Since many have been watching television since they were children for two to four hours a day, it is impossible to turn on a television and not expect fairly high quality.

Educational television (now called public television) has always struggled with the issue of production quality. For years, educational television's production quality (or lack thereof) limited mass viewership. Recently, however, many programs have successfully combined educational information and production to produce more viewable programs. One of the limiting factors with many educational television stations has been the lack of funds to produce high-quality efforts. By pooling resources, public television stations have been able to overcome some of the problems associated with attempting to produce high-quality programs locally. There is a parallel between the plight of the hometown educational television station and full-motion teleconferencing—the financial burden of enhanced production quality is great.

Almost all of our experience with full-motion television has been associated with commercially produced entertainment programs. Even educational or instructional television has fallen prey to the use of endless production techniques to keep our attention on the screen. Initially, there was considerable use of special effects simply because they were new and available, with little regard to how they supported or enhanced the content of the program. In many cases, the production value is used to generate interest in a program that has little content to offer—little material of substance to keep our attention. Production effects are one method of artificially creating interest in the visual image. The danger, however, is when production technique gets in the way of the content and distracts from the viewer's absorption of the information. We have become so accustomed to a fairly high level of sophisticated production that when we are exposed to programs of lesser production value, regardless of inherent interest in the content, we may tend to initially discount the program as less than professional. *However, I have found that the greater the viewer interest in the content, the less important the production value.*

Earlier in the book I mentioned that the level of production quality does not have to be as high when the content is of interest to the viewers—to a point. After viewing many dedicated and *ad hoc* video teleconferences, my assessment is that the production quality has been substandard. The one saving factor for video teleconferencing, however, is that those attending have a high interest in the information that will be covered in the teleconference. The exception to this case is the large *ad hoc* teleconference, which will be covered later in this chapter. The role of production values in video teleconferencing will change as use of the medium increases. There are two possible directions: either video teleconferencing will become so commonplace that we no longer worry about production value (our use of the telephone may be an appropriate analogy), *or* production value will have to be increased in order to maintain interest (here commercial television is the best example). At the present time, the trend is toward increasingly sophisticated production techniques.

## Maximizing The Visual

Very few video teleconferences make effective use of this visual medium. The bulk of video teleconferences one sees today are nothing more than a closed circuit version of *Meet The Press*—a group of individuals lined up, with each talking in turn with little movement. The vast majority of the programs could have been distributed via audio with little impact on the content. *For the most part, these programs consist of "talking heads"*—a term used to describe a situation where the bulk of the program is nothing more than a head-and-shoulders picture of a person talking. It is doubtful if the nonverbal communication that takes place in these programs merits the tremendous increase in expense. Obviously, the answer is to concentrate on using the power of visual communication if your choice is video teleconferencing. A video teleconference should seek to use materials beyond simple graphics, such as demonstrations and videotape, to supplement discussions. Some examples of how to increase the visual quality of a presentation might include:

1. Previously recorded videotape to depict information that is being discussed.
2. Colorful graphics to show financial trends.
3. Breaking the total information package into smaller units (packets) and using several individuals to present the information (visual variety).
4. Frequent interactive sessions to increase involvement and level of attention.
5. Portions of the presentation originating from other locations around the country.
6. Automated camera control equipment in dedicated facilities which will change the image depending on the individual talking.

Remember that while we are interested in the nonverbal communication that is taking place during a conference, we are also interested in "seeing" the problem so that the group members can focus their attention. The key is to "Show the problem, don't just describe it!"

## System Costs

As soon as you begin to consider full-motion teleconferencing, the cost becomes much higher than that of any of the other systems we have been discussing thus far. Of course, the cost is relative. An organization may find that such a system will enable it to reach thousands of potential clients instead of hundreds for about the same cost. A company with considerable need for full motion might save much more than the cost of the system in travel displacement. There are three major factors that contribute to the high cost of full-motion teleconferencing: the capital equipment, production, and communication costs. The capital equipment costs are normally associated with a dedicated facility, while production costs are normally incurred in an *ad hoc* teleconference. The communication costs are common to both efforts. In the following section, we will take a look at some of the cost factors associated with satellite communication. Let me point out, however, that it is not within the scope of this book to give you all the necessary information to set up your own satellite event. UNLESS YOU ALREADY KNOW THE SATELLITE INDUSTRY, USE ONE OF THE SEVERAL FIRMS SKILLED AT SETTING UP SATELLITE PROGRAMS. THIS IS NO AREA FOR THE NOVICE. See chapter 14 for further information on resources.

### Getting To The Satellite

From a pure communication standpoint, there are a number of paths the video signal must travel to get from an originating location to the other participating sites. As an example, let's take a look at a satellite full-motion teleconference. First, getting the signal from the originating location to the satellite uplink. The uplink is the equipment that transmits the visual signal to the satellite. While the cost of equipment to receive satellite signals has declined considerably over the past few years, the cost of transmitting equipment (uplinks) has remained high. It is not uncommon for an uplink to cost between $150,000 and $250,000. As a result, there are only a few uplinks scattered across the United States. So the first cost will be associated with either establishing microwave transmission facilities between the originating location and the uplink or renting a transmission channel from the telephone company. The second option is to move the originating location to the same town as the uplink, thereby saving a portion of the communication cost. The first step is one of the most complex parts of the process. The hourly costs are based on the distance between the originating location and the uplink. In the midwest, where uplinks are few and far between, getting to the uplink can be almost as expensive as the satellite and reception costs combined.

### Using The Satellite

Now that you have engineered getting the television signal to the uplink, the next cost is for use of the satellite itself. There will be an hourly cost for using the uplink facility once you have found a way to get the signal to the uplink. Hourly prices vary, but you can expect to pay anywhere from $200 to $500 an hour to use an uplink. Each satellite has 24 television channels, called "transponders," that pick up the signal from the uplink and retransmit the signal back to the earth. These transponders are used by the major networks to move sports, news, and other programs around the country. Firms that offer premium movies, like Home Box Office, also use one or more transponders to distribute their signals to the many cable television systems around the country. While the availability of satellite time has been increasing, it is still important to reserve time as far in advance as possible. There will be openings for those that need to use a communication satellite at the last minute, but it still makes sense to make your reservation between three and six months in advance. Just to be on the safe side, it is also advisable to have two or three times and dates in mind, in case of a time conflict. In many instances, transponder time is acquired from a time broker—someone who buys large blocks of time and then resells the time. Depending on the time of day, transponder time can cost from $300 to $1,000 an hour, with discounts available for heavy users.

One complicating factor should be kept in mind. The receivers back on earth are normally pointed at only one satellite and cannot be easily moved. You may find, for example, that the antennas at locations you wish to reach on the east coast are pointed ("look at") one satellite, while the west coast locations look at another satellite. In this case, it may be necessary to have the east coast satellite signal picked up by a receiver in the mid-west and sent to another uplink pointed at the west coast satellite. One program I evaluated not too long ago had a complex distribution scheme. The program was first uplinked from a location in the southwest to a satellite that serviced a portion of the receiving locations. To reach the others, the program was received and uplinked again in California. To reach Canadian viewers, the signal from the second satellite was picked up at the Canadian border, microwaved to another uplink in Canada, and sent to a third satellite which could finally be received by the Canadian participants. There were some technical problems because of the complexity. This is one of the reasons why I recommend using an experienced satellite transmission company; there are too many potential problems for the newcomer. Mistakes can be costly.

### Receiving The Signal

Of all the details, finding reception sites is probably the easiest task. Just about every town now has a cable television system capable of picking up the signal. Public television stations are now opening their doors to host satellite gatherings. Even some private hotel/motel owners have purchased their own receivers to attract business groups. But the largest group of satellite receivers are owned by the major hotel chains across the country as a method of increasing their convention business. Finally, there is a growing number of businesses that have portable receivers that can be driven to the locations you want to include in your program. The costs can range from $100 to use existing receiving facilities to $1,000 for a portable unit to travel to a rural location. A good satellite transmission company will work with all the necessary owners of reception equipment to fulfill your needs.

### Other Transmission Options

In the case of dedicated facilities, it is becoming more common to see the use of video compression systems (codecs) so that the picture information can be sent via more economical data networks. By using codecs that compress the video signal to a rate that can be handled by a T1 carrier channel (1.544 Mbps), significant cost savings can be achieved. In some cases, a T1 channel will cost $20,000 a month, while the cost of a noncompressed television link would run $100,000 per month. While the cost of codec equipment is high (approximately $100,000 per installation), heavily used video teleconferencing rooms can demonstrate a rapid payback period. As was noted earlier, considerable research is in progress to reduce the transmission requirements even further. Full-motion television has been successfully demonstrated using data transmission speeds as low as 56 Kbps, and further refinement of image quality will be forthcoming.

For major corporations that already use T1 carriers to link various locations for data and telephone transmissions, the Action/Honeywell Roadrunner can perform the necessary re-routing so that compressed video teleconferencing can use the same T1 carrier line. Since all the voice and data links would probably not be in use at the same time, the cost of having the voice and data traffic use other transmission systems would be less than establishing two T1 carrier services.[1]

## The Small Ad Hoc Business Meeting

As far as pure business meetings go, it may be best to start at the low-risk end of the spectrum. There are firms that currently offer public full-motion electronic meeting rooms that can be rented so that participants can meet instead of flying around the country. The costs for such a service are in the $750 to $1,500 an hour range. This may seem high, but when you add up the travel costs for coast-to-coast travel, it may be fairly inexpensive. The recent air carrier price wars may have brought the cost of travel down to under $200 for a round-trip ticket, but the hotel, food, and taxi costs may easily double the travel cost. The advantage, of course, is that the communication cost is fixed, so you can pack as many of the executives from each office into the electronic conference room as you like—which lowers the per person meeting cost dramatically.

The best known electronic video meeting room service is AT&T's Picturephone® Meeting Service (PMS). See Figure 11-1.

Currently serving many of the major metropolitan cities, PMS will be expanding over the next year to over 20 locations around the country. The PMS is a very straightforward, people-oriented facility. The cameras are switched by the participant's voices so that the image seen by the other location is of the person speaking. A camera over the conference table is pointed at a viewbox which can be used to present paper information or transparencies. Another camera is directed toward the blackboard for more spontaneous interaction. See Figure 11-2.

All in all, a good facility which has been well designed by the AT&T engineers. The system uses a video compression scheme which is quite good, and few users can detect any difference between a PMS image and what they would see on their home televisions.

AT&T has produced a number of excellent guides for users of their facilities, which I would recommend you acquire well before you use the PMS. Several

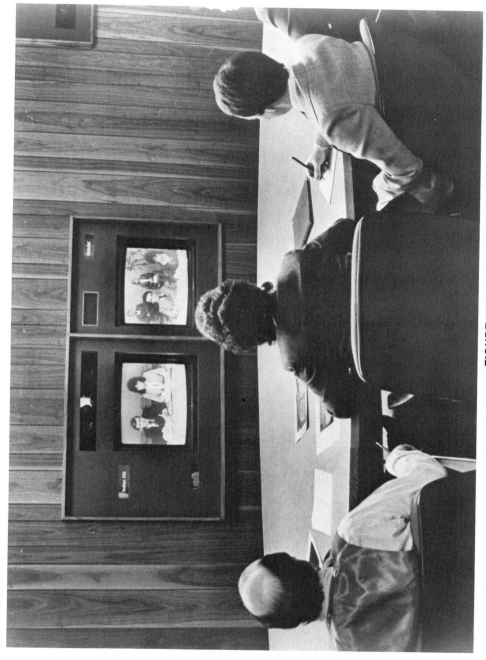

**FIGURE 11-1**
Picturephone® Meeting Service
Video Teleconferencing Room

*Credit: Reproduced with permission from AT&T.*

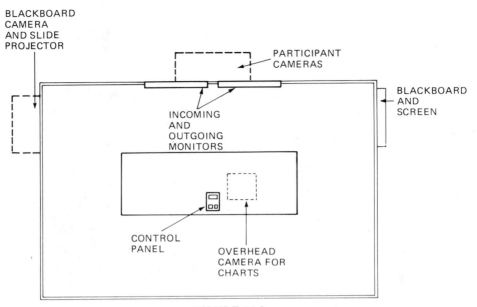

**FIGURE 11-2**
Basic Design of Picturephone® Meeting Service
Video Teleconferencing Room

*Source: AT&T.*

weeks prior to the meeting, several of the key participants should visit the PMS location for an introduction. Take along some graphic information which is representative of the material that you will be presenting during the meeting. Here is a simple list of the areas you should check out when visiting the PMS room:

1. Take your camera. Take several pictures of the room from different angles so that those that could not attend with you have some reference prior to the meeting. The pictures can serve you well when describing the facility to other new users as well.

2. Try out the microphones. See how the switching of the camera takes place when various members of the group talk. Try to disrupt the image by coughing or moving the microphone to determine what will happen.

3. Use the overhead camera. Test the controls. Determine how well your transparency or sheet of paper is seen by the camera. Since material on a sheet of paper is higher than wide (unlike a television screen which is wider than high), get a feel for how much information on the paper can be easily seen on the television set. Mark on your paper the ideal area to contain information.

4. Test the camera that is directed at the blackboard. As with the paper, determine how much the camera must zoom in for the

writing to be seen easily on the television set. With the camera zoomed in enough so that your writing is legible, mark off the top/botton and left/right limits of what can be seen on the television and measure the dimensions so that you can mark off the area before the start of your meeting.

5. Describe to the Bell representative the nature of the meeting and some of the visual materials that you plan to use and ask for suggestions. Even though I have participated in hundreds of video teleconferences, I *always* learn something new from other users. It does not hurt to ask!

6. When you get back to your office, write up a brief site visit report and circulate it to those that could not attend the visit. Describe the setting, the cameras, and the monitors. Circulate the pictures you took during the orientation. Since the presentation of graphic material is what gives most users problems, sketch some templates to be used by others as they develop their graphic information.

Since the presentation of graphics gives users of video systems so many headaches, one of the reasons for visiting the PMS room early is so that you will have time to revise materials before the actual meetings.

On the day of the conference, try to arrive 45 minutes prior to the meetings so that the graphics can be tested, the blackboard marked, and materials placed in a logical order for the presentation. Those who were not able to attend the introductory session can also experiment with the equipment and get used to seeing themselves on the television monitor. For subsequent meetings, it is not important to arrive as early, but the first session is a learning experience and arriving early will serve to reduce some of the natural anxiety that goes along with a new experience. *Seek to help others relax. Following the first 30 minutes of experimentation, lead the group through a discussion of the objectives. This will begin to focus their attention on the business at hand and away from the technology.*

Concerning the meeting itself, if you are not part of the discussion, you might want to make some notes on the meeting. This in-progress evaluation will help you in taking corrective action before the next teleconference.

1. Could the participants see all the relevant material?
2. Was time wasted in moving from one image to another?
3. Could everyone hear clearly?
4. Were the expected outcomes achieved?
5. Were there any inefficiencies?
6. What would you have done differently?

Write down your observations and keep them on file as reminders for the next meeting. Following the session, personally talk to *each* of the participants to assess their reactions to the meeting. You may wish to write a memorandum to all the participants outlining the positive results of the meeting, along with constructive comments that would improve the quality and productivity of the next session. *Make sure that those in upper management not present at the conference receive a straightforward review of the event, with several suggestions for future applications.* It may be worthwhile to consider having a public relations photographer take a few pictures before the conference and a few as the conference begins, and then have the photographer leave so he or she does not disrupt the meeting. You can use the pictures in the company newsletter or annual report to indicate to others the strides the firm is making to increase productivity.

Due to the recent breakup of the Bell System, the rates for PMS and other services have been in a state of flux. The chief advantage of a PMS-like facility is that you do not have to worry about a capital investment or maintaining the equipment, and you can use the facility on an as-needed basis. However, at roughly $1,000 an hour one thinks twice about scheduling too many meetings that may not have required travel, but would be important to the organization from a coordination and productivity standpoint.

## The Dedicated Facility

Once you have used a public meeting room facility and demand increases, the next step would be a dedicated electronic meeting room at your organization to

**FIGURE 11-3**
ISACOMM's Full-Color, Full-Motion Teleconferencing
Facility Located At United Telecom's Corporate Center,
Westwood, Kansas

*Credit: Courtesy of ISACOMM, Inc., a United Telecom Company.*

link with other high-communication-density locations. An excellent example of a well-thought-out video teleconferencing facility is one designed by ISACOMM (see Figure 11-3).

ISACOMM works with customers to tailor the facility to meet each organization's unique teleconferencing needs. The ISACOMM basic design (see Figure 11-4) is very functional and offers an excellent environment for meetings. As has been mentioned previously, the critical questions before making this step are:

1. Is it absolutely clear that a full-motion visual capability is critical to accomplish the teleconferencing mission?

2. Will the travel savings and increased productivity justify the initial investment and ongoing communication costs?

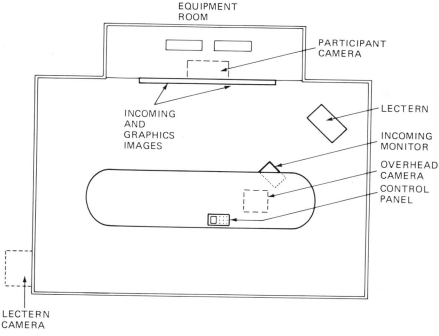

**FIGURE 11-4**
Basic Diagram Of ISACOMM Teleconferencing Facility
In Westwood, Kansas

If the answers to these questions are "yes," then you can proceed to explore a dedicated facility in more detail.

## Human Factor Considerations

When preparing to establish a dedicated facility, there are some technical details that should be considered. It is strongly recommended that you get a consultant to assist you in this area. Room design, equipment selection, acoustics, and establishment of transmission systems are a few of the details that must be considered. Since the costs of each video teleconferencing room can range from $100,000 to $500,000, a consultant can be considered good insurance that the room will function as desired.

## Room Placement

I have found that it is important to place the teleconferencing room near the group that will be the heaviest users of the facility. If you place the room too far away, utilization will be lower than anticipated. *It is amazing how much utilization can decline when a facility is moved just one floor away.* In the initial stages, participants will not be in the habit of using teleconferencing, and "out of sight, out of mind" certainly applies to the location of the room. However, you must balance placement with perceptions of territorial ownership. Be sensitive to the fact that there may be some users who will not use a facility because it is located in a particular department or location. Strive for a neutral placement.

In one situation, I spoke with an organization that placed the meeting room in the executive suite. Although the identified high-volume users were not the executives, placement was made for political reasons. The implementer discovered that the low utilization was due to the perception that the facility was reserved for only upper management. Even after the implementer attempted to make it clear to everyone that the facility was open to all those in the organization, there was continued resistance due to a reluctance on the part of some major users to journey into "executive territory." There was the perception that if the room was utilized, there had better be a darn good reason, in case one of the executives stopped by to see what was going on. Once the teleconference room was moved out of the executive suite, utilization more than doubled. Sometime later, the implementer learned that the executive group had some misgivings about the initial placement in their area, but were giving the benefit of the doubt to the implementer. So the implementer's perception that establishing the room in the executive suite was critical for political reasons was unfounded and, in the end, lessened his credibility with management.

## Room Design

One could easily emulate the Picturephone® Meeting Service design and have a workable facility. In fact, AT&T has several publications which can give you some ideas. The best overview is an AT&T publication entitled *Quorum*™ *Teleconferencing System Room Guidelines* (SP-4390-6/82). There is quite a bit of useful information packed into this ten-page booklet, covering location, space considerations, room environment, equipment placement, and acoustics. The basic designs that have been discussed thus far are certainly workable; however, I would suggest a few revisions. See Figure 11-5.

This design has two major changes from the other designs. First, the table is designed to facilitate more intragroup communication. As I have discussed previously, placing the participants more in a conventional seating arrangement reduces the "us versus them" syndrome, which can result in debate rather than

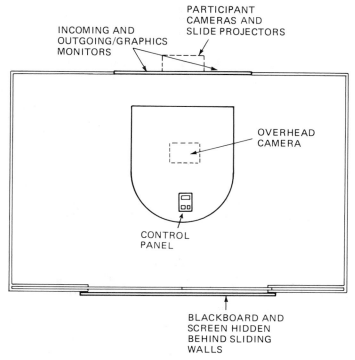

**FIGURE 11-5**
Video Teleconferencing Room Design To Duplicate
Normal Participant Eye Contact

dialog. Second, the blackboard is *behind* the participants rather than off to the side. In AT&T's configuration the advantage is:

1. From the camera's perspective, the wall behind the participants is not cluttered and will provide a cleaner-looking image of the participants.

2. The participants will not have to turn around to see what is being written on the blackboard.

Since eye contact between parties is important in our culture, let's see what happens when someone at location #1 begins to present information at the blackboard. The camera used for the blackboard is switched on. From an eye contact point of view, the blackboard camera represents the eyes of those at location #2. However, the presenter will attempt to maintain eye contact by looking at the main television monitor showing those at location #2. The distant location will constantly have the feeling that the presenter is looking off to the side rather than at them. The presenter, on the other hand, will be bothered by the fact that even though he or she has moved over to the side of the room, the distant participants continue to look straight ahead; after all, they are still looking at the monitor in front of them. Those sitting at the table in location #1 will be bothered by the fact that those at location #2 appear to be looking at them instead of at the presenter.

In my configuration, the blackboard camera is in the same cluster as the other cameras looking at the group, so the focus of attention does not change. Eye contact continues to be natural. Granted, the participants at location #1 have to turn their attention from the television monitors in the front of the room to the blackboard, but this is also a natural approximation of a real meeting. If both video teleconferencing rooms are configured the same, when the presenter sees the table at the distant location in the monitor at the end of his or her table, the impression will be that the table actually extends to the distant location—that the participants are gathered around a common table. As for the background looking cluttered when a normal discussion is taking place, the installation of a sliding panel to hide the blackboard when not in use cleans up the visual image. I also have increased the size of the light box area so that larger blueprints and diagrams can be laid out on the table for discussion.

ISACOMM's approach is a little different. A lecturer faces the local participants to maintain eye contact. To provide more normal interaction between the lecturer and the remote participants, ISACOMM uses a monitor placed in front of the lecturer (see Figure 11-6). From the lecturer's position, both the local and remote participants can be easily seen. ISACOMM also uses its television monitor system a little differently. The two monitors in the front of the room (see Figure 11-3) display the incoming group video and the common graphic being discussed. Many other systems use the second monitor to display the outgoing group image. The common graphic screen is an excellent concept, although some might prefer to see the outgoing group image. By pressing a "preview" button on ISACOMM's control panel, it is possible for the local group to see their own image, but there is the potential for users to become lax and not pay appropriate attention to the visual aspect of the teleconference.

## Video's Need For Constant Feeding

Unlike captured frame and audiographics, the visual image will need constant attention. Since we are accustomed to the constant camera switching on regular television, it may be difficult for some participants to get used to the fact that there is no director making sure the visual images are the best possible. The use of voice-activated automatic switching of the cameras so the image seen is of the person talking certainly is a valuable addition, but none of the systems on the market feature equipment that automatically zooms in or out; these modifications are left up to the participants. There will be three stages that users will go through:

1. Considerable attention to the visual image. A significant amount of time will be consumed as the participants attempt to create the kinds of close ups seen on television when a person is talking. Since they are new to the camera manipulation effort, the users will be fairly ineffectual.

**FIGURE 11-6**
View of ISACOMM Teleconferencing Room From
Lectern

*Credit: Courtesy of ISACOMM, Inc., a United Telecom Company.*

2. Some attention to the visual image. The amount of camera movement will decrease, but user manipulation skills will increase so that less time is wasted in positioning the cameras.

3. Little attention to the visual image. Users will simply leave the cameras alone, except when it is very important to show an item of significance.

The more that you can automate some of the camera control function, the more consistent the image will be over time. However, automation dictates that you have a good grasp of the demands that will be placed on the system—the specific kinds of camera and lens positions that are most commonly used. Given the recent interest in developing more sophisticated control systems, *it may be worthwhile to implement a basic camera switching system and add more sophistication once your organization's visual communication requirements have been identified.*

I believe it is important to implement automatic control functions before your users reach Stage 3, as identified above. With a decreasing concern with the visual element, there is a reduction in full-motion's importance. In Stage 3 presentations, the users set the camera so that as many of the participants as possible can be seen by the camera. At that point, the details of facial expression become lost, and only gross nonverbal communication is exchanged. If one of the basic reasons for implementing full motion is the nonverbal aspect, then the rationale for full motion is reduced.

### The Nerd Factor

In a recent announcement of its report on teleconferencing, International Resource Development, Inc., (IRD) noted that one reason why visual teleconferences are not a success is that participants

> . . . have their ties askew, don't always look at the camera, and may pick their noses and seem unsure what to say. To their dismay, some executives find that teleconferencing . . . portrays them as nerds.[2]

Frankly, I agree. The reason, again, is that we enter the video teleconferencing event with years of television viewing habits that change the way we perceive a meeting. The full-motion television medium changes our expectations. *Certainly, no one would mind if a participant in a face-to-face conference had his or her tie askew or that his or her hair was not perfect, but with full-motion television we expect perfection—that is what we are used to seeing.* Over time, our attitudes change, but those first few encounters can certainly be critical. I would certainly recommend that a little extra attention be given to the participants' looks, just to be on the safe side. In a recent installation, I installed a one-way window looking in on the conferencing room. Not only does this permit unobtrusive monitoring of the event, but the mirror surface lets participants take a quick look at their appearance before the session begins.

The International Resource Development release went on to say that teleconferencing fails to communicate some of the more subtle nonverbal aspects of a face-to-face meeting—namely body odors. A number of serious researchers believe that odors are important to the communications event. Efforts are underway to isolate the relevant odors and develop equipment that will detect and release similar odors at distant locations. *Without very convincing experimental evidence, it is difficult to attach a high priority to the development of "Tele-Smell-O-Vision," especially when compared with the other problems facing users of teleconferencing.* Planning, goal setting, education and sensitivity to electronic group process factors would rank considerably higher on my list for a successful teleconference than the presence of body odor.

### Audio

Users of full-motion systems expect the audio quality to be much better than that of audio conferencing systems and tend to be far more lax in their use of existing microphones. Once again, we are used to fairly high-quality sound from our home televisions and expect similar quality in a full-motion teleconferencing environment. Higher quality audio requires greater communication bandwidth, hence increased communication costs. While the relative cost of high-quality audio is inexpensive when compared with the visual information, the cost is certainly greater than simple voice grade lines. Since the predominant amount of information transfer will be via audio communication, it is advisable to spend a few extra percent to make sure the sound quality is excellent. While a bandwidth of 7 to 9 KHz is adequate (about the same as AM radio), I would recommend a 15 KHz bandwidth (the same as FM radio). The human voice does not generate very much energy at those higher frequencies, *but if the participants in the teleconference will be presenting advertising campaigns, recordings, or other audio material that will appear via other media to the general public, then a true high-fidelity audio system is very useful.*

The tendency for users of a full-motion video system to avoid microphones might seem a little unusual. In other teleconferencing systems, users seem to warm right up to the microphone, but full-motion participants have a negative reaction. Our clue to this problem comes from regular television once more. Generally, the only time we see microphones on television is during the news and when someone is singing; the rest of the time we hear people fine and they do not appear to be wearing devices. In regular television and film, production teams use a boom microphone to pick up the actors' voices. These are sensitive microphones placed on a long boom and suspended above the actors, just outside the camera's field of vision. Comments like "it's just like a face-to-face meeting" do not help the situation. After all, when was the last time you were at a traditional meeting when you had to use a microphone so that the person at the end of the table could hear you? Talking about the problem with participants will help, but letting them hear how they sound to others provides a more direct kick in the right direction. All too many room designers spend time on the visual aspect of the facility and neglect the audio portion, when the bulk of our idea communication is verbal.

One of the best teleconferencing audio systems to appear on the market is the AMS8000 manufactured by Shure® (see chapter 8). The low-profile microphones provide excellent quality and are not obtrusive. Shure® has gone one step further with the addition of electronic switching equipment that will automatically select cameras based on a speaker's location.

**Multisite Communication**

Even with dedicated facilities, there are times when participation by more than two locations is desirable. Unfortunately, almost all the systems are limited to full two-way visual communication between just two locations. While the science fiction movies show a teleconferencing room with a television monitor representing each participating location, we are a long way from that kind of capability. Although possible, the cost for the communication circuits to link all the locations so that each site can see all the participants is tremendous. One method of achieving a similar result is to have all the visual signals converge on a central distribution control room where the engineer sends back out to all the participants the image of the person talking. While this is effective, an engineer's cost can be fairly substantial, and the system may not be available while the engineer goes to lunch, is sick, or goes home for the night.

In New England, I designed an automated system to perform many of the functions of the engineer that was much faster than its human counterpart and was available 24 hours a day. The design was based on the premise that in a multisite conference there is generally one location that is the focal point for the event. Very often it was the location with the chairman, moderator, or presenter. Basically, the system operated in the following manner:

1. The conference chairman's location uses a control panel to indicate to a central computer the locations that will be participating in the conference. Those locations not selected cannot eavesdrop on the conference.

2. At the start of the conference, all the locations see the chairman on their monitors. The chairman sees the participants at one of the other locations.

3. When someone at a participating location wants to ask a question or make a comment, he or she presses a small button on their microphone. The system will then redistribute all the television signals so that all locations can see the person making the comment, while the person making the comment continues to see the chairman.

4. After making the comment, the individual releases the button. The system will reconfigure the system so that all locations again see the chairman. The chairman will continue to see the person who made the comment for any nonverbal feedback (a quizzical look, head nodding, etc.).

5. Each time a participant makes a comment, the system will repeat the process: everyone will see the individual talking, while visual communication between the individual and chairman is maintained. At the conclusion of the comments everyone would see the chairman, and visual communication between the individual and chairman will not change.

All of this fancy electronic footwork takes place in less than .2 seconds and creates a highly interactive visual environment for the participants. While this design still does not permit everyone to see everyone else all the time, it does enable participants to see what is really important—the person making the comment—and establishes a continuous visual link between the chairman and individual for nonverbal communication.

### Building The Facility

Unless your firm has an excellent electronics capability, I would strongly suggest using one of several of the major full-motion teleconferencing vendors to construct the facility. MA/Com, ISACOMM, Satellite Business Systems, and others are all experienced in the design and construction of full-motion teleconferencing rooms. AT&T can even build the facility for you and charge a monthly rate just as though you were installing a sophisticated telephone system. I would suggest that you seek two types of input as you consider the development of your facility. First, find a vendor that is willing to develop the kind of facility that makes sense in your organization—a firm that will listen to your needs and will then suggest a solution that fits the communication requirements of your users. Second, seek out a consultant who is not associated with a major vendor and who has hands-on experience with the type of teleconferencing you plan on initiating. Few of the vendors actually use teleconferencing on a daily basis, so their comments concerning the human factor side of teleconferencing may be limited. While the vendors that I mentioned do use teleconferencing for technical dialogs, their experience may not be applicable to your situation. A third party, not associated with a vendor organization, may be able to provide valuable insights as to some of the day-to-day implementation and utilization problems that you will face.

### Dedicated System Summary

The dedicated system is the most expensive form of teleconferencing. The establishment of such a system demands that adequate cost justification be made, with sufficient attention to detail to make sure that the facility will be utilized. Due to the expense involved, anyone considering a serious commitment to full-motion facilities should begin with a pilot program between two locations and then expand to develop a network once the company's unique communication demands have been identified.

## Large Ad Hoc Events

If you want to reach large, specific audiences, then the *ad hoc* teleconference may be just what you are looking for. There is no doubt in the minds of many users that using teleconferencing to reach widely separated geographic locations (generally via satellite) is extremely beneficial. For the most part, events developed by major corporations for marketing and educational events originated by professional organizations differ little from the traditional concept of closed-circuit broadcasting or narrowcasting—broadcasts that reach a narrow segment of the population. What separates these teleconferences from closed-circuit broadcasts of world championship boxing matches is the interaction between the originating and receiving locations. *Ad hoc* teleconferences require considerably more planning, and since the program will be seen in a host of cities, a great deal of coordination and attention to detail is necessary.

### The Pheromone Factor

The large scale *ad hoc* teleconference has the highest Pheromone Factor. People are still awed by all the trappings surrounding space age communication. The major attractions of a large-scale satellite program are:

1. Its newness. "Live via satellite" still has the power to draw attention to itself. The satellite antennas and the specialized hardware give off a "state-of-the-art" message. Early programs emphasized this aspect over all other factors as a way to draw people to the

various receiving locations. However, as the number of satellite programs have increased, the newness has been wearing off. Many professionals who have been exposed to satellite programs are no longer attracted to the event simply because it is coming in via satellite. There are many other groups, which have not had previous contact, that are still in awe of the technology and would attend an event just to see what it was all about.

2. Feeling special. Even old hands at satellite teleconferences will comment that going to a closed-circuit satellite broadcast still makes them feel that they are part of a unique national group. An elite collection of individuals who will be receiving information not available to others. There is a sense of community that develops—that they belong to a select group.

3. Knowing the latest information. A good satellite program will promote the fact that the information presented is new and not widely available. Very much like a news program, the program should focus on the latest information not yet available in the journals, magazines, and other media. The key element is salience. The information that will be presented will have *immediate* impact on the participant's work. The information must be practical and useful; otherwise the timely quality is not important and the participant will wonder if reading a book would have accomplished the same objective.

4. Interacting with experts. Remember it is the interactive capability that sets a teleconference apart from a closed-circuit broadcast. Just knowing that a participant can ask a question has quite a bit of attraction. My discussions with participants indicate that when they hear a peer from somewhere else in the country ask a question, the overall evaluation of the program is more favorable. Actually hearing the voice of the peer, as opposed to someone reading a question submitted by a participant, has the greatest positive impact on how the participants rate the effort.

All of these factors add up to a high Pheromone Factor. The newness of the information is emerging as the critical marketing element to attract people to a teleconference, while the interaction process appears to be important in the overall assessment of the program.

**The Production Value**

Since many of those who will be viewing or participating in an *ad hoc* teleconferencing event will not have had any previous exposure to the process, the expectation level will be based on past experience with traditional television. Production value must be high in order for the program to maintain content credibility. There is a continuing debate on exactly how "flashy" the program should be.

Current programs range from "talking heads" discussing a topic in a round-table format to extravagent productions that resemble a television variety special, complete with guest stars, actors, and animation. The type of audience and the desired outcomes from the event should indicate the type of communication approach used. Some common sense is indicated. Generally speaking, however, a professional-level audience will be less impressed by "flash" and more interested in production value that supports the information to be communicated.

A factor that is common to all groups is the need to convey information graphically—to use the visual impact of television. The phrase "Don't talk about it. Show me!" is very applicable to this form of communication. Television news is an excellent model to follow for a large-audience satellite conference. Television news has certainly come a long way from someone sitting in front of the camera reading the news to the audience. Now, we have on-the-spot, live reports from locations of interest with interactive discussion taking place between the anchor and reporter. The feeling is immediacy. "This is happening NOW." There are several ways to achieve immediacy in a teleconference:

1. The live remote report. Taking the lead from television news, these live reports originate from the scene. Remember, in a satellite conference any location near an uplink can reach all the participating locations. Even though a moderator is in Chicago, a remote report on new regulations could come from Washington—either from a studio or from the steps of the Capitol. Similarly, a report on new automation techniques in an automobile plant could originate from the assembly line. To extend the current news practice of the moderator and reporter talking, the question could come from a participating viewing site just as easily.

2. The prerecorded insert. In this case, the moderator turns the program over to a reporter in the same studio who then introduces a prerecorded videotape which describes the activity visually. The reporter can either describe what is being seen (called a "voice-over"), or the reporter can be part of the prerecorded material as well. Following the prerecorded tape, discussion between the moderator, participants, and the reporter can be initiated. An analogy would be the type of discussion that takes place on a television news program such as "20/20" between the reporter and the moderator before and after the pre-recorded news story.

There is tremendous power in the live event. I recall watching a program on television news aired over PBS called *Media Probes* in which a media consultant said that live programming redefines our perceptions of what is important. The old adage "If a dog bites a man it isn't news, but if a man bites a dog—that is news!" changes when we add a live component. If a dog bites a man on live television, it becomes immediately interesting again. This immediacy, the sense of being there, is what is so powerful about television and, by extension, is what can be powerful about a video teleconference. To harness the power of the medium requires creativity and planning, little of which has been apparent in many of the current visual teleconferences. I would estimate that well over three-fourths of today's teleconferences are nothing more than people sitting around a table talking about a subject. Obviously, some topics do not lend themselves to graphic depiction, but those topics are in the minority.

### Handling Interaction

High production value means that considerable planning has taken place and events are timed to the second. The rehearsals and scripts ensure that the program content is well defined and nothing is left to chance. Unfortunately, interaction by its very nature is spontaneous and unpredictable. This is one reason why television producers responsible for a major teleconference are apprehensive about interaction. Interaction is totally out of the realm of their experience and, as a result, interaction becomes only a small part of many teleconferences. Very few production teams in the country have been responsible for more than one teleconference. While major organizations seek out experienced firms to handle the logistics of a major teleconference, the production crew from a local television station is generally hired to handle the actual program. The production team's inexperience with interactive events can lessen the impact of the effort. However, there is an increasing trend to use production crews that have experience with video teleconferencing—an option I *strongly* recommend. This is one reason why some organizations seek out a consultant familiar with teleconferencing to act as the executive producer to oversee the efforts of the technical group and production team. A creative executive producer can focus the creative energy of both groups to develop innovative approaches to the interaction problem.

Let's look at some of the methods used to promote and handle the interaction process:

1. The use of planted questions. One of the concerns is that the participants asking questions will be inarticulate. A common problem. Most of us do not ask clear questions; we tend to ramble a little. Some have used their marketing people to isolate major relevant questions, identify individuals in selected locations, write up the questions, and have those individuals ask the questions as if they were their own. Although it may appear to be an underhanded approach, it works quite well: the question is asked succinctly, there are few surprises, and the participants feel that an important question has been asked. *To be effective, however, the question must be important to the participants. If marketing has failed to identify real, "hard-core" issues, then the planted question will be a waste of time.* Since some groups are more reluctant to get started in the interaction process than others, I normally insist that arrangements be made for several planted questions to be used if interaction is slow in starting—questions to "get the ball rolling."

2. The use of question takers. In this approach, participants call an intermediary who writes down the question and passes it along to the presenter. Some like this approach because of its controlled nature. Questions can be screened, rewritten to make more sense, and prioritized. Most participants, on the other hand, feel somewhat frustrated by the process because they know that their comments will be edited. *One caution: select the toughest and most sensitive questions first.* Since word-of-mouth is still one of the most effective forms of communication, ignoring tough questions can have a serious backlash as those that asked tough questions begin to talk up the fact that the organization censored the questions. Although some would disagree, I recommend the questioner's name being used over the air. Participants respond better when they know the question comes from a real person. I would also reecommend that an "anonymous" option be provided for those concerned with political ramifications of the question.

3. The use of local moderators. Instead of questions going to a centrally located question taker, questions can be given to a local moderator and forwarded to the originating location. In this case, it is recommended that the local moderators be put on the air to ask the question. Although this method is somewhat unpredictable, individuals at each site will feel themselves to be a part of the event if their moderator goes "on the air." Take special care in selecting the local moderator in order to minimize uncertainly. Hold a conference call with the moderators several days prior to the event to go over all the ground rules and protocols. From a production standpoint, it is recommended that pictures of all the moderators be gathered and placed on the air so that all can put the face with the voice.

4. The use of participants. The most unpredictable, but the most interesting form of communication for the other participants. Actually putting an individual on the air does wonders for the interest factor. There are two basic approaches to direct participant interaction from a production standpoint: the live question and the recorded question. First, the live question represents maximum risk (obscene comments, libel, etc.), but it does permit a real dialog between the presenter and the participant. From a technical standpoint, there are constant problems with feedback (the telephone being too close to the teleconference speakers). Second, the recorded question permits the participant to ask a question in his own words and enables the producers to screen blatant problem questions. Since there is generally little dialog between the presenter and the participant after the initial question has been asked, a recorded approach can sound quite natural. Technical problems are avoided, and the participant can rejoin the conference to hear himself ask the question. A smart

producer will stay one step ahead of the questions and provide the presenter with a brief statement concerning the nature of the question prior to playback so the presenter can collect his or her thoughts. For obvious reasons, I recommend the prerecorded approach for larger conferences when questions are unpredictable.

In addition to the obscene caller I discussed earlier, I have seen many interaction disasters. In one case, there were no provisions made for a telephone at a particular site, even though the program was to be interactive. Questions were written down, and then a runner took the questions up one flight of stairs and gave them to a secretary to call in. I can recall sitting in the audience as the presenter acknowledged a question coming from our group . . .

PRESENTER: I see we have another question from Chicago. Your question please?

SECRETARY: Hello?

PRESENTER: Yes, I can hear you. Go ahead with your question.

SECRETARY: (Reads question very poorly. Several medical terms mispronounced.)

PRESENTER: (Unaware that someone other than an actual participant is asking the question.) Uh . . . could you explain the nature of the problem a little more?

SECRETARY: (Unaware that her voice was being heard live.) The problem? The problem is that I have tons of work to do and these people keep bringing me these little notes to read. Are you ready for the next question?

Everyone at our location sank lower into their seats. A horrible feeling!

In another situation, the producers forgot to arrange for a telephone in the viewing auditorium for participants to use in calling in their questions. There was no local moderator, since the participants were to call in directly with their questions. Someone with a burning question found a pay telephone down the hallway, but did not have any change. He came in the door by the side of the stage, where the wide-screen television was located, looked up at the group, and said, "Does anyone have 20 cents for the pay phone so I can ask a question?" A roar of laughter came from the group as everyone dug into their pockets. Within a few minutes there must have been $15 worth of change on the table at the front of the room for those with questions.

But the most frustrating situation is when all the necessary site provisions have been made, but too few incoming telephone lines are available at the presenter's location. I can still hear the voice of one moderater over the din of the broadcast at a recent teleconference, "Ladies and gentlemen. I've been trying for 20 minutes to get your questions in, but the lines are all busy! I'm sorry, but I'll keep trying." At that moment, the presenter on the television said, "I am surprised we haven't heard from Kansas City." Then he turned to the other presenters. "Perhaps they know all the answers!" The presenters laughed, and the Kansas City group booed at the television screen. The solution to the problem is to have each of the participating sites call a bridging company, like Connex, and stay on line for the duration of the event. Certainly, the extra $50 per location is well worth it to avoid some of the problems I have described here!

## Cost Factors

There are so many variables involved that it is difficult to say what a large teleconference will cost. Generally speaking, an average figure would be $25,000 to $35,000, with a range of $5,000 to $500,000. Here are some of the factors which will impact the cost of a major conference:

1. Production level. The amount of material that has to be pre-recorded, the size of the production team, the types of graphics that will be necessary, the number of locations from which program content will originate, and the design of the television set and lighting.

2. Access to and number of viewing sites. If the receiving locations are in major urban centers, then the probability of satellite receivers being available is quite high. Additional expense is involved if portable units have to be sent to locations where no equipment is available.

3. Number of participants at each site. Small groups can use public broadcast studios or small meeting rooms in equipped hotels or motels. Large groups, on the other hand, will require special television image projection equipment, and site preparation will be more costly.

4. Access to uplink facilities. The greater the distance between the origination point and the uplink, the greater the cost. If the uplink is too far away, then there will be costs for either moving the presentation to the uplink facility or renting a portable uplink.

5. Time of day and length. Satellite time between 4:00 p.m. and 2:00 a.m. (eastern time) is most expensive. However, the uplink and receiver costs may be higher at other times.

6. Type of interaction. If a very low level of interaction is desired, simply calling the origination facility collect is possible. For high levels of interaction, the use of a conference bridge with all sites fully linked for the duration of the teleconference is necessary.

7. Insurance. If the program is an expensive one, then program insurance should be obtained in the event of a technical failure.

Before you call a major specialist in satellite teleconferences, prepare answers to the above questions. This will enable you to focus more directly on the type of presentation and will speed the process.

### Security

Large-scale teleconferences have a problem with information security. Due to the increase in the number of private satellite receivers scattered around the country, eavesdropping is common. Satellite broadcasts can be received by anyone (or company). In a recent satellite conference, a major corporation outlined a national sales strategy for its offices and announced a new "800" number for prospective clients. Within hours, the corporation was receiving calls on the "800" number from people who just happened to listen in.

The problem is complex. It is possible to "scramble" a television picture so that only those with "unscramblers" can make any sense out of the information. Unfortunately, if you are trying to reach a large audience, the receiver locations may not be equipped with unscrambling equipment. The problem with the scrambling equipment today is that the process degrades the television image quality, which may be a high price to pay—not to mention the cost of equipping all the receiving locations with the necessary hardware. Even if you decide to scramble information, it is fairly easy for those with some electronics experience to build unscramblers with just a handful of parts. The recent announcements that satellite premium-movie distributors are considering scrambling their broadcasts has created quite a number of articles in the magazines aimed at the home satellite owner. In light of the problem, many users simply do not worry about security. After all, much of the current *ad hoc* use of satellites is promotional in nature. The lack of security is only a problem for those who use a satellite broadcast to discuss strategic planning or other sensitive topics.

Those users of compressed video equipment, as opposed to regular wideband television, have less of a problem with security. Due to the signal processing techniques, these pictures cannot be readily intercepted by unauthorized individuals. Since the compressed video signals are digital, a number of firms offer high quality encryption/decryption equipment that creates an extremely secure communications channel. Keep in mind though, that such equipment is not applicable to mass distribution systems; it is only for those with dedicated teleconferencing systems and some specialized public teleconferencing rooms.

It is easy for users of satellite systems to believe that their communications are secure. Always remember, however, that if your teleconference is using any satellite for the distribution of regular television signals, YOUR COMMUNICATIONS ARE NOT SECURE. I would strongly recommend that you advise your participants that their comments will be overheard and they should speak accordingly.

### The Public Service Satellite Consortium

For my money, the Public Service Satellite Consortium (PSSC) is one of the best-equipped organizations to coordinate a large-scale satellite teleconference (see Figure 11-7). The PSSC was formed in the late 1970s by a number of farsighted individuals, many of whom were participating in the government's first major ex-

**FIGURE 11-7**
*Ad Hoc* Teleconference

Credit: *Courtesy of the Public Service Satellite Consortium, Washington, D.C.*

periments with two-way satellite television. The PSSC then hired many of the technical experts at the conclusion of those experimental broadcasts and began to assist business and industry to use this new form of telecommunication. With over 230 video teleconferences under its belt, the PSSC knows the ropes and has an excellent staff. Although technically oriented in the beginning, the PSSC has been expanding its expertise into market analysis, production, and education. Recently, the PSSC has formed a new subsidiary called Services by Satellite (SatServ) which services corporate satellite communication needs. Basically, the PSSC/SatServ services include:

1. Telecommunication consulting, market requirement studies, and needs assessment.
2. Full video teleconferencing services. including planning, networking, production, and facilities arrangements.
3. Engineering studies and technical planning.
4. Operation and lease of a major satellite access facility in Denver, Colorado (see Figure 11-8). The facility consists of a teleconferencing studio, a network control center, and an uplink capable of accessing the majority of the commercial satellites.
5. Operation and lease of portable uplink equipment which can be located at the most convenient origination point.
6. Sponsorship of one of the largest annual conferences in the satellite communication field.
7. Regular workshops on how to conduct successful satellite teleconferences.

The list of PSSC/SatServ clients is indeed impressive: DuPont, Hewlett-Packard, Petro Lewis, the major television networks, United Technologies, Tandem, Digital Equipment, and a host of professional organizations.

For those seriously interested in pursuing satellite communication further, I would recommend attending one of the PSSC workshops to learn more about the field. Following the workshop, return to your organization and work up several application concepts and discuss them with the PSSC representatives. I would advise that you take your time and look for a satellite application roughly a year down the road. This will give you enough time to develop a solid case for your proposal, to obtain the necessary consultive input, and to make all the arrangements so that the program will be a success.

## Summary

Full-motion video teleconferencing can be divided into large- and small-group efforts. The smaller groups tend to use either *ad hoc* public teleconferencing rooms or dedicated facilities, while the teleconferences to reach larger groups

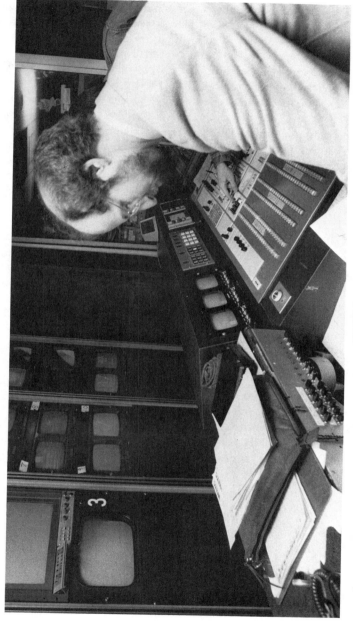

**FIGURE 11-8**
Public Service Satellite Consortium
Network Control Center Near Denver, Colorado

*Credit: Courtesy of the Public Service Satellite Consortium, Washington, D.C.*

generally use a fairly sophisticated satellite distribution system. Both are expensive and require a great deal of preparation prior to the event. Before using video systems, make sure either that the visual element is indeed necessary in order to communicate the message or that marketing factors demand a visual medium. Before implementing a full-motion dedicated facility, it is essential that consultive input be obtained by both hardware and human factor experts. In the case of a large-audience effort, obtaining advice from those with solid experience is even more critical. The financial exposure is too great to be left to beginners.

Without question, the use of satellite technology to reach large audiences on an *ad hoc* basis with important information can be extremely cost effective. Numerous companies are announcing products and holding national press conferences every day. However, the implementation of dedicated full-motion video teleconferencing facilities for routine meetings may be costly and counterproductive. For a significant number of businesses, full-motion television is simply not necessary and solid audio communication supplemented by slow scan or shared-screen equipment will meet their communication needs at a significantly reduced cost.

For those considering a dedicated full-motion facility, it may be wise to provide both full-motion and slow scan television (with various transmission speed options). With such a facility, participants could use the most cost-effective teleconferencing system: full motion for major presentations and slow scan for technical discussions in which static images are common. Using an Action/Honeywell Roadrunner, the teleconferencing system would use only as much bandwidth as necessary and thus contain communication costs. Integrating voice, data, and teleconferencing may provide additional organizational savings, but considerable evaluation will be necessary to determine the most cost-effective approach.

With those cautions in mind, I would certainly recommend that larger corporations give serious thought to full-motion teleconferencing. A well-designed system can be easy to use and can lead to enhanced productivity. There is little question that executives find full-motion teleconferencing an excellent means of maintaining "executive presence" in geographically separated locations without travel costs or lost productivity.

## Chapter 11 Notes

1. J. Van Pelt, "Cost effective, two-way full motion, color video networks." *Business Communications Review,* November-December 1982, 14–18.

2. "IRD nerd report." *TeleSpan Newsletter,* March 15, 1983, 23.

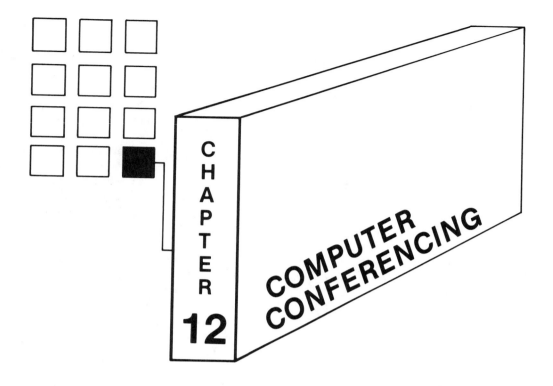

CHAPTER 12

COMPUTER CONFERENCING

"The sleeping giant!" That is the best description of computer conferencing. Although it is not flashy and does not have a high Pheromone Factor, computer conferencing is one of the best productivity-enhancing teleconferencing systems. What is computer conferencing? It consists of communication terminals which are used by participants to access a central computer. The central computer stores the text information entered by a user and forwards the information to other users when they call the computer. This "store and forward" feature is the basis for increased productivity. In some respects, computer conferencing is similar to electronic mail.

## Development of the Technology

Many years ago, there was a need for information to be sent to locations and appear in typewritten form to ensure accuracy of communication. By combining a typewriter with electromechanical circuits, the teletype was born. A large network of teletypewriters grew across the country as businesses found that the teletype was a better way to transmit order information between locations. As an example, the famous "hot line" between the United States and the Soviet Union is not a telephone but a form of teletypewriter—again because of the need for message accuracy. Gradually, the applications expanded as the teletype machines were used to transmit time-critical correspondence. To connect all of these teletypes, a number of dedicated networks emerged, the most famous being the Western Union Telex system. Much as with a telephone network, users referred to their directory and called other teletype terminals when there was information to exchange. Gradually, all electronic typewriters (called "terminals") have started to replace the older electromechanical devices. The new terminals have few moving parts and are more reliable than the older teletype terminals. In addition, the electronic terminals have become more sophisticated and even portable.

Some companies had hundreds of teletype terminals scattered across the country and getting a single message to all of them became very time consuming. Then someone decided to use the power of a computer to call all of the locations and send the messages. The user would simply provide the computer with a list of the terminals to be contacted and then type the message in just one time. In some cases, the computer was told to "store" the information until late at night, when the communication rates were the lowest, and then "forward" the messages on to the various identified locations. The "store and forward" era was born.

There have been countless variations on this theme, but rapid dissemination of "record" communications has come of age. For those using portable terminals, the messages were placed in an electronic "mail box" so that when the mobile user had some free time, he or she would call the central computer and retrieve the messages in the mail box. Today, we call all of this "electronic mail," and its use is growing in leaps and bounds.

Users of store and forward systems discovered that they could cut down on the number of telephone calls. Callers, especially those dealing with offices and clients in different time zones or overseas, would not have to be concerned with someone being in the office at the time the communication was sent. As a side benefit, users discovered that there was a substantial reduction in "telephone tag" (you call me, I am out, you leave a message, I return the call, you are out, I leave a message, etc.). With store and forward, the full message is communicated without the need to go through a secretary, reducing the risk of the message being taken incorrectly.

The move from electronic mail to computer conferencing took place when it was realized that the computer could do far more than simply store and forward text information. Instead of thinking in terms of mail boxes, innovators began to think in terms of file folders. Logically, there would be a file folder for you, for me, and for the other participants in which our messages would be placed. In addition, file folders could be assigned a topic rather than a person's name and, as with any file folder, a number of readers could look through all of the messages in the file at any time. The concept of computer conferencing was born—asynchronous teleconferencing.

Let's look at an example of how such a system would work. There is a large corporation with regional offices across the United States, including an Alaska/Hawaii region. Each region has its own personnel director, and there is a corporate director of personnel in New York. There has been a recent change in wage-and-hour law, and the personnel policies need to reflect those changes as soon as possible. The problems are simple: the time zone differences between New York and

Hawaii create a very narrow "business window" (the time when the people in New York and Hawaii are in the office), and the personnel directors have a busy schedule, making it difficult to get together via audio or visual teleconferencing. In a computer conference environment, the corporate director would open a conference (a file) on "wage and hour" and restrict access to include only the other personnel directors. First, the corporate director would state the problem and ask for initial comments. Each of the personnel directors would "check in" to the computer conference when their schedules permitted, review the comments of the others, and add comments as appropriate. After the problem had been broken down into sections, the group would contribute to the formation of a new policy that reflected the unique problems in their individual regions. At the end of the conference, the New York office would have a completed policy, with a high probability that the policy would meet the corporation's needs due to the involvement of the regional directors.

Computer conferencing has been successful even when time zone problems were not a factor. In some firms, conflicting schedules prohibit face-to-face meetings even when the participants are in the same building, but competitive demands require immediate action. The computer conference permits the individuals to meet electronically, exchange thoughts, and arrive at action plans without the traditional face-to-face meeting.

Let's look at some of the components of today's computer conferencing systems:

1. Message creation. Basic to the system is the ability to create a document. This includes the capacity to edit and refine the text. Some systems offer the option to check for spelling and grammatical mistakes.

2. Private messages. The ability to send the same document to one or more specific individuals. These messages cannot be read by other users of the system, nor can they be copied and sent to others without the permission of the author.

3. Public messages. The ability to send open messages to all the users of the system. Announcing a new product, the Christmas party, or changes in the organization are all public messages. Some use the analogy of the electronic bulletin board to describe the public section of the system. In addition, it is possible to use the public message feature to create divisional electronic newsletters to keep users up-to-date.

4. Conferences. Private communications relating to a specific topic or task. New participants can review previous comments to gain a perspective on the topic. Some computer conferences allow conference participants to vote (public or secret ballot) on motions and other items when concensus is required. Public conferences are also possible so that a broad cross section of users can contribute to a particular topic.

5. Private notebooks. A collection of communications on any topic. Participants can work for several days in their notebooks preparing a major item to be inserted in a conference. A user can permit others access to the notebook for comments.

6. Support features. Included in this area would be any features that make life easier for the user. A spelling checker, a directory of users and conferences, the ability to customize the computer's output to match the type of communication terminal being used, and voting are a few examples of common support features.

A number of the new electronic mail systems, such as GTE/Telenet's system, are offering mail communication options that are becoming more like those offered by computer conferencing systems. This trend is a natural extension of the current electronic mail technology. At the present time, many of these electronic mail firms are allowing the user to establish his or her own filing system so that communications can be saved and reviewed at a later time. Movement away from paper storage to electronic storage makes retrieval of information much easier in today's complex business environment. Many of our memos and letters have more than one topic, and electronic systems enable users to file a document in as many file folders as there are unique thoughts in the text. Many professionals waste hundreds of dollars in time trying to locate documents. How many times have we searched in vain for an important paper placed somewhere where we would not forget it! Multiple filings increase the chances that we will remember at least one location that might contain the document. Some of the systems permit those receiving information to assign key words that describe the content of the message. To retrieve a misplaced document, the user has the computer search all of the messages and display those with the desired key words.

In addition to some of the benefits mentioned thus far, computer conferencing is fairly inexpensive. With a computer conferencing service, there are four costs. First, there is the capital cost of the communication terminal. Many users purchase a portable terminal for less than $1,500, but a sizable group use their personal home computers that have been equipped for communications or make use of their company's word processing equipment. Second, there is a monthly "membership fee" associated with the computer conferencing service bureaus, which runs between $50 and $100 per month. Third, there are the actual usage costs. Users are assessed these charges for the amount of time they are actually connected to the main computer and associated communication costs. These charges range from as low as $7 per hour to $30 per hour—still less than many telephone calls. Fourth, there are a range of charges for storage and text manipulation. Some systems charge for storage at a rate of $.001 per month per 2,000 characters to 10 cents per month per 1,000 characters, while others charge 5 cents for each message sent. Each system is different. The charges for text storage are the ones to watch. While the cost may appear quite low, there is a tendency to amass stored information just as we store paper. So it is a good idea to periodically "clean house" and reduce the amount of irrelevant information stored in the computer.

In order to keep communication costs to a minimum, a number of communication terminals have internal-storage capability so that longer messages can be composed and edited prior to connecting with the computer conferencing system. Since few executives can type as fast as the communications network can receive information (about 300 words per minute), a heavy user can save a significant amount of money by preparing the information ahead of time and letting the communication terminal transmit the information as fast as the communication channel will allow. Many vendors offer "smart terminal" software for home computers that permit these personal machines to prepare text prior to linking with the larger computer.

One of the problems with electronic mail and computer conferencing systems is that they are generally not compatible with many of the larger computers used by businesses. Historically, many main-frame computers were implemented to support financial activities, and using such computers for text manipulation has never received a very high priority. In addition, low-cost portable communication terminals and main-frame computers speak different communication languages. Many corporate data processing directors have been reluctant to support such systems for a variety of reasons. *First,* additional hardware is necessary to act as a translator between the main frame and the portables. *Second,* there are few good computer conferencing and electronic mail software packages available for the larger companies, and on-site programmers lack sufficient experience to author solid, user-friendly text softwear. *Third,* computer conferencing requires considerable storage space for messages, which equates to increased hardware costs.

Normally, using a company which sells computer conferencing services (service bureau) presents few initial problems. If a company is new to electronic mail and computer conferencing, using a service bureau affords it an opportunity to understand how its firm communicates so that the firm can later purchase software more intelligently. A big problem faces the corporation that decides that advanced electronic mail or computer conferencing makes sense, but finds out that (a) its computer does not support the appropriate communications and (b) the firm has just committed large sums to place color graphics terminals in the offices of those who would be ideal candidates for computer conferencing. The new color machines may have considerable difficulty "talking" with the computer conferencing service.

Data processing must take the lead and seek to meet the new demand for text-related computer use. The first step is for data processing to understand what electronic mail and computer conferencing is all about. The programmers and directors should attempt to get as much actual "hands on" experience as possible to get a feel for the workings of a good electronic text system and expand their knowledge to include the languages and communication protocols used. With these new technologies, data processing should be actively exploring current offerings and recommending to management, rather than the other way around. The move is toward greater integration of computer-related services in a data processing department, and by being reactive, data processing is always ''behind the power curve'' and unable to integrate effectively.

Before we discuss some of the unique communication factors, let's review some of the applications:

1. Collect the thoughts of those who cannot meet regularly face-to-face or by another form of teleconferencing.

2. Distribute timely information. Such items as computer newsletters that are updated daily or special-purpose bulletin boards can keep those with a ''need to know'' current with fast-changing developments.

3. File messages electronically in a fashion that permits rapid retrieval.

4. Keep a written record of a communication, thus reducing the potential for error in taking a message over the telephone.

5. Reduce ''telephone tag,'' since the complete message is transmitted, reducing the need for telephone communication.

6. Reach individuals in other time zones more easily.

7. Communicate with others from any location in the world with a telephone.

8. Expand participation to a broader cross section of the organization to capture new, creative ideas.

## People And Computer Conferences

Now let's look at some of the human factors involved in computer conferencing.

### Social View Of Typing

There are many who refuse to use any text-based system because of a widely held view that typing is something done only by secretaries. While many innovative executives do not seem to be bothered by typing, there are a number of middle- to upper-level executives that feel that they are above typing. It is not uncommon for some executives to delegate the manipulation of the terminal to their secretaries and dictate information to be sent. Actually, if this approach works, there is nothing wrong with using a secretary. At least the executive is participating in the activity, and information is being exchanged much faster than it would be by traditional mail or telephone. On the negative side, the executive is not actually learning anything about the technology and the manipulation of the equipment. If the executive goes on the road and needs to communicate with the system, it is likely that he or she will have to call his or her secretary long distance to pick up the latest mail, since the executive will have insufficient skills to use up the portable terminal.

The president of the Western Behavioral Science Institute, Dr. Richard Farson, recently reported on Western's experience in teaching executives via computer conferencing. The educational programs were offered to busy executives who were unable to leave their company, but wanted the ability to participate via a communication terminal. Dr. Farson noted:

> We find that a number of things we thought would be a problem are not. We were told that executives would not want to work with these computers because they had keyboards. We have no difficulty getting the participants in our program to learn it and enjoy it. We find that those who don't type, and most don't, send longer messages than those who do.[1]

There is no doubt that use of the keyboard intimidates some individuals, but many of the new-rising executives are taking typing so that they might use their new personal computers more effectively. By learning new computer-related skills, these new executives believe that they are learning to "work smarter."

## Message Characteristics

Murray Turoff of the New Jersey Institute of Technology has studied computer conferencing for many years. Turoff noted that the average message between individuals was fairly short, about 175 words, while comments made in a multiple-participant computer conference were almost 300 words.[2] On the average, 75 percent of the messages originated by a user were *sent* to specific individuals, while the remaining 25 percent were computer conference comments. On the other hand, the messages *received* by a user regarding computer conferences increased to 50 percent, due to the wide distribution of conference comments. Turoff's findings support the contention that computer conferencing can distribute considerable amounts of information to others.

Dr. Farson, of Western Behavioral Sciences Institute, noted that:

> Messages are rich, and colorful, and detailed, and precise, and deep, and complex, and individualized. They are anecdotal. . . . They have engaged their executive classmates in complex discussions of course work, or philosophical or practical matters relating to their own work situations.[3]

Some have noticed that the traditional "memo style" becomes modified in a computer setting. These more colorful messages may be compensating for the lack of visual contact. In my experience, there are definite style differences in messages exchanged between (a) those you have met face-to-face and (b) those that you have met electronically via computer conferencing. When interacting with a someone new, there tends to be more personal information exchanged so that the reader can get to know the author better. New users of a computer conference system should be a little more expansive than usual with their messages in order to impart more subtle information that will assist others in "reading between the lines." This will compensate for some of the initial feelings that the participants are missing the visual and verbal nuances. Messages should be limited to one major thought, and do not attempt to cover all possible topics in one message. A "one message, one thought" approach enables readers to absorb information easier.

Probably some of the most exciting work in the field of computer-based writing is being done by David Hughes of Colorado Springs. Hughes feels that computer text is as different from paper text as paper text is from the spoken word. Hughes has noted:

> It is my absolute conviction that until the people working with words begin to understand computing in a cultural context . . . not as a clerical skill, not as a computer skill . . . [until] they see telecommunications as a device that can do things other technologies cannot do, then we're not going to drag . . . the human race into this. A lot of word processing assumes the name of the game is to sit and use the screen to reproduce Gutenberg *en route* to a piece of paper, but I think you can do things on a screen you can't do on a piece of paper.[4]

One of the aspects Hughes eliminated was punctuation. Since commas serve to add pauses in written communication to compensate for the lack of verbal communication, Hughes' terminals pause as they display text—as if the words were being spoken.

The very process of letters appearing on the communication terminal invokes a new way of looking at messages. For example, some terminals send text in only upper-case letters, thus giving messages more emphasis than normal. In addition, there is considerable variation between terminals as to how many characters appear on each line—anywhere from 40 to 132. A financial table produced on an 80-character-per-line machine is almost illegible on a 40- or 64-character-width machine. It is important, therefore, to make sure that there is consistency between the format of the machines that you use, or at least that you are fully aware of any variations that might exist and prepare messages that can be easily read on the machine that prints the fewest characters per line. As Hughes says, " . . . in electronic speech, if you want to be an effective writer, you have to be acutely conscious of what a person is reading, how they're reading it, and the rate they're reading it." According to Hughes, if you cannot visualize the other person reading your information "you don't know how to speak to another person." Murray Turoff, of the New Jersey Institute of Technology, has suggested several methods of adding subtle qualities to text information through the use of symbols. For example:

( + ) Smile

)-( Frown

– ! Decrease the emotion

+ ! Increase the emotion

I would not be at all surprised if others add to these symbols to create an expanded set of characters that serve to enhance the "tone of voice" of a message.

## Tone Of Message

There is one negative aspect of electronic messages with which you should be concerned. A short message tends to be abrupt and to the point. While effective, short messages also tend to be less than diplomatic at times and can lead to emotional overreaction. An initial short message can trigger a series of messages between individuals, each a little more combative than the first. This reaction is one reason I recommend that new users write just a little more than they think is necessary and be cautious about making absolute or categorical statements. It is too easy to hit a nerve and unleash more response than expected. Be cordial. In a face-to-face meeting we tend to watch for visual clues that indicate we may have stepped on a few toes and immediately start to provide more information to defuse the situation. Since electronic messages lack immediate feedback, it is important to be sensitive to reader reaction to our statements.

I can recall making a few suggestions in one conference and receiving a rather terse reply from one participant indicating that he had considerable expertise in the field of discussion and that I was way off base. I perceived some negative tone in the message, so I sent a message directly to the person who had made the comment and explained a little more about the rationale for my statement. I received a notification from the computer system that the message had been received, but there was no reply. I sent another message. To this date, I have never received a reply, and my opinion of that person is fairly negative. From a personal relations standpoint, it is a good idea to acknowledge that you have received a message from someone and comment on the content.

## Suggestions For Conference Moderators

Each computer conference should have a moderator or chairman. The role of the chairman is to set the objectives of the specific conference discussion and keep the discussion on track. Here are a few suggestions:

1. Use a number of smaller messages, rather than one long message. This permits the chairman to subsequently modify a comment without forcing the other members to reread irrelevant material.

2. In the first conference comment, state the objective of the conference (why the meeting has been called). Attempt to state the desired outcomes.

3. In the second conference comment, set a few of the ground rules. State the timetable for the conference, how frequently participants are to check the conference for comments, and who will be participating, and make sure to indicate any other individuals outside the conference who will be reading the comments.

4. In the third conference comment, propose a draft agenda for the conference. Clearly state that the agenda is a draft so that members will have the feeling that they are involved in a participatory event.

5. Open the conference for the first series of comments. Comments should be restricted to the gathering of more information relating to the problem. This is to make sure that the conference members can present relevant information on their perceptions of the problem. *No suggested solutions are to be given at this point.*

6. At an appropriate point, the chairman closes this initial round of input and restates the problem in light of the information received.

7. The chairman then opens the conference for solutions to the problem. The solutions should avoid specifics at this point in time. Stress general approaches that fit with corporate goals and objectives.

8. Following a solid round of suggestions, the chairman can either call for a vote or indicate his or her preferred solution. If a decision is made without voting, an explanation is in order before proceeding to the next phase.

9. The chairman then opens the discussion for proposed action plans. The objective is to determine the best method for implementing the decision.

10. Following the discussion, the chairman either calls for a vote or indicates that a certain action plan will be used.

11. The next step is task assignment. The chairman proposes a draft of the various tasks assigned to the appropriate participants to implement the action plan. Comments are then requested.

12. After the comments, the task assignments are finalized.

13. The last portion of the meeting should be the establishment of the action plan monitoring mechanism. The chairman states how frequently the members are to enter their progress reports into the conference to monitor the situation. *Ad hoc* problems are to be discussed as they arise.

14. The conference now enters a free-form mode in which reports and observations are entered. Should the implementation plan begin to have obvious problems, the problem/solution process is initiated once more.

The objective is to precisely define the steps needed to reach a solution and to give focus to the conference. Without guidance the conference can wander and lack direction. It is not uncommon for participants to send private messages to each other discussing the direction of the conference and methods of achieving a particular outcome. These messages may have a strong political overtone, and a careful chairman can see the results of private messages in the conference comments as sides are taken. Naturally, a chairman can and should use private messages to influence the process of the conference. The degree of confidential tampering should be restrained, if possible, to assure that others feel a part of the decision process and can "buy into" the solution.

## The Electronic Information Exchange System

The Electronic Information Exchange System (EIES, pronounced "eyes") was developed by the New Jersey Institute of Technology almost a decade ago to explore new issues of computer technologies as part of the decision support system. Users have been departments of the federal government, state agencies, educational institutions, and private individuals. Currently, there are over 1,000 individuals and groups using EIES on a regular basis. The applications are as varied as the users themselves, but they include preplanning for face-to-face meetings and conferences, follow-up evaluations to meetings, surveys, writing meeting minutes and reports, cooperative writing of longer documents (grants, business plans, articles), project coordination, and crisis management—just to name a few.

Recently, I was part of a national team charged with evaluating a large satellite video teleconference. Few of the team members had ever met one another prior to the program. Before the conference, the chairman introduced the team members and outlined the objectives of the evaluation effort. A list of evaluation questions was presented. Following the teleconference, each of the participants entered their responses. After all the responses had been entered, the group then shared additional reactions to the program. The chairman took the comments and developed the final evaluation report for his client. Within 24 hours of the program's conclusion, a significant amount of evaluation information had been collected; certainly there would have been no other way to gather such complete information so quickly. Even after the formal evaluation was finished, several of the members continued to enter comments, which led to further private communications and additional conferences to discuss more specific suggestions concerning visual teleconferencing.

The EIES system is both simple and sophisticated. Simple in terms of basic operation and sophisticated in terms of the vast array of options available to the users. The basic system supports private messages, public and private conferences, newsletters, notebooks, and the ability to directly link two or more communicating terminals for "live" interaction. The live feature is interesting. I have participated in several events where an individual attending a major event over 4,000 miles away acted as a court reporter and kept participants informed of the discussion taking place in a large face-to-face conference.

To support users, there are a variety of user-friendly options:

1. There is extensive word processing support for text editing and spelling correction.

2. The main computer can automatically adjust text composed on an 80-character-per-line terminal so that it will look good on a 64-character terminal.

3. There are public conferences on how to use the system which permit new users to practice entering and manipulating messages.

4. There is an extensive directory of users which contains a brief biography, address, and telephone information. Users can have

the computer search the directory for key words so that it is possible to locate others with similar interests.

5. The system operator is always available and can link directly with a user to assist with problems.

6. There is access to the power of the computer to tabulate surveys and conference votes.

7. There is a newsletter for users.

8. There are nonbusiness conferences for those interested in French, those wishing to sell items, announcements of conferences, those with new personal computers looking for operational hints, and a number of other special purposes that create a sense of community among the members of EIES.

In order to get a better "feel" for a teleconference, let me show you a sample encounter with the system.

---

### SAMPLE COMPUTER CONFERENCING SESSION ON EIES

1. WELCOME

   NAME OR #? 271

   CODE?

   NJIT Electronic Information Exchange System (032583)

2. ROBERT COWAN (ROBERT A, 271) on at 3/25/83 10:47 PM EST

   via Uninet USA Collect

3. Last Active: 3/23/83 6:35 PM

   Note: See important money-saving information. Enter:

   +CHIMO

4. LIST THOSE NOW ON LINE (Y/N)? Y
   - 16:    5:14 PM    Beverly Post (Bev,130)
   - 43:    7:45 PM    Charles Nelson (Chuck,700)
   - 47:    8:00 PM    John Ellis (JE,222)
   - 50:   10:47 PM    ROBERT COWAN (ROBERT A,271)

5. Waiting:

   1 Confirmation

   3 Private messages

   Pending:

   M 3118

   M 3250

   M 3280

6. M 3047 Received by Beverly Post (Bev,130) 3/24/83
   12:03 AM

7. M 3118 Beverly Post (Bev,130) 3/24/83 12:21 AM
   L:2
   TO: Phyllis, ROBERT A, ARLENE
   IF YOU MESSAGE 1594 OR CONTACT BY PHONE OUR
   PRESS OFFICE THEY CAN ARRANGE TO SEND YOU
   PHOTOS

8. M 3250 Charlton Price (Charlton,116) 3/24/83 7:55 PM
   L:7 KEYS:/TELESPAN/WEEKENDS/HOSPITALITY/
   A:3005
   You said that the mention of the teleconference
   seminar was in an issue of Telespan newsletter. Am
   anxious to see how they handled it. Also want to get in
   touch with them again.
   I'll be traveling the next two weeks but hope we could
   see you folks on the weekends, when I'll be home.
   Please call.
   M 3280 Jack Dawson (Jack,1599) 3/25/83 5:00 PM
   L:2 KEYS:/GRANT/NTIA/
   BOB-- CHECK TODAY'S FEDERAL REGISTER FOR
   GRANT ANNOUNCEMENT IN TELE-
   COMMUNICATIONS. LATER . . .

9. INITIAL CHOICE?
   ACCESS TO:
   | | |
   |---|---|
   | MESSAGES | (1) |
   | CONFERENCES | (2) |
   | NOTEBOOKS | (3) |
   | BULLETINS | (4) |
   | DIRECTORY | (5) |
   | EXPLANATIONS | (6) |
   | COMPOSITION | (7) |
   | MONITORING | (8) |
   INITIAL CHOICE? 2;558
   Private Conference: TELECOMMUNICATIONS IN
   HEALTHCARE (558)
   You are the only member active.

10. UP TO 29: WILSON AMES (WILL,220)

    UP TO 25: JACK DOUGLAS (DOUG,994)

    UP TO 29: Pat Schneider (Pat,567)

    UP TO 25: ROBERT COWAN (ROBERT A, 271)

    <BREAK>

11. 29 Items. CC29 Written on 2/20/83 11:15 AM

    4 New text items.

    ACCEPT ABOVE ITEMS (Y/N/#)? Y

    C558 CC26 JAMES JONES (JJ,599) 2/10/83 3:27 PM L:34

    KEYS:/CHANGE/

    One of the critical elements of computer conferencing,
    particularly the conference discussion mode, seems to
    be the ability of the moderator to stimulate discussion
    relevant to the topic at hand. This of course requires
    that the moderator spend a good deal of time monitoring
    the comments and responding or stimulating further
    response from other participants. I certainly
    <BREAK>

12. CONFERENCE CHOICE? --

    ROBERT COWAN (ROBERT A,271) OFF AT 3/19/83
    11:55 PM

13. USED:              $0.00

    PERIOD TOTAL:  $0.00

    TIME USED:          : 1

    CUMULATIVE    120: 4

---

## EXPLANATION OF EIES SESSION

1. Signing onto the system. Each user has a unique identification
   number and password.

2. The system identifies the user by number, date, and time.

3. CHIMO is the name of the electronic newsletter for all of the
   EIES members.

4. The system indicates who is currently using the system, in case I
   wanted to send someone on-line a message that would be received
   immediately.

5. Indicates that one "receipt of message" confirmation is waiting
   and three messages are waiting.

6. The system indicates precisely when a message was received by the addressee. The "M 3047" refers to the message number, in case I want to review it later or modify it and forward it to others. I also know exactly when the message was written.

7. The first message. I know that the same message was sent to two other individuals.

8. In the second message, various key words are supplied by the sender for easy retrieval. The "A:3005" refers to an associated message. In this case, I had sent a message (number 3005) to Charlton and he is responding to a comment that I made.

9. These are the basic system options. The most commonly used features are messages, conferences, notebooks, and composition (text generation).

10. After joining a private conference, a user can see the number of items read by each of the authorized participants.

11. The computer conference remembers the last message you read and will notify you when there are new messages.

12. Signoff.

13. Final cost and usage information. Cost for the session is indicated, along with the total for the billing period. The system also tracks the total number of hours a user has accumulated since first established on the system.

As you can see, EIES is not a complicated system for a beginner to use. There are a number of advanced features available once the basic skills have been mastered.

## Summary

Computer conferencing offers an excellent supplement to other teleconferencing modes, as well as providing users with excellent "stand-alone" capabilities. The benefits are many: a lower conferencing cost, reduced turnaround time on messages, reduction of telephone tag, participants always feeling in touch with the organization, increased participation, resultant face-to-face meetings shortened, items in writing with telephone message errors avoided, and participants being able to contribute when they have the time. The lack of visual and verbal cues, loss of pressure to do the work, potential for misunderstandings, and potential for managerial resistance to typing are disadvantages.

In all probability, some of the greatest growth in the teleconferencing field will be in increased audio and text communication. If you have not considered computer conferencing for your organization, you would be well advised to explore the area further.

## Chapter 12 Notes

1. "Asynchronous teleconferencing." *TeleSpan Newsletter,* July 15, 1982, 8–10.

2. M. Turoff, "The EIES experience: Electronic information exchange system." *Bulletin of the American Society for Information Services,* 4(5), 1978, 9–10.

3. "Asynchronous teleconferencing." *TeleSpan Newsletter,* July 15, 1982, 8–10.

4. J. P. Mellow, Jr., "Networking poet laureate: E-poet says micros will shatter Gutenberg literature." *80 Micro,* December 1982, 404, 406, 408.

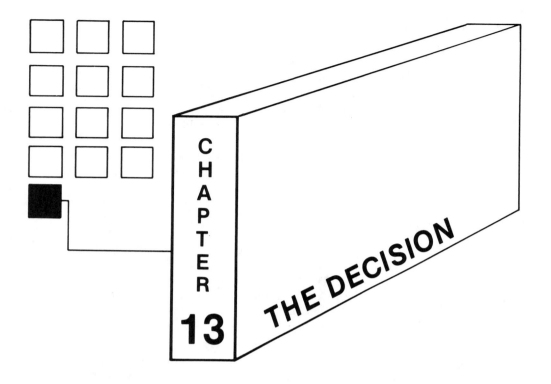

CHAPTER
13

THE DECISION

Thus far, we have reviewed the major teleconferencing modalities available. Now we come to the decision process—going through the steps to initiate a teleconferencing capability. In this section we will review the needs analysis, the financial analysis, selecting the equipment, and implementation. There is much that has been covered thus far in the book that pertains to needs assessment and implementation, so the sections dealing with those topics will briefly review some of the past statements.

## Needs Analysis

The more closely the teleconferencing effort supports the organization's mission statement, the greater the probability for success. Always try to keep in mind that the system's objectives are to assist users to be more effective in their work, to cut costs, and to enhance the firm's position in the marketplace. The raw data is difficult to acquire, but here are some hints on how to begin collecting information that might lead to the application of teleconferencing:

1. Talk with people. Informal questions concerning travel and expansion may provide valuable insight into some of the organization's communication problems. You should seek out people in education and training, marketing and sales, and management. It is best to start with those who have responsibility which extends outside the

walls of the facility. Data of interest include the level of frustration due to travel, critical training that cannot be delivered, customers lost due to time-consuming travel, the competition initiating new communication programs, and the need for greater communication between geographically separated locations to reduce coordination problems.

2. Get access to the facts. Informal discussions are a good start, but actual data is needed to support what you have learned. Since much of the travel information and examples of cost overruns due to lack of coordination require access to financial information, it may be appropriate to develop a preliminary proposal for management. The paper should state a few of the observations made, listed in prioritized order consistent with the mission statement. If you wish to develop teleconferencing for a department or division, then the request should be made to the appropriate manager. In your paper, briefly review what other companies are doing with teleconferencing. Request access to appropriate records and key individuals to conduct your survey. Provide a timetable for the study.

3. Collect the hard data. Since many managers are interested in hard savings, first look at the travel expenses, e.g., air fare, hotels, tips, dinners, transportation. Calculate the travel time involved and arrive at a travel time cost based on estimated salaries. Determine if additional staff are to be hired to assist travel-intensive employees.

4. Collect the soft data. Discuss the concept of teleconferencing with potential users. Seek their input as to the number of trips that could be displaced if a system was in place. This will be a conservative estimate, because those you approach will tend to underestimate their use of teleconferencing as a travel substitute. If they say that a system would eliminate only one or two trips per year, do not attempt to persuade them that they would use the system more. Do not push your potential users. The success of a system will depend on aggregate use, and there is more to be gained by using a low-key approach at this stage. Have the potential users estimate additional revenue that could be generated if they did not have to travel as much. The individuals may tend to overestimate what they would be able to accomplish with new free time, so you may wish to consider discounting estimates by between 10 to 50%. Try to identify problem areas that indicate communication problems, such as individuals who are too busy to travel to other locations and provide the necessary management input. Have the individuals you interview place some of their projections in writing. Having the data in writing helps when talking with management. At minimum, draft a summary of a meeting with an individual and forward it to the person for any corrections or additional comments. At least you have offered him or her an opportunity to correct your assumptions.

5. Collect media-related data. As you talk with the various potential users, seek out specific examples of visuals and other information that may indicate that a particular teleconferencing modality might be appropriate for their needs. How fast information needs to be exchanged, whether hard copy is necessary, the types of visual information used, the locations involved, and the locations that will be presenting the bulk of the information—all of these factors will impact the specific technology selected.

6. Write an interim report on your findings. Document the needs assessment process to keep management informed of your efforts. Basically, this is to keep them up-to-date. KEEP IT BRIEF. Managers have many other topics competing for their attention, and unless you maintain some visibility, there is a high probability that they will forget what your study was all about. Seek comments from management concerning areas that you might have missed or incorrect assumptions. Specify the steps you will be taking and the date for the next report.

As a result of your analysis, you should have documented evidence that both hard and soft dollars could be saved with the implementation of a teleconferencing system. You will have a reasonable idea of travel displacement, new revenues that could be generated, critical problem areas that cannot be solved without additional staff or new technology, and general communication/coordination problems that could be addressed to some degree by an advanced communication system.

## Determining The Medium

The results of your needs assessment will give you a good idea of the type of teleconferencing technology that would best suit your particular organization. Oddly enough, new users tend to opt for an audio or a satellite conferencing system as first choice. Audio conferencing is selected when the organization is looking at teleconferencing as a method of reaching a variety of locations with routine tactical communication. Those that select the satellite route tend to look at teleconferencing from a marketing approach. The one factor that you should remember is that each of the technologies has its own unique application in an organization. Teleconferencing is more than audio-only, satellites, or captured-frame communication; it is an awareness that there are many other options to face-to-face communication. Some organizations support more than one form of teleconferencing. For example, there could be weekly audio conferences between managers, a computer conferencing system to provide text support for the teleconferencing effort and strategic planning, captured-frame for education and engineering groups, and satellite communication for marketing and annual meetings. Again, look for an appropriate mix of technologies, rather than assuming that one modality will do all things well.

Obviously, cost will be a primary consideration in the development of teleconferencing. As you look at the financial section, you may wish to develop cost data on several different approaches to the problems and opportunities in your firm. Naturally, there will be a slightly different set of users for each mode, but your needs assessment will have provided you with the necessary information to determine who would be best served by a specific technology.

Briefly, let's look at some of the advantages and disadvantages of each of the modalities discussed thus far:

## Audio-Only

Advantages: low cost; able to link telephones anywhere in the world; no special equipment required; visual information can be discussed if sent to participants prior to the event; vocal inflection communicates additional information; meetings tend to take less time; financial risk low; potential for being highly interactive. Disadvantages: unable to handle *ad hoc* needs for visual information; low Pheromone Factor; lack of visual cues a problem for some participants.

## Audiographic

Advantages: able to demonstrate visual information more readily than audio-only; electronic blackboard devices permit display of limited *ad hoc* visual information; a higher Pheromone Factor than audio-only; excellent for business and educational "chalk talk" presentations; can have a high "presence" level if used intensively; uses low cost voice grade telephone lines. Disadvantages: lack of visual cues; communication costs higher than audio-only; requires special equipment; number of participating locations become limited to those with advanced equipment.

## Slow Scan Television

Advantages: able to use any visual information from a television camera; able to present images of people as well as graphics; able to use low-cost voice grade telephone lines (dedicated lines permit faster image transmission); multiple images can be discussed using computer memory; users only have to worry about the images that are to be transmitted next; sophisticated camera operation equipment not required; excellent for users who have a great need for the presentation of graphics. Disadvantages: equipment costs higher than audiographic; some negative user reaction to having their image on television; additional session time consumed in presentation of images; lacks full motion; length of image transmission time too long for some users.

## Videographics

Advantages: essentially the same as slow scan television and audiographics; users can make notations over the SSTV image; multiple-site participation in image development possible; multiple colors identify sites; preprogrammed symbols can be used; uses low cost voice grade telephone lines; highly effective for problem solving that relates to graphic information; high level of "presence." Disadvantages: full motion not possible; equipment more expensive than SSTV; communication sites limited to those with equipment.

## Full-Motion Television

Advantages: perceived as having a high Pheromone Factor; excellent for marketing purposes; excellent when motion is required; environment close to actual face-to-face meeting; fairly easy for new users to enter into the dialog; number of locations that can be reached with satellite television higher than audio-plus systems due to high number of satellite earth stations. Disadvantages: costly equipment and high communication charges; considerable user attention to the images unless camera controls are automated; high production level necessary in most situations; information security is low without scrambling.

## Computer Conferencing

Advantages: low equipment cost; communication costs low; users can participate when they have the time; a written record is provided; equality of participation possible; users can participate from any location with a telephone; considerable participation and input possible. Disadvantages: loss of visual and verbal communication cues; need for message diplomacy; some resistance to typing possible; information overload (junk mail) a problem; may be more difficult to keep participants "on the right track"; decisions may take longer.

## Summary

There is considerable overlap in each modality's potential applications, so it is necessary to take a detailed look at the precise needs of the user population. The selection of more than one medium is not uncommon. Each mode has unique advantages, but actual hands-on experience is recommended before any major purchases are contemplated. One of the major determining factors will be the costs of the technology versus the savings and benefits.

## Preparing The Financial Data

Few managers have a solid financial background. Many have developed management responsibility because of their knowledge of a product or a market, personal skills, and so forth. There are some basic reasons why it is important to develop a few budget and financial skills. First, the financial aspect of a project will be one of the top two factors in the decision process. Second, you cannot trust a financial analysis performed by a vendor; vendors will not have all the data concerning your organizational needs. Third, as you look at different equipment options, which will have differing costs and lifetimes, it is important to convert the costs to present value terms. Otherwise, you will be comparing apples with oranges. Fourth, the more that you know about finance, the greater your upward mobility in a financially driven organization.

In the following section, we will discuss the budget for a teleconferencing project in terms of capital equipment, expenses, savings, depreciation, and present value.

## Expenses

In this section we will cover the expenses associated with the project, with the exception of the actual equipment purchases.

*Personnel.* This includes all or part of the personnel expenses associated with the operation of the project. Included would be secretarial support, assistants, the project coordinator, and other individuals associated with the project at distant locations. The wages should include the base salary plus any fringe benefits.

*Communication costs.* Based on your estimates of teleconferencing frequency, locations involved, and duration, develop a monthy utilization table which is broken down by time of day. Add to your estimates an additional 20% which will be used in actually managing the network, elements such as discussions via teleconferencing on how to train users, changes in the conference schedules, and any special demonstrations that might take place. Having the data by month is necessary when obtaining quotations from the telephone company or other carriers. For example, while WATS expense increases with distance (called "bands"), it also declines with both utilization and time of day. Unfortunately, the number of hours of WATS use accumulates only during the billing month, so having the monthly estimates of teleconference use is important. The location information will permit you to determine the most economical method of reaching the various locations. Since communication costs can easily be the greatest continuing expense, it may be appropriate to get the advice of a communications consultant familiar with the various alternative rates.

*Maintenance.* Although difficult to estimate in some cases, a minimum of 10% of the purchase price per year is recommended. If the locations are rural, increase your percentage to compensate for increased charges for travel. In the case of a number of rural locations, or if it is critical that the network have minimum "down time," the purchase of additional equipment to be used in the event of a failure is recommended. Installation of the equipment can be entered as an expense or part of the capital equipment expense, but it should be included.

*Travel.* Actual visits to operational installations by you and other key decision makers may be beneficial. Along this same line, you will want to know more about teleconferencing, and expenses associated with attending one or more of the national teleconferencing seminars should be included in the budget. In addition, when a system is first implemented, there will be considerable initial travel. In order to defuse possible negative reactions to teleconferencing as impersonal, face-to-face training is recommended.

*Rent/Space.* If a dedicated teleconferencing room is established, there will be a cost associated with that area: renovation, construction, or rental. Even if the space was not being used, the electronic meeting room will cause new space to be acquired for personnel expansion.

*Supplies.* These are any consumables associated with the operation of the project. Included would be postage for visual information, audio or videotapes, and special graphics material. There are a number of journals to which you may wish to subscribe, along with one or two of the major teleconferencing newsletters.

*Insurance*. In the case of an operational network, make sure that all equipment is fully covered. You may wish to check into options that will cover a major system failure, in which costs associated with emergency repair are reimbursed. If you are conducting an expensive *ad hoc* satellite teleconference, I would strongly suggest insuring the event in case of technical problems.

*Rentals*. Equipment rental/lease is not a capital equipment expense and cannot be depreciated. Lease/purchase agreements are considered the same as equipment purchase.

*Sales and property tax*. If you work for a nonexempt organization, be sure to ask your financial people for estimates. Non- and not-for-profit organizations may be exempt from these taxes. Remember that the taxes apply to the equipment purchases and supplies, and can also apply to communication costs and maintenance.

*Education and promotion*. Education and promotion are key elements in the implementation of a teleconferencing effort. Development of training programs (audio and videotapes, training manuals) can be expensive. Artwork, typesetting, layout, and poster costs can add up.

*Consultants*. As I have recommended throughout this book, the need for input from both vendors and independent consultants is critical to the success of an operation—especially for the first-time user. In addition to the front-end advice on the development of a system, plan for an additional visit in six to nine months for assistance with the project implementation review. Consultants are available to act as facilitators in computer conferencing systems, assisting in conference design and guidance, needs assessment, equipment and room design, development of training programs, training audio bridge operators, evaluation, and user training.

## Hard Savings

Hard savings consists of actual dollars that will be saved, as opposed to the more vague productivity savings.

*Personnel*. Individuals could be laid off due to other workers becoming more productive. If a planned position will be eliminated, it is also treated as a hard savings.

*Travel*. All expenses associated with travel that will be eliminated are hard savings. Transportation, meals, and room costs are included. If possible, try to review actual expense report sheets to obtain projections, since there may be other entertainment expenses.

## Soft Savings

Soft savings are productivity or value-added savings that do not result in additional available cash to the organization.

*Personnel*. The primary issue in this category is the value of a worker's time. The extent to which a value is attached to nonproductive time (time in travel) varies from organization to organization. Some managers will say that professional level nonproductive time should not be given any value, since the professional is paid to "do whatever it takes to get the job done." This means that if a salesman spends two hours on the road during the day and does not get the paper work finished, he is expected to work late to get it done. Other managers will place a value on nonproductive time equal to productive time. In other words, a $50-an-hour professional on the road for two hours costs the company $100 in nonproductive time. At the extreme, a few managers will assign a value to a professional's time based on the individual's worth to the company, not the actual wages paid. As an example, the time of an $80,000 salesman who generates $1,000,000 in sales is worth more than just the $80,000; more available productive time may net revenue beyond a simple hourly wage. On the average, many corporations assign the same value to nonproductive time that is used for productive time in order to compute travel time savings.

Another personnel-related savings that is often overlooked is associated with the mass distribution of information. For example, a personnel manager who needs to present a two-hour seminar on benefits to ten locations will only have to give the presentation one time instead of ten. So in addition to the travel time savings to the ten locations, there is an additional savings of nine presentations, for a total savings of 18 hours. If there are a number of locations to be linked via teleconferencing, the mass distribution savings can be significant.

*Publicity*. If handled properly, the fact that an organization is using teleconferencing can result in considerable free publicity. It is fairly common to see articles on the organization's efforts in major trade magazines and in the local press. Some corporations have included in their savings analysis the projected cost of traditional publicity which would result in a similar exposure.

*Enhanced productivity*. Boeing reported that its teleconferencing system enabled it to finish a contract 30 days ahead of schedule, saving hundreds of thousands of dollars. An organization may wish to consider tracking projects which use teleconferencing to see if the new communications medium results in projects being completed earlier than the historical average. It is recommended that firms contemplating teleconferencing review work objectives and increase expectations in light of probable productivity increases.

*Increased revenue*. Like savings, revenue contributes to a positive bottom line. If there is a likelihood that teleconferencing will result in increased sales or client activity, then that should be factored into the analysis. Some firms base their territory on the driving time from the headquarters. Teleconferencing can expand the territory, while retaining the similar level of communication.

## The Financial Analysis

Once the raw data has been assembled, then it is time to plug the information into the analysis. In this section, we will take a look at the capital purchase, depreciation, tax computations, present value, and consolidation of the information.

### Capital Purchases

The purchase of major hardware (items over $200) can provide an organization with some immediate tax benefits. The Investment Tax Credit (ITC) is available to taxable organizations as an incentive to purchase new equipment with an expected life of seven to ten years. At the present time, the tax credit is 10 percent of the purchase price of the equipment. That means that a $50,000 purchase will result in an ITC of $5,000. It is important to remember that the ITC is a *tax credit*, not simply a reduction in gross income. After computation of the company's taxable income and tax, the ITC reduces the tax liability directly. There have been some recent IRS changes that may impact the ITC; check with your financial officer.

## Depreciation

Depreciable life is a term used in defining a standardized life for a piece of equipment. Equipment may be "useful" for either less or more time than the depreciable life. There are several ways of computing depreciation: straight-line and double-declining balance. The following calculations do not include any salvage value of the equipment. One of the reasons is that in seven to ten years the equipment will be worth very little, given the steady decline of electronic equipment prices and the introduction of new technology. Any residual value will probably be negated by the time, energy, and expense in trying to find someone to buy the equipment.

*Straight-line depreciation.* The straight-line approach is the most simple. Literally, you take the purchase price of the equipment and divide it by the depreciable life. For example, a piece of equipment with a seven year life would depreciate like this:

| Year | Value | Depreciation |
|------|-------|--------------|
| 1 | $5,000 | $714 |
| 2 | 4,286 | 714 |
| 3 | 3,572 | 714 |
| 4 | 2,858 | 714 |
| 5 | 2,144 | 714 |
| 6 | 1,430 | 714 |
| 7 | 716 | 716 |

For a variety of reasons, it is better to accelerate the depreciation of equipment at a faster rate.

*Double-declining balance.* In this method, the value of the equipment for each year is divided by its depreciable life and multiplied by two.

| Year | Value | Depreciation | Formula |
|------|-------|--------------|---------|
| 1 | $5,000 | $1,429 | ($5,000/7) × 2 |
| 2 | 3,571 | 1,020 | (3,571/7) × 2 |
| 3 | 2,551 | 729 | (2,551/7) × 2 |
| 4 | 1,822 | 521 | (1,822/7) × 2 |
| 5 | 1,301 | 372 | (1,301/7) × 2 |
| 6 | 929 | 265 | (929/7) × 2 |
| 7 | 664 | 664 | (remaining balance) |

There are other approaches to depreciation so that there is zero-value remaining in the last year, but the formula is a little more complex and you may wish to review the technique with your financial officers.

## Present Value

The rationale behind present value (PV) is to give the user an understanding of the future value of money. Given our inflation rate, I would certainly prefer to receive $5,000 now than seven to ten years from now. By investing of the money, hopefully, it would be worth more in the future to compensate for the declining value of the dollar. Given that teleconferencing should be viewed as an "investment," it is appropriate to compare the financial benefits of teleconferencing with investing the money in some other venture. Key to the PV calculation is the "discount rate"—the rate at which the dollar is devalued or the company's normal return on investment. The precise rate used will vary from organization to organization and is normally higher than the interest rate available if the money were placed in a long-term, high-yield investment. If there is a great deal of ambiguity about the assumptions used in the development of the cost/savings data, the discount rate may be even higher. While it is essential that you consult with your accountant, let's look at the PV formula and then perform several quick calculations:

$$\text{Present Value} = \text{Future Value} (1 + i)^n$$

where "i" is the discount rate and "n" is the number of years following the investment.

For those with personal computers, a program in BASIC would look like this:

```
10 INPUT "ENTER THE DISCOUNT RATE";DR
20 INPUT "ENTER THE YEAR (99 TO END)";Y
30 IF Y = 99 THEN END
40 INPUT "ENTER THE FUTURE VALUE";FV
50 PV = FV/((1 + DR)↑Y)
60 PRINT "THE PRESENT VALUE OF"; FV; " IN YEAR";
   Y; " IS "; PV
70 GOTO 20
```

After you subtract expenses from savings, use the PV to determine the cost of the project in present-day dollars. Rather than going through the complex formula each time, it is a little easier to develop a PV factor which can be multiplied by your savings-minus-expenses line. Using a Future Value of $1.00, the factors look like this:

Discount Rate = 15%

**YEAR**

|              | 0      | 1      | 2      | 3      | 4      | 5      |
|--------------|--------|--------|--------|--------|--------|--------|
| Future Value | $1.00  | $1.00  | $1.00  | $1.00  | $1.00  | $1.00  |
| PV Factor    | 1.0    | .8696  | .7561  | .6575  | .5718  | .4972  |

Discount Rate = 20%

**YEAR**

|  | 0 | 1 | 2 | 3 | 4 | 5 |
|---|---|---|---|---|---|---|
| Future Value | $1.00 | $1.00 | $1.00 | $1.00 | $1.00 | $1.00 |
| PV Factor | 1.0 | .8333 | .6944 | .5787 | .4823 | .4019 |

As you can see, it is best to try to recover your investment as early as possible. After a few years go by, a fairly significant positive cash flow is necessary to offset early losses.

In order for any of this to make any real sense, you have to add up the present-value cash flows (savings minus expenses) for all the years of the project. Generally, a five-year projection is all that is necessary. Because of our economy, it may be risky to base a venture on anticipated profits beyond year five. This will give you the "net present value" (NPV) of your project. If the NPV is close to zero, then your project will provide about the same investment opportunity as a long-term note, and your firm may wish to consider the project more in terms of marketing appeal and other soft benefits. If the NPV is positive, then it would appear that the project is a worthwhile investment.

## Cash Flow Spread Sheet

Now that we have covered most of the financial bases, you can put your financial data on a spread sheet for analysis. Here is a sample spread sheet:

|  | 1 | 2 | 3 | 4 | 5 |
|---|---|---|---|---|---|
| Capital Purchase | ___ | ___ | ___ | ___ | ___ |
| ITC | ___ | ___ | ___ | ___ | ___ |
| 1. SUB-TOTAL | ___ | ___ | ___ | ___ | ___ |
| Expenses | ___ | ___ | ___ | ___ | ___ |
| Savings | ___ | ___ | ___ | ___ | ___ |
| 2. SUB-TOTAL | ___ | ___ | ___ | ___ | ___ |
| 3. DEPRECIATION | ___ | ___ | ___ | ___ | ___ |
| CASH FLOW (1 + 2 + 3) | ___ | ___ | ___ | ___ | ___ |
| PRESENT VALUE FACTOR | ___ | ___ | ___ | ___ | ___ |
| PRESENT VALUE CASH FLOW | ___ | ___ | ___ | ___ | ___ |
| CUMULATIVE FLOW | ___ | ___ | ___ | ___ | ___ |

Now you have all the necessary information for your financial officer to review concerning the project. There is one final factor that the accounting people may add to the spread sheet.

## Taxes

Taxes may have some impact on your calculations, but do not attempt to calculate the tax impact yourself. The tax laws change too much and vary from state to state. Basically, taxes impact your revenue and expense picture, with taxes reducing the impact of your revenue faster than reducing your expenses. Since this aspect can be confusing, talk it over with your firm's accountants. Organizations not subject to taxation certainly save themselves considerable additional calculation.

## The Proposal

Now you have done all of your needs analysis and financial homework and are ready to develop the proposal. Each organization has its own unique set of questions that a proposal should address, but let's go over some guidelines. Executives reviewing the proposal are concerned with several aspects. First, does the idea make sense? If the concept does not make common sense, then the proposal may have difficulty. In addition, the project should also address the future expansion of the project: "Where is all of this going?" Second, does the idea make sense for the organization? While an idea may be sound, it may not be appropriate for the firm in light of the strategic plans and the mission statement. Third, what is the cost of the project and what are the benefits? Finally, do the financial assumptions appear to be complete? This last step is tied closely with the third question, but it should be considered a separate item.

Harry Newton has proposed several steps that should be followed in the preparation of a proposal that has been modified for teleconferencing:

1. Find out what business your company is in.
2. Determine the one thing your company does better than anyone else and how teleconferencing can improve that capability.
3. Seek out the company's new directions and expansion (new businesses and new products).
4. Find out what is happening in the business environment over which your firm has no direct control (federal and state regulations, for example).
5. Note related developments in other communication technologies and office automation. How will they impact your efforts?
6. Develop scenarios for the business, marketing, and technological alternatives.
7. Finally, determine the unknowns, the assumptions, the anticipated time frames, and the fall-back strategies.[1]

No executive expects you to know the future. Your projections are not cast in concrete, but the very fact that you have gone through the process communicates to management that you have taken the necessary steps to ensure the success of the project and to determine the best organizational match.

As you write your proposal, it may be wise to develop the financial analysis using some of the harder savings; there may be too many variables beyond your control. Instead, pay special attention to weaving those softer savings into the proposal narrative so that if the NPV is marginal, there will be additional incentives for the project, but they will not be overtly included in the project's evaluation criteria. One final thought as you consider the various teleconferencing options: if teleconferencing is new to your organization, seek to put into place a system with strong, rapid, easy, and quantifiable cost savings. This will give you organizational credibility and will make it easier to get approval for other more esoteric proposals.

## Getting Your Equipment

Since the number of vendors and equipment options in the teleconferencing field are increasing, it is important to approach equipment purchase in an organized fashion. Here are some of the steps which will lead to a greater probability that you will have the kind of system you want.

### System Functions

What do you want your system to do? Make a list of mandatory and optional functions the system is to perform. This is your teleconferencing "wish list." You should have a pretty good idea of what the system should be able to do from your needs assessment. Try to think in terms of what the users need to carry out their communication. By prioritizing, you will be focusing your mind on the most important elements. Develop your thoughts in a narrative fashion; walk the readers through the operation. Do not be afraid to be wordy; the more the vendors understand why you want a system to perform a certain way, the more creative they can be in meeting the need. If you do have some technical capability in the organization, I would strongly recommend that you avoid being too technical. Remember that the state-of-the-art is changing so rapidly it would not be in your best interests to get locked into a design specification that is obsolete.

### Request For Information

The request for information (RFI) is your way of picking the vendors' brains. Send your narrative description of the system to all those that might have the remotest possibility of responding. What you will be looking for are various approaches to the design and new product enhancements that have not been widely released. In addition, vendors may indicate that their experience has shown that one or more of your ideas do not work well. Do not take this as an insult; rather consider their comments as an opportunity to rethink your approach. The RFI is really an opportunity for the vendors to introduce you to new products, and it can be a learning experience. If a vendor makes a suggestion that opens new doors, then consider the RFI exercise a success.

### Request For Proposal

Now you are getting down to business. Once you have reviewed the RFI and have reprioritized your mandatory and optional list, you are ready for the request for proposal (RFP) (some call this a Request for Quotation as well). First, consult with your purchasing agent for suggestions concerning the wording of the RFP. Some of the items that you might want to include are:

1. The right to reject any or all of the proposals. Do not lock yourself into the lowest bidder.
2. Systems must meet your stated specifications. Vendors may be required to prove that their equipment meets those specifications.
3. Welcome alternative proposals.
4. Set a cut-off date beyond which proposals will not be considered.
5. Have the vendor warrantee the equipment for one year.
6. Make sure appropriate training is included, both operational and technical. Request a fixed price for additional training should you have staff turnover.
7. Make sure there is *one* vendor responsible for potential interface problems should there be a mix of hardware.
9. Be sure the vendor includes sufficient replacement equipment in case of a hardware failure and states how major equipment problems will be handled.
10. Each proposal should include a list of references and the firm's financial statement.

Following the issuance of the RFP, hold a bidders' conference at which the vendors can clarify points in your proposal. Make sure that the vendors have ample time to review the RFP prior to the conference. Tape-record the conference, have it transcribed, read it to make sure your responses are correct, and send the edited transcript to the vendors as an addendum to the RFP. If a vendor calls with a question, make sure you write down question and response for your records.

### RFP Analysis

Many times attempting to determine the best RFP is frustrating at best. Sometimes you might think that putting the vendor names on a dart board and just throwing blindly would be easier. The biggest problem will be in trying to sort out how well a response meets your mandatory and optional needs. There is a fairly easy way to approach the problem. First, return to your prioritized list of needs. Second, determine a "weighting factor" for each of the priorities. Do not give equal weight to every item. Since you ranked the items, you should feel that one item is more important than another and your weighting factors should so indicate.

Another common mistake is to decrease the rating factors in a linear fashion. For example,

| Priority | Weighting Factor |
|----------|------------------|
| 1 | 5 |
| 2 | 4 |
| 3 | 3 |
| 4 | 2 |
| 5 | 1 |

Unfortunately, this approach may not take into account that priorities 1 and 2 are much more important than 3, 4, and 5. Your factors should try to reflect as closely as possible your actual assessment of their importance.

| Priority | Weighting Factor |
|----------|------------------|
| 1 | 8 |
| 2 | 7 |
| 3 | 4 |
| 4 | 3 |
| 5 | 1 |

Next, develop a form that includes enough space for your priorities, weighting factors, and the vendors. For each square, assign a value which relates to how well the vendor's response meets the priority (5 = excellent and 1 = low). Be sure to leave enough room to make notes concerning unusual characteristics associated with a vendor's response to your priority areas. After you enter the vendor's value, multiply each value by the weighting factor to obtain a vendor score for each priority. Then add all the scores to arrive at a total, which will indicate the most logical choice for the contract.

| Priority | WF | Vendor 1 Value/Score | Vendor 2 Value/Score | Vendor 3 Value/Score |
|----------|-----|----------------------|----------------------|----------------------|
| 1 | 8 | 3/24 | 3/24 | 4/64 |
| 2 | 7 | 5/35 | 2/14 | 4/28 |
| 3 | 4 | 3/12 | 4/16 | 5/20 |
| 4 | 3 | 2/6 | 3/9 | 4/12 |
| 5 | 1 | 5/1 | 3/3 | 4/4 |
| **TOTAL SCORE** | | 78 | 66 | 128 |

This approach will provide a much clearer indication of the best product choice for your situation.

If there are any final negotiations involved, there are several points worth remembering. Be sure and focus on the most important points; do not get sidetracked by minor points. Give yourself a little time to think; do not sign on the dotted line too quickly. Do not be overly concerned about getting the lowest price. A recent article in *The Business Owner* (1983) made an interesting statement worth remembering:

> It's unwise to pay too much,
> And it's unwise to pay too little.
> When you pay too much, you lose a little
> money, that is all.
> When you pay too little, you sometimes lose
> everything,
> Because the thing you bought was incapable
> of doing the thing you bought it to do.
> The common law of business balance prohibits
> paying too little and getting a lot.[2]

## Summary

The decision process is never easy. It requires thought and attention to detail. By following some of the suggestions in this chapter, you will have explored the various options and performed the necessary financial analysis to determine whether teleconferencing is indicated. By preparing the proposal with the organization in mind, you will be enhancing both the system's probability of success and the proposal's probability of approval. Finally, you have some guidelines for dealing with vendors that will assist you in assessing the offerings in light of prioritized needs. Remember, there are always risks in business and there always will be. Even if your proposal is not accepted, you will have learned more in the process that will benefit you in the future. As the saying goes: "HIGH RISK, HIGH REWARD!"

## Chapter 13 Notes

1. H. Newton, "Communication lines." *Business Communications Review*, January-February 1981, 31–35.

2. "Negotiations: How to get what you want at the 'best' price." *The Business Owner*, January 1983, 10–12.

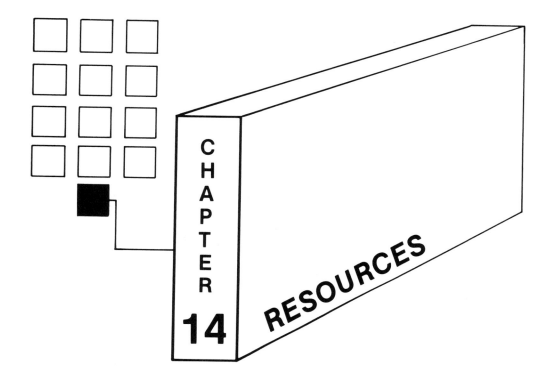

# CHAPTER 14

# RESOURCES

The field of teleconferencing is changing very rapidly. New equipment is being introduced every month. New office automation equipment is starting to feature options which support teleconferencing efforts. New users of teleconferencing are trying exciting variations in their approaches to teleconferencing. This chapter will seek to provide some suggestions as to literature, seminars, and educational programs not mentioned in the previous text that may be of interest to you. The following information is not exhaustive, but rather very selective. As you develop expertise, you will discover new avenues of information, but the information covered here will get you started.

## TeleSpan

A few years ago, Elliot Gould initiated the *TeleSpan Newsletter,* which specializes in the latest information on new equipment, current teleconferencing activity, new regulations and tariffs, and case studies from all sectors of the economy. The articles are generally brief and to the point. Included with each article are all the necessary telephone numbers to get more information. One of the more interesting aspects of the newsletter is the special features on user responses to new technology. For example, *TeleSpan* recently hosted a ''progressive dinner'' in which participants were able to test many audio conferencing bridges in sequence for evaluation purposes. In a rather unique twist, others could listen by dialing a "900" number. Truly a unique approach. *TeleSpan* also provides readers with commentary from other teleconferencing users around the country that cuts to the heart of some of the implementation problems they faced—no holds barred. With no advertising, *TeleSpan* is free to act as teleconferencing's *Consumer Report* and has a high credibility rating in my opinion. The annual subscription rate is $115 and is well worth the money. I would let many other subscriptions lapse before discontinuing *TeleSpan*.

In 1983, *TeleSpan* produced the *TeleSpan's Definitive Guide to Teleconferencing Products and Services.* For the beginner and the seasoned veteran alike, this 150-page notebook is one of the most complete collections of teleconferencing-related products and services available. For those interested in teleconferencing, this publication is required reading. As with the *Newsletter,* the *Guide* has complete address, telephone number, and contact individual information. Products are briefly described, and price ranges are included. Included is an excellent glossary of terms, which is constantly being refined in the *Newsletter.* In order to make the most of the *Guide,* however, the reader should be familiar with some of the more common terms and have a basic understanding of the technologies involved. The technical information presented early in this book should provide you with the necessary background to understand the *Guide.*

As you can tell, I am very impressed by the *TeleSpan* offerings. The *Newsletter* and *Guide* are not the typical high-gloss publications found in the electronics industry, and that is part of their appeal. The publications get down to basics and provide solid survival information. Remember that one of the reasons that your firm may wish to enter teleconferencing is for competitive edge, but you will not be able to maintain your position without keeping current with the ever changing state-of-the-art. Address: *TeleSpan,* 50 West Palm Street, Altadena, CA 91001, 201-797-5482.

## Publications

There are a number of relevant publications you may wish to receive as part of your continuing education. Not only do each of the following publications have excellent articles, but they include information on new products on the marketplace.

1. *Business Communications Review.* 36 South Washington Street, Hinsdale, IL 60521. $54 annually. Jerry Goldstone produces an excellent publication which deals with a broad scope of communication issues. While the focus of the publication is on telephone technology, there have been a growing number of articles on teleconferencing, business planning, and electronic mail. The regular contributions by Ronald Frank and Harry Newton are excellent. No advertising.

2. *Computer Decisions.* P.O. Box 13802, Philadelphia, PA 19101. $28 annually. The bulk of this glossy publication is computer-related

articles, but there have been a growing number of articles on electronic mail and how computers can become a larger part of a decision support system. The jargon in the advertising can be overwhelming, but be patient; after reading a few of the articles, the jargon becomes understandable.

3. *Data Communications.* McGraw-Hill Building, 1221 Avenue of the Americas, New York, NY 10020. $18 annually. A technical hard hitter, but the articles are understandable. There have been excellent articles on teleconferencing, electronic mail, videotex, portable communication terminals, and the latest trends in networking. As with many of the other technical publications, the true value is in the concepts being proposed, not the actual technical details. Advertising.

4. *Desktop Computing.* 80 Pine Street, Peterborough, NH 03458. $25 annually. Wayne Green is outspoken and controversial—and good. Starting by publishing material for amateur radio operators, Green has branched out into the computer field. His editorials are well worth the price of the magazine. Although he has a technical background, his ideas challenge readers to view the emerging technology from a different perspective. He always maintains a "bottom line" approach to his ideas, which adds to his comments. The articles are for businessmen who are interested in what computers can do for them, not how they work. With the increased market penetration of smaller computers, anyone considering electronic mail or computer conferencing should be aware of the personal computing devices on the market. Advertising.

5. *Educational and Industrial Television.* C.S. Tepfer Publishing Co., 51 Sugar Hollow Road, Danbury, CT 06810. $14.75 annually. EITV now has regular features on teleconferencing, although from a satellite/full-motion video approach. EITV is aimed at those involved in the production of television programs. There are occasional articles on how to improve visual images, which can be helpful to non-production-oriented individuals. Advertising.

6. *The Futurist.* 4916 St. Elmo Avenue, Bethesda, MD 20814. $20 annually. Published by the World Future Society, *The Futurist* is a superior magazine. While some may consider the articles as "off-the-wall science fiction," the authors are well known experts in business, education, and industry. There have been a number of communications and Office-of-the-Future-related articles in *The Futurist* over the past year. The World Future Society's 1982 conference on "Communications and the Future" was outstanding, and selected portions appeared in the magazine, as well as in a special WFS publication on the conference. The most interesting aspect of *The Futurist* is its attention to the IMPACT of

technology on our lives today and tomorrow. As a sidelight, there are a number of local WFS societies which host their own special-interest programs. Participation in these meetings can be most enlightening. Minimal advertising.

7. *High Technology.* P.O. Box 2810, Boulder, CO 80322. $15 annually. An outstanding magazine. All the latest technologies from bioengineering to computer sciences are explained in layman's terms. In addition to the articles are business outlook "snap shots" for investors and stock reports. Advertising.

8. *Modern Office Technology.* P.O. Box 91368, Cleveland, OH 44101. $30 annually. This magazine takes a fairly broad-brush look at the work environment, with emphasis on how the office is being enhanced by technology. Subjects of articles range from facsimile to typewriters to computers to satellites. The articles are aimed at giving managers decision information, rather than explaining the inner workings of the technology. Advertising.

9. *Satellite Communications.* 6430 South Yosemite Street, Englewood, CO 80111. $20 annually. The editor, Kim Degnan, has been actively involved in the satellite communications business for a number of years. Her work in Washington and with consulting firms gives Kim an excellent background for leading this publication, which deals with satellite applications and technology.

10. *Telecommunications.* 610 Washington Street, Dedham, MA 02026. $36 annually. This magazine not only gives you the latest information on satellite systems, but gives you a world-wide perspective as well. The articles are both practical and introduce readers to state-of-the-art communication systems.

11. *Telemarketing.* Technology Marketing Building, 17 Park Street, Norwalk, CT 06851. $39 annually. This is a high-gloss, well-thought-out publication that covers the telecommunications front from a marketing perspective. There have been several fine articles on audio and video teleconferencing. This is an excellent publication that your marketing people should receive to see how a multiple modality approach can work to increase sales. Advertising.

12. *Video Systems.* P.O. Box 12912, Overland Park, KS 66212. $25 annually. If you are interested in every aspect of video communication, then this magazine should be on your list. Past articles have covered everything from production to video art to satellites to 3-D television. I think that the articles have become more thoughtful over the past several years, and while there is still a fair amount of "how to" information in the publication, there have also been extremely interesting items on the future of the industry. Advertising.

If you subscribe to even half of these magazines, you will learn much about the industry. I should add that the prices quoted here may change, and I would recommend you contact the publishers for the current prices. For those in the industry, some of the journals may be available at no charge.

## Books

There are few books on the topic of teleconferencing available, but new offerings will be appearing as the demand increases. The books listed here serve two purposes: to provide additional information concerning teleconferencing and to provide some insight as to the emerging integrated nature of information systems.

1. *Electronic Meetings: Technical Alternatives and Social Choices* by Robert Johansen, Jacques Vallee, and Kathleen Spangler (Reading, Mass.: Addison-Wesley, 1979). The book takes a critical look at teleconferencing and the promise of increased communication effectiveness. Included in the book are a series of scenarios which highlight the strengths and weaknesses of the various modalities available (audio, video, and computer conferencing.). Required reading.

2. *Global Talk* by Joseph Pelton (Rockville, Ind.: Sijthoff and Noordhoff, 1981). An interesting approach to the emerging trends in global communication. This book may be of interest to communicators in multinational corporations.

3. *Imperial Earth* by Arthur C. Clarke (New York: Ballantine Books, 1979). Although this book is science fiction, Clarke presents one of the best descriptions of integrated personal communication and teleconferencing I have read. His descriptions have been the basis for some of my system design objectives.

4. *Megatrends* by John Naisbitt (New York: Warner Books, 1982). Naisbitt's view of our changing environment, especially his commentary on the information age, is worth reading. The book's popularity with upper-level management may assist you in promoting some of the networking aspects of teleconferencing. Although Naisbitt feels that teleconferencing lacks the "high-touch" aspect of face-to-face meetings, there is no question that some of the modalities and approaches described in this book would appeal to his belief that information must be managed in a more productive manner.

5. *Profiles of the Future.* by Arthur C. Clarke (New York: Popular Library, 1977). Originally written for major corporations, the book provides some insightful glances at classic failures of individuals to move with the technology flow.

6. *TeleGuide: A Handbook for Video-Teleconference Planners* by the Public Service Satellite Consortium (Washington, D.C.). A good analysis of the steps necessary to ensure a good satellite event. The PSSC brings many years of experience to the book, and it can be most helpful.

7. *The Network Nation: Human Communication via Computer* by Starr Roxanne Hiltz and Murray Turoff (Reading, Mass.: Addison-Wesley, 1978). A classic work on the emergence of new human networks via computer-based text systems. Many in the field consider this book required reading.

8. *Teleconferencing: A Practical Guide To Teaching By Telephone* by Ricki Ann Bronstein, Jack E. Gill, and Elmer W. Koneman. (Chicago, ILL.: Society of Clinical Pathologists Press, 1982). An excellent book on the educational applications of audio teleconferencing. Good sections on delivery styles and preparation of visual information.

In each of the books, review the bibliography for items which may be applicable to your organization.

## Conferences

There are a host of conferences which specialize in teleconferencing being held each month. Of the group, there are two worth special consideration.

*Teleconferencing and Interactive Media.* Presented by the Center for Interactive Programs at the University of Wisconsin Extension at Madison, Wisconsin, each May. For a number of years, Lorne Parker and Chris Olgren have hosted one of the best conferences on teleconferencing. Of course, there are the traditional presentations by vendors, but the real satisfaction is in meeting kindred souls and sharing war stories. The programs also include presentations from users in all the modalities included in this book, but with concentration on audio and video systems. Those who attend are from both education and industry, and I have found the educators more willing to share the pitfalls and problems than the corporate telecommunicators. Contact Chris Olgren at 608-262-4342.

*PSSC's Users Conference.* Held in Washington, D.C. each October, the Public Service Satellite Consortium's annual meeting is an excellent forum for those interested in satellite communications. The attendees represent major corporations and government, with some educational representation. The speakers are from high levels of government, and the presentations tend to be concerned with policy and impact issues. In addition to the speakers, the PSSC hosts a variety of workshops. Contact the PSSC at 202-331-1154.

Each month, the *TeleSpan Newsletter* highlights other conferences and seminars around the country. Many of the periodicals I have mentioned include such a calendar, but *TeleSpan*'s tends to be more complete.

## Formal Education

For those interested in a more intensive educational experience covering a broad spectrum of telecommunication issues, the most logical choice is the Interactive Telecommunications Program at New York University. Some of our country's finest minds in the field are at the NYU program. Students can explore both teleconferencing and the newer medium of teletext. The broad background of the graduates make them excellent choices to implement and direct corporate and educational teleconferencing programs. The program's main attraction is that it concentrates on the human factor aspects of the media, rather than the purely technical portions. Today, there are more than enough individuals available who can handle the electronic portions of teleconferencing, but the missing ingredient has been those sensitive to human communication issues who can direct the technicians to develop the appropriate hardware so that the communication system can support an organization's unique information exchange problems. Contact the Interactive Telecommunications Program, School of the Arts, New York University, 725 Broadway, New York, NY 10003, 212-598-3338.

## International Teleconferencing Association

Literature and conferences are one way to keep pace with the changes in the field, but joining an organization of teleconferencing users can provide access to valuable human resources. The ITCA is a recently formed association for those interested in the field. Its membership consists of many of the "old hands" in teleconferencing, as well as the newer users of the technology. Promotion, education, and information exchange are some of the objectives the ITCA will be addressing over the next few years. In addition, the ITCA plans to become active in the regulatory and legislative areas as well. For more information, contact the ITCA at 1299 Woodside Drive, Suite 101, McLean, VA 22102, 703-556-6115.

## Consultants

At the present time, there are many teleconferencing consultants across the nation. Unfortunately, there are few consultants I would classify as excellent. In selecting a consultant, check for the following:

1. What is the consultant's track record? Does he/she have *direct* experience with the type of teleconferencing you want to investigate?

2. Has the consultant supplied a list of past customers? Be sure to call at least three and see how well the consultant performed for them.

3. Is the consultant's philosophy of communication similar to your firm's? If not, WATCH OUT! The consultant's product may not fit in with your objectives. You can get a feel for the consultant's

approach through telephone calls and by reading any papers the consultant has provided.

4. What contacts does the consultant have with other experts? The teleconferencing field can be complex, and *no one* knows it all. You want to feel confident that the consultant will tap other resources to ensure the success of your effort. You want to avoid the situation where you are providing ''on-the-job training'' for a consultant. A good consultant will let you know his or her strengths *and* weaknesses.

If you are looking for consultants, first approach the vendors and have them recommend several you can contact. In all probability, the vendors will have had some dealings with the consultants they recommend, and it is in their best interests to recommend reliable individuals or firms. It is also probable that they will recommend consultants who have purchased the vendor products, so be careful about the recommendations. Apply the above criteria to find the best match. *TeleSpan* has been accumulating a list of consultants, some of which appear in the *TeleSpan Guide*. While there is no organization that can give you a list of all the consultants, a few phone calls will provide you with a list from which you can start.

## Other Firms Worth Noting

In addition to the firms that have been discussed in depth, there are several other companies that deserve mentioning.

### Ad Hoc Production Companies

1. Spotlight Presents, New York, N.Y.
2. TAP Productions, Norwalk, Conn.
3. TeleConcepts, New York, N.Y.
4. TNT Communications, New York, N.Y.

### Ad Hoc Distribution Companies

1. HI-NET Communications, Memphis, Tenn.
2. Public Service Satellite Consortium, Washington, D.C. (mentioned in the text).
3. Robert Wold Company, Los Angeles, Calif.
4. VideoNet, Woodland Hills, Calif.
5. VideoStar Connections, Atlanta, Ga.

### Engineering Consultants

Richard K. Miller & Associates, Alpharetta, Ga.

**System Designs**

1. ISSACOM, Atlanta, Ga. (mentioned in the text).
2. Peirce-Phelps, Video Systems Division, Philadelphia, Pa.

**Audio Bridging**

1. Connex International, Danbury, Conn. (mentioned in the text).
2. Kellogg Communications, Denver, Colo.

Again, the best way to locate the best firm to serve your needs is to first purchase a copy of *TeleSpan*'s *Definitive Guide to Teleconferencing Products and Services.*

## Summary

Even though teleconferencing has been with us for many years, widespread interest has only recently developed. There is no single source of information that covers all the aspects of teleconferencing. The state-of-the-art is changing both in the area of technology and in the understanding of the human factors. Much like any other area of mediated communication, successful teleconferencing is both a science and an art. Research continues to seek out the key factors, while daily practitioners continue to gather anecdotal information on approaches which work in selected environments. Unfortunately, the experimental research to date only gives us vague clues as to the potential of teleconferencing in larger group settings. We still have little insight about new electronic group process techniques for smaller, multisite encounters. For this reason, it is essential for anyone considering a major teleconferencing effort to keep current with the activity of others. If teleconferencing is to be part of your competitive advantage, simply getting started is not enough. You must actively seek out new information and applications and filter that information to other users and potential users in your organization. The broader the participant base in teleconferencing, the greater the potential benefit. Your strategic plan must include ongoing surveillance of the field and integration of that information to maintain your competitive investment.

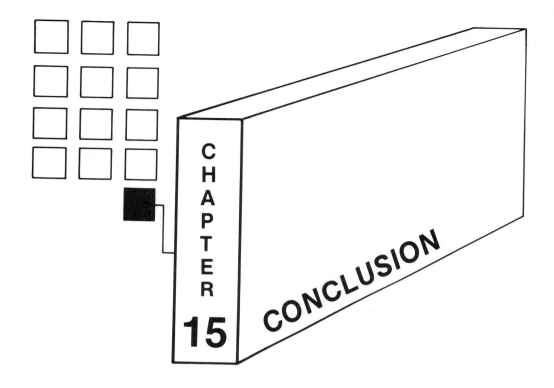

**C H A P T E R 15**

**CONCLUSION**

**W**e have covered quite a bit of territory in this introductory book to teleconferencing. As you have learned, there are many teleconferencing options currently available and more will be emerging over the next few years.

/ **Trends** /

There are three major trends worth watching over the next few years:

1. The increasing number of combination telephone/microcomputer devices will begin to have an impact on teleconferencing. These devices have telephone directories and other voice support features, while also providing computer functions and serving as communication terminals to access larger computers. It is not difficult to imagine a group of users sitting at their work stations, with their telephones linked via audio conference and their terminals linked via computer conference, discussing charts and graphs prepared earlier. Along this same line, we may see conferences in which both voice and computer information have been stored so that we can gain the advantages of both textual and voice store-and-forward communications.

2. Continuing progress will be made in the compression of video images. At transmission speeds below 56 Kbps, visually based teleconferencing will become more affordable and usable by middle managers who deal primarily in static images, but who also need some motion capabilities.

3. The desirability of videographics will increase as costs decline. The advantages of full-motion notations on static images will create additional demand for such equipment.

All of these trends will lead to the development of what Arthur C. Clarke calls "COMSOLES"—COMmunication conSOLES. These devices will support:

1. Advanced voice communication support.

2. Computer communication and local computing.

3. High resolution monitors for the display of computer graphics and slow scan or compressed video.

4. Stylus devices for videographic notations.

5. Removable storage so that events and notations can be recorded locally or prepared ahead of time.

6. Camera equipment and/or the ability to play back video images previously recorded.

While this may sound like a return to the old Picturephone® concept, it is important to realize that the major thrust is audio, graphics, and real-time stylus notations: the "people pictures" are purely supplementary. The technology currently exists to integrate many of the components, but the major barriers are a lack of (a) information communication standards and (b) computer software to handle the multiple communication modes with a minimum of user attention to the details. Apples's *Lisa* computer is probably the best example of user-friendly software that interfaces a number of small, discrete programs. In a COMSOLE, the master software would extend to teleconferencing functions as well.

On the applications side, declining hardware costs will push all of these technologies out of the board rooms and executive offices and further down the organizational ladder. A broader distribution of these technologies will provide organizations with increased access to human resources, but will also create new organizational problems and challenges. In all probability, this new situation will call for further interaction between Information Resources and Human Resources divisions. These two divisions will become the most critical elements in an organization—a major change from the old perceptions concerning the roles of data processing and personnel!

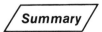

**Summary**

Fortunately, the increased use of teleconferencing is providing valuable information on how individuals communicate, which is refining the types of technologies being introduced. There are a few final statements I wish to emphasize.

1.  TELECONFERENCING MUST SUPPORT THE ORGANIZATION'S MISSION STATEMENT. Communication technologies do not stand alone; they must seek to enhance the types of communications which increase productivity in the right direction. Due to the variations in objectives, there is no single teleconferencing system that meets all needs, nor is there just one type of teleconferencing system to consider. Develop a strategy that includes all of the media mentioned in the book so that you will provide your organization with the best available options.

2.  TELECONFERENCING WILL CHANGE THE NATURE OF THE ORGANIZATION. Increased vertical and horizontal communication will take place, which may not always prove beneficial in some organizational settings. Since the precise dynamics of an organization's reaction to teleconferencing cannot be reliably predicted, implement teleconferencing in small, incremental steps using those areas with a great need to communicate for pilot projects.

3.  DO NOT BE TOO IMPRESSED BY THE TECHNOLOGY. It is easy to become overly awed by the hardware and forget that it is the users of the system who will determine the success of teleconferencing. The system must meet their needs. Keep the design and sophistication simple, but always have the option available to keep pace with demand.

4.  CONSTANTLY EVALUATE TELECONFERENCING. Teleconferencing must pay its own way, either in decreased expenses in other areas or by the generation of additional revenue. Even soft benefits should translate to saving or increased revenue. Develop mechanisms to monitor the users, uses, and outcomes of teleconferencing. Make sure that successes are well documented and passed along to management. Keep in constant touch with the users and be especially sensitive to the problems encountered. If the system is unreliable, do all that is necessary to correct the situation. If the system needs to be modified and your assessment indicates that such modification would increase participation or suitability, seek to modify the system as quickly as possible.

5.  DEVELOP AN ONGOING TRAINING PROGRAM FOR USERS WHICH INCLUDES BASIC COMMUNICATION SKILLS. Teleconferencing can intensify communication difficulties. Since those who do well with teleconferencing are those with a solid grasp of basic interpersonal skills, make sure that participants have at least minimal proficiency.

6. SEEK ADVICE. Teleconferencing can be expensive, both in terms of initial capital and ongoing expense, so make use of consulting input to guide the initial steps. Expert advice is strongly recommended for those considering the use of large-scale satellite teleconferencing—both technical and human factor advice. Read as much as possible, attend one or more of the national conferences, and join a teleconferencing association. Keep current.

7. THE TRUE ADVANTAGE OF TELECONFERENCING IS INTERACTION. Interaction is what separates teleconferencing from broadcasting and the distribution of prerecorded materials. Seek to promote, not limit, interaction. In mass audience efforts, work with production personnel to handle interaction creatively in a way that will support the need for high-quality production and participation.

8. PREPARE FINANCIAL JUSTIFICATIONS ON HARD-DOLLAR SAVINGS ONLY. However, include significant data on benefits that may impact the organization's bottom line in the test of the proposal. Do not overestimate savings; be conservative. Work with financial officers in the development of the proposal so they will feel a part of the proposal. Make sure financial questions have been addressed prior to submitting the proposal to management.

9. LACK OF ATTENTION TO THE HUMAN FACTORS, NOT THE TECHNOLOGY, IS THE PRIMARY REASON WHY TELECONFERENCING FAILS. Since teleconferencing is simply another form of communication, it is imperative that you communicate with the potential users and seek their input. A teleconferencing system will not exist in a vacuum; it requires a broad base of users to be effectively utilized.

10. START SMALL. Look for areas in which the probability for success is high and concentrate on the people in those areas. Seek out the failure-tolerant individuals first and build on the experience. It may take as long as two to three years to reach high levels of utilization. Set realistic expectations for yourself and others. Above all, make no promises that you cannot keep concerning the capabilities of the teleconferencing system.

11. KEEP A BROAD PERSPECTIVE ON THE COMMUNICATIONS FIELD. There will be a merger of computer, audio, and visual communication. Integration is natural and desirable. Those who seek to keep technologies separated will neither be helping themselves nor their organizations. Be proactive, not reactive. If you plan to adopt a position of leadership in implementing teleconferencing in your organization, maintain the momentum and continue to assume a position of leadership.

12. FINALLY, TRUST YOUR INSTINCTS. You know your organization and you know the people in it—rely on that knowledge. While consultant input is helpful, never adopt advice that seems to go against your better judgment. The consultant should never be the decision maker, only a resource. After all, you will be the one held accountable for teleconferencing.

Teleconferencing is not a technology in search of a problem; it is one approach to human logistics in an organization. Intelligent teleconferencing may not require substantial financial commmitments, but it does require common sense and knowing your organization's problems and needs. Teleconferencing is not simply an investment in hardware; it is an investment in human communication—maximizing human potential.

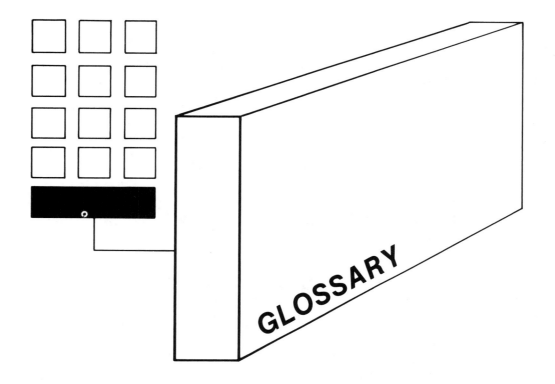

*Acoustics*—The properties of sound. Used to describe the quality of sound in an electronic meeting room. A room with "good acoustics" has a good balance between sound absorption and reflection of sound for a normal-sounding voice when picked up by a microphone.

*Ad Hoc*—Irregularly scheduled teleconferences. A special meeting.

*Analog*—Continuously variable waveform information. Examples would be the human voice, regular television signals, and AM and FM radio.

*ASCII*—American Standard Code for Information Interchange (pronounced "ask-ey"). A standardized set of digital signals representing letters and other characters for computer communication. Many personal computers and portable terminals communicate using ASCII characters.

*Asymmetrical Communication*—When there is inequality of communication capability. Can pertain to either inequality of communication equipment or a teleconference that fails to make use of interactive capabilities. For example, a one-way video satellite transmission with telephone communication for interaction.

*Asynchronous Communication*—When individuals can exchange information without the need to be connected to a communications system at the same time. Examples would be a letter, electronic mail, and computer conferencing.

*Audiographics*—An audio-conferencing system with the capability of remotely controlling graphic equipment. Included in the category would be remote control slide projectors, telewriters, and electronic blackboards.

*Audio teleconferencing*—Multiple locations linked via microphones and loudspeakers.

*Background*—(a) The transmission of information to a receiving site which does not affect the image currently seen by the distant participants; (b) when two images are superimposed, as in videographic systems, the static image is called the background image.

*Bandwidth*—The maximum amount of information that is carried by a communications link, or required by a communicating device. Expressed in cycles per second or bits per second.

*Bits Per Second (bps)*—The number of digital "on/off" signals transmitted in one second.

*Bolding*—Type that is produced by word processors and electronic typewriters when letters are struck many times, thereby darkening their appearance.

*Bridge*—A device which enables a number of telephone lines to be connected together so that the parties can hear one another.

*Broadcast Band*—The band of frequencies assigned to AM and FM stations.

*$C^3I$*—Command, control, communication, and intelligence. Used in the military to describe the spectrum of equipment to support tactical and strategic operations.

*CBBS*—Computer-based Bulletin Board Systems. An electronic mail system which uses small personal or minicomputers. Supports basic store-and-forward features.

*Clarke Orbit*—The orbit used by communication satellites, located over the equator and 22,300 miles above the surface. Satellites in Clarke Orbit appear stationary to observers on earth. First theorized by Arthur C. Clarke in 1945.

*CODEC*—COder/DECoder (pronounced "CO-DECK"). Devices that compress analog signals so that less-expensive transmission channels can be used.

*Common Carrier*—A firm that sells communication channel capability. Common carriers include the telephone company and firms that provide specialized services to link locations.

*Compressed Video*—A television signal that has been processed by a CODEC.

*Computer Conference*—A sophisticated electronic mail system which enables participants to discuss task-related information. Computer conferences support a variety of functions, such as voting, which assist users in reaching decisions more effectively.

*Conference Bridge*—See bridge.

*Conference Call*—A bridging service provided by the telephone company.

*Continuous Presence*—The ability to see all participants in a visual teleconference without interruption. The phrase was coined by Earl Brown of Bell Labs in 1978.

*CONUS*—CONtiguous United States. A term used in conjunction with communication satellites to describe their primary service area.

*Cost Displacement*—Costs that are not eliminated. Expenses that shift from one cost center to another.

*DDD*—Direct-Distance Dialing. Use of the public switched network as a means of linking locations in a teleconference.

*Dedicated Line*—A telephone line that can only be used to communicate with one other location.

*Default*—The manner in which an electronic system will operate when power is first applied, or when no user intervention is made.

*Depth of Field*—The distance between the closest and furthest point in focus without adjustment of a lens.

*Digital*—The on and off pulses used by computer devices to communicate.

*Dish*—An antenna for the reception and transmission of extremely high-frequency signals from satellites and microwave transmitters.

*Downlink*—The equipment associated with the reception of information from a communications satellite.

*Duplex*—The ability of two signals to move in opposite directions through one communication channel at the same time. An example would be a normal telephone conversation between two individuals.

*Earth Segment*—Satellite transmission and reception equipment located on the earth.

*Echo Suppression*—Electronic circuitry which compensates for the time delays experienced in satellite communication.

*Electronic Blackboard*—A device consisting of a blackboard device which is sensitive to surface pressure and television monitors which display pressure movements on the blackboard.

*Electronic Mail*—Text information that is communicated via electrical signals between two or more locations.

*Facsimile*—A device which scans a printed page, converts the image to electrical signals, and transmits the information to one or more locations where the information is used to recreate a duplicate of the image on a piece of paper.

*Failure Tolerant*—A characteristic of individuals who tend to be involved in new innovations. Individuals who are not dissuaded from participating in a new technology because of technical or implementation problems.

*Fault Tolerant*—Equipment which has sufficient electronic circuit redundancy so that it will continue to operate in the event of a component failure.

*FCC*—Federal Communications Commission. The federal agency responsible for the regulations governing the communications industry.

*Feedback*—(a) To receive immediate response concerning a statement or assertion; (b) a high-pitched howl which occurs when a microphone is placed too close to a loud speaker.

*Fiber optics*—Strands of an extremely pure glass-like substance used to conduct light from a laser.

*Foreground*—(a) In an electronic system capable of performing several tasks at the same time, the task most visible to the user; (b) in a videographic system, the real-time graphic notations superimposed over another image.

*Four wire*—A telephone link which allows duplex communication. Normally a dedicated line.

*Frame*—(a) The information seen on a television screen; (b) one complete transmission of a single television image. There are 30 such frames transmitted each second in normal television.

*Frame tension*—A psychological state of anxiety when the viewer believes that the television camera is not showing all the pertinent information in a scene.

*Frequency response*—The range of frequencies that can pass through a transmission without degradation.

*Full-motion television*—The type of television seen on home television sets, including all characteristics associated with the transmission and reception of the image information.

*Geostationary Orbit*—See Clarke Orbit.

*Graphics*—Any two-dimensional information which will be photographed by a television camera or presented in a teleconference.

*Half-duplex*—When two or more communication locations can only speak or transmit visual information one at a time.

*Hard switching*—A form of switching used by speaker telephones in which the alternation between speaking and listening is very noticeable.

*Hertz (Hz)*—One cycle per second. A term named after Heinrich Hertz used to describe the frequency of wave information.

*Hop*—The distance between a radio transmitter and receiver.

*Hot Stand By*—(a) A backup power system which will immediately supply electricity to electronic equipment in the event of a power failure; (b) a second set of electronic systems which will become activated in the event of an equipment failure.

*Information utility*—A company that sells access to a variety of information-related computer services.

*Interface*—An electronic unit which controls several other devices and is designed to simplify the operation of a system.

*Invisible systems*—Electronics and transmission systems which are not readily apparent to the user and operate without user intervention.

*Iris*—Thin metal blades in a lens which open and close to control the amount of light reaching the light-sensitive surface of a television camera.

*ITC*—Investment tax credit. A tax credit given to encourage the purchase of new equipment.

*Joy stick*—A device which controls camera movements in four directions: up, down, left, and right.

*Landline*—A telephone line which does not use a communications satellite; a physical wire link between two or more locations.

*LASER*—Light Amplification by Stimulated Emission of Radiation. A technology which superimposes information on a beam of light.

*Linear array microphone*—A microphone with specially designed sound pick-up devices situated in such a way as to be most sensitive to sound from individuals seated at a conference table.

*Local loop*—A telephone line between a user's location and the telephone company switching equipment.

*Look angle*—The angle between the horizon and a communications satellite. Used in conjunction with the placement of a communications satellite receiving or transmitting antenna.

*Loop*—See local loop.

*Microwave*—A range of frequencies above 1,000 MHz. The band of frequencies used for the transmission of information to or from communication satellites and used to distribute television information on the earth.

*MODEM*—MOdulator/DEModulator. A device which converts digital computer information into audio tones for transmission over telephone lines.

*Monitor*—A professional quality television set, normally designed just for the display of television information from a camera or other video source, with no provision for the reception of regular television channels.

*Narrowcast*—A communication to a special, limited audience. In contrast to "broadcast," or communicating to very large audiences.

*Net present value*—A method of converting dollars in the future to their current worth.

*Noise*—Nondesirable information. Noise can be static in an audio communication or "snow" in a television image.

*Nominal Group Technique*—A form of "brainstorming" in which there is a more controlled idea generation structure.

*Omnidirectional*—A reception or transmission device that radiates energy in all directions. For example, an omnidirectional microphone will pick up sound from all directions.

*One way*—A communication that originates in one location is heard or seen in other locations with no provision for interaction or response.

*On-Line*—When two or more locations are linked electronically.

*Packet switching*—A long-distance communication system for computer devices. Instead of information being transmitted in a continuous stream, the data is divided into smaller packets, thus increasing the efficiency of the communication network.

*Password*—A computer "key." A series of characters assigned to an individual which will permit access to a computer device.

*Pan*—To move a camera left or right.

*PBX*—Private Branch Exchange. Telephone switching equipment located on a user's premises. A user's telephone call is routed through the PBX and then to the telephone company.

*PET*—Portable Earth Terminal. A satellite antenna and reception equipment on wheels which can be easily moved.

*Pixel*—A picture element. The smallest unit of resolution in a visual communication system (facsimile or television).

*Presence*—The sensation that the participants in a teleconference are in the same location.

*Proportional spacing*—A form of spacing used by typesetters and the new electronic typewriters and word processors. Instead of each letter consuming the same space on a line, the space is varied according to the width of the character.

*Public switched network*—The public telephone network in which calls are routed based on the digits dialed by the user.

*Raster lines*—The fine lines across the face of a television screen.

*Real time*—When actions appear to happen without time delay. For example, when notations on a videographic screen appear at the same time on all other screens, then the notations appear in real time.

*Record communication*—Any communication which produces a copy of the information transmitted on some form of media that can be archived.

*Repeater*—An electronic device which receives a radio signal and retransmits the signal to the next location.

*Resolution*—The amount of detail which can be seen following the transmission of visual information. A high-resolution system would enable users to see very finely detailed information.

*RS-232C*—A digital communication standard used by most information utilities, small computers, and portable computer terminals. The standard describes in considerable detail the specifications of the communication signal.

*Satellite*—A radio repeater located in orbit around the earth.

*Slow Scan Television (SSTV)*—Equipment which can transmit still video images via telephone lines or other narrow-bandwidth transmission systems.

*Soft switching*—A method of switching used in some speaker telephones in which the loudspeaker and microphone are turned up and down rather than simply switched on or off, making the switching less noticeable to the user.

*Space segment*—The portion of a communications link which is located in outer space.

*Symmetrical communication*—When all teleconference locations have similar communication equipment.

*Synchronous*—(a) A teleconference in which all participants must be present at the same time in order to communicate; (b) a communications protocol used by some larger computer systems.

*T1 Carrier*—A standardized bandwidth communications channel which is capable of transmitting 1.5 Mega bits per second (Mbps) over a single pair of wires.

*Teleconference*— An electronic means of communication between three or more individuals in two or more locations.

*Television projector*—A device which can display television images on a single screen for large audiences.

*TET*—Transportable Earth Terminal. A portable satellite transmission device.

*Time broker*—A firm that buys and resells time on a communications satellite.

*Touch Tone*[TM]—A method of telephone dialing which uses a series of audible tones to represent digits.

*Transceiver*—Transmission and reception electronics built into a single package.

*Transparent*—Any technology which operates without the knowledge of the users. Also see "invisible systems."

*Transponder*—One of the many transceivers located in a communication satellite. A transponder is normally designed to handle a single full-motion television signal.

*Two-way*—A system which enables the teleconferencing locations to interact.

*Unidirectional*—When energy is either received or transmitted in a single direction. For example, a unidirectional microphone will pick up sound in primarily one direction.

*Uplink*—The equipment associated with the transmission of information to a communication satellite.

*User friendly*—Electronic equipment designed for ease of user operation.

*User hostile*—Electronic equipment that is difficult to operate.

*Video*—The picture portion of a television communication.

*Videographics*—The combination of slow scan or freeze-frame television with real-time, full-motion graphics.

*Visible systems*—Those electronic devices which can be seen by users. Normally, microphones, television cameras, interface equipment, and video monitors.

*Voice grade*—A standard telephone line designed to carry only frequencies below 3,400 Hz.

*Voice switching*—Equipment that switches television cameras based on sound.

*WATS*—Wide Area Telephone Service. A telephone long-distance service that in many instances is less expensive than direct long-distance dialing "1 plus."

*Zoom lens*—A lens in which the optical elements can be changed to give the impression that the camera moves closer or further from the subject without physical movement of the camera itself.

# INDEX

Italicized page numbers indicate material in tables or illustrations.